# Basic Concepts in Physics

# BASIC CONCEPTS PHYSICS

**C. Boyle**
*B.Sc.(Hons), M.Sc., P.G.C.E. C. Phys.,
M. Inst. P., A.F.I.M.A.*

**Checkmate/Arnold**

© C. BOYLE 1986

First published in Great Britain 1986 by Checkmate Publications.
4 Ainsdale Close, Bromborough, Wirral L63 0EU.

This edition published in association with Edward Arnold (Publishers) Ltd.,
41 Bedford Square, London WC1B 3DQ.

Edward Arnold (Australia) Pty Ltd., 80 Waverley Road, Caulfield East,
Victoria 3145, Australia.

Edward Arnold, 3 East Read Street, Baltimore, Maryland 21202, U.S.A.

Boyle, C.
Physics.——— (Basic concepts)
1. Physics
I. Title        II. Series
530              QC21.2

ISBN 0 946973 38 5

Text set in 10/12 pt Times
by Merseyside Graphics Ltd., 130 Meols Parade, Meols, Wirral L47 5AZ
Printed & Bound by Richard Clay (The Chaucer Press) Ltd., Bungay, Suffolk

# TABLE OF CONTENTS

## AREA 6 : WAVE PHENOMENA

# AUTHOR'S FOREWORD

The text book author's role is to present his subject in a thorough, comprehensible and refreshing way. It is particularly important for him/her to keep abreast of new material and discard any superfluous material without omitting any mundane but fundamental ideas.

This book aims to fulful the above requirements. It deals with the nationally agreed core syllabus in 'A' level physics and it is organised into topic areas as outlined in this new syllabus. Each topic area is subdivided into appropriate chapters and provides a new approach to the subject matter concerned.

In addition to providing a basic grounding in 'A' level physics, the other important purpose of this book is to provide the student with a thorough preparation for the 'A' level examination. In his experience as a lecturer and examiner, the author subscribes to the view that some basic yet fundamental concepts are not fully understood by some students. Such concepts are explained very thoroughly yet, hopefully, not pedantically in the hope that their true beauty and simplicity shall become evident to the student.

This text should be used in conjunction with its companion text, "Questions & Answers in 'A' Level Physics".                                    C.B.

# AREA 1 : PHYSICAL QUANTITIES

## Chapter 1
## QUANTITIES, UNITS and DIMENSIONS

### 1.1 QUANTITIES

The exact description of a physical quantity consists of the product of two factors — a pure number and a given unit.

Virtually all quantities in physics have a unit attached with the obvious exception of quantities such as relative density which is a ratio of two quantities and their associated units.

The pure number must be a measure of some basic or derived quantity.

We use the Systems International (S.I.) in which the basic or fundamental quantities are:

      length
      mass
      time
      current
      temperature interval
      amount of substance

The above quantities are fixed by convention and all other physical quantities — known as derived quantities — may be defined in terms of them.

Definitions of derived quantities may be given in terms of a word equation. Specific heat capacity is defined as the thermal energy needed to increase the temperature of 1Kg of a body by 1K.

Therefore as a word equation

$$\text{Specific Heat Capacity} = \frac{\text{Thermal Energy Transfer}}{\text{Mass x Temperature Change}}$$

It is only possible to write this equation in symbols if the symbols are defined.

## 1.2 UNITS
### 1.2.1 The definitions of the base units are as follows:—

metre (symbol m). The metre is the length equal to 1650763. 73
wavelengths in vacuum of the radiation corresponding to the
transition between the levels $2p_{10}$ and $5d_5$ of the krypton –86
atom.

kilogram (symbol Kg). The kilogram is the unit of mass and is equal
to the mass of the international prototype of the kilogram which
is a cylindrical piece of platinum-iridium alloy kept at Sèvres.

second (symbol S). The second is the duration of 9192631770 periods
of the radiation corresponding to the transition between the two
hyperfine levels of the caesium 133 atom.

ampere (symbol A). The ampere is that constant current which, if
maintained in two straight parallel conductors of infinite length,
of negligible circular cross section, and placed one metre apart
in vacuum, would produce a force of $2 \times 10^{-7}$ Newton per metre
between the conductors.

kelvin (symbol K). The Kelvin is the unit of thermodynamic or
Kelvin temperature and is the fraction $1/273.16$ of the
thermodynamic temperature of the triple point of water.

mole (symbol Mol). The mole is the amount of substance of a
system which contains as many elementary units as there are
carbon atoms in 0.012Kg of carbon 12. The elementary unit may
be an atom, a molecule, an ion or an electron etc. but it must be
specified.

The definition of the ampere sets a value for an important constant
$\mu_0$, the permeability of free space.

The force between two current carrying straight wires of length l
carrying currents $I_1$ and $I_2$ and situated a metre apart, is given by

$$F = \frac{\mu_0 I_1, I_2 l}{2\pi r}$$

Now from the definition of the ampere, when $I_1 = I_2 = 1A, l = 1m$ and
$r = 1m$ then     $F = 2\pi \times 10^{-7}$

thus     $2\pi \times 10^{-7} = \frac{\mu_0}{2\pi}$

$$\mu_0 = 4\pi \times 10^{-7} \text{ Units (Hm}^{-1})$$

1.2.2 The units of some derived quantities are given below:

| QUANTITY | UNIT |
|---|---|
| Area = length x width | $m^2$ |
| Volume = length x width x height | $m^3$ |
| Speed = $\dfrac{distance}{time}$ | $ms^{-1}$ |
| Velocity = $\dfrac{displacement}{time}$ | $ms^{-1}$ (in given direction) |
| Acceleration = $\dfrac{velocity\ change}{time}$ | $ms^{-2}$ (in given direction) |
| Force = mass x acceleration | N or $Kgms^{-2}$ (in given direction) |
| Momentum = mass x velocity | $Kgms^{-1}$ (in given direction) |
| Work = force x distance | J or Nm |
| Power = $\dfrac{work}{time}$ | W or $Js^{-1}$ |
| Pressure = $\dfrac{force}{area}$ | Pa or $Nm^{-2}$ |
| Density = $\dfrac{mass}{volume}$ | $Kgm^{-3}$ |

1.2.3 In practice we may wish to measure either very large or very small quantities. In order to avoid writing very large or very small numbers we often use multiples of units — when dealing with very large quantities or submultiples (fractions) of units — when dealing with very small quantities.

**Common multiples**

| Multiple | Name | Symbol |
|---|---|---|
| $10^3$ | kilo | K |
| $10^6$ | mega | M |
| $10^9$ | giga | G |
| $10^{12}$ | tera | T |

**Common Submultiples**

| Submultiple | Name | Symbol |
|---|---|---|
| $10^{-3}$ | milli | m |
| $10^{-6}$ | micro | $\mu$ |
| $10^{-9}$ | nano | n |
| $10^{-12}$ | pico | p |

## 1.3 DIMENSIONS

The dimensions of a physical quantity is its relationship to the basic units of mass, length, time, currents and temperature denoted by $[M]$, $[L]$, $[T]$, $[I]$ and $[\Theta]$

The dimension of any derived physical quantity may be derived by the use of dimensions in any defining equation.

The dimensions of some derived quantities are given below:

| QUANTITY | DIMENSIONS |
|---|---|
| Area = length x width | $[L^2]$ |
| Volume = length x width x height | $[L^3]$ |
| Speed = $\dfrac{\text{distance}}{\text{time}}$ | $[LT^{-1}]$ |
| Velocity = $\dfrac{\text{displacement}}{\text{time}}$ | $[LT^{-1}]$ |
| Acceleration = $\dfrac{\text{velocity change}}{\text{time}}$ | $[LT^{-2}]$ |
| Force = mass x acceleration | $[MLT^{-2}]$ |
| Momentum = mass x velocity | $[MLT^{-1}]$ |
| Work = force x distance | $[ML^2T^{-2}]$ |
| Power = $\dfrac{\text{work}}{\text{time}}$ | $[ML^2T^{-3}]$ |
| Pressure = $\dfrac{\text{force}}{\text{area}}$ | $[ML^{-1}T^{-2}]$ |
| Density = $\dfrac{\text{mass}}{\text{volume}}$ | $[ML^{-3}]$ |

A quantity which has no units also has no dimensions. Therefore constants and quantities which are defined as a ratio do not have dimensions. The dimensions of speed and velocity are identical, i.e. they are scalars.

There are two uses of dimensions. Firstly to check a formula and secondly to derive an equation. In checking a formula we use the fact that the dimensions on both sides of an equation must be identical. In deriving an equation we recognize the fact that the method only enables a proportional relationship between variables to be established — any constants of proportionality cannot be found by the method of dimensions and a full rigorous mathematical analysis is required to establish the complete equation.

**EXAMPLES**

1) To check the hydrostatic pressure formula
$$p = \rho g h$$
p = hydrostatic pressure due to a column of liquid
$\rho$ = density of liquid
g = acceleration due to gravity
h = depth below free surface of column

Dimensions of left hand side of equation = $[ML^{-1}T^{-2}]$
(see table)

Dimensions of right hand side of equation =
$$[ML^{-3}][LT^{-2}][L] = [ML^{-1}T^{-2}]$$

The dimensions of both sides of the equation are identical, therefore the equation is correct.

2) To derive an equation for the period of oscillation, T, of a simple pendulum.
We assume that the amplitude of oscillation is small and ignore all dissipative forces such as air resistance.

Suppose the period of the pendulum depends upon the following factors:

  1) the mass of the pendulum bob
  2) the length of the pendulum
  3) the acceleration due to gravity

Since the exact nature of the dependence is not known, we assume arbitrary powers for each variable.

Period $\alpha$ (Mass)$^{\alpha}$ x (Length)$^{\beta}$ x (Acc due to gravity)$^{\gamma}$
If a constant of proportionality, K, is introduced then
Period = K x (Mass)$^{\alpha}$ x (Length)$^{\beta}$ x (Acc due to gravity)$^{\gamma}$

Change each side of the equation into dimensions
Dimensions of Period = $[T]$
Dimensions of K = none
Dimensions of Mass = $[M]$
Dimensions of Length = $[L]$
Dimensions of Acceleration due to gravity = $[LT^{-2}]$

Therefore
$$[T] = [M]^{\alpha}[L]^{\beta}[LT^{-2}]^{\gamma}$$

Collecting together indices on the right hand side of the equation
$$[T] = [M]^{\alpha}[L]^{\beta+\alpha}[T]^{-2\gamma}$$

Now any quantity raised to the power zero is 1

For the left hand side of the equation

Power to which [T] is raised  =  1  (1)
Power to which [M] is raised  =  0  (2)
Power to which [L] is raised  =  0  (3)

For the right hand side of the equation

Power to which [T] is raised  =  $-2\gamma$  (4)
Power to which [M] is raised  =  $\alpha$  (5)
Power to which [L] is raised  =  $\beta + \underline{\gamma}$  (6)

Using the fact that the powers on both sides of the equation must be identical then
from (2) and (5)     $\alpha = 0$
from (1) and (4)     $1 = -2\gamma$ or $\gamma = -\frac{1}{2}$
from (3) and (6)     $0 = \beta + \gamma$
                    $= \beta - \frac{1}{2}$ or $\beta = \frac{1}{2}$

Substituting for $\alpha, \beta$ and $\gamma$ into the original equation
Period = K x (Mass)$^0$ x (Length)$^{\frac{1}{2}}$ x (Acc due to gravity)$^{-\frac{1}{2}}$
i.e.   $T = K\, l^{\frac{1}{2}}\, g^{-\frac{1}{2}}$     where   l = length
                                   g = acc due to gravity
                                   T = period
or   $T = K\sqrt{\dfrac{l}{g}}$

A full analysis shows that the value of K is 2

Note that any false assumption — such as the dependence on mass — disappears in the mathematics.

## 1.4  HOMOGENEITY OF PHYSICAL EQUATIONS

For an equation to be correct it must be homogeneous with respect to units and dimensions, that is, the units and dimensions must be identical on both sides of the equation. It should be noted that although homogeneity is necessary it is not in itself a sufficient test for correctness.

## QUESTIONS

1) Use the method of dimensions to show that when a body moves through a fluid the retarding force acting on the body depends upon the density and coefficient of viscosity of the fluid but is independent of the velocity of the body (dimensions of coefficient of viscosity = $[ML^{-1}T^{-1}]$).

2) Use the method of dimensions to check the formula for centripetal acceleration

$$a = \frac{V^2}{r}$$

$a$ = acceleration,   $V$ = speed of body,   $r$ = radius of orbit

3) Supposing the velocity of deep water waves to depend upon the density of the water, the acceleration due to gravity and the wavelength, use the method of dimensions to derive an equation for their velocity.

## Chapter 2
## SCALARS and VECTORS

### 2.1 DEFINITIONS

A scalar quantity is one which has magnitude only. Examples are distance, speed, volume, temperature, mass, energy and power. Scalars are combined arithmetically.

A vector quantity is one which has both magnitude and direction. Examples are displacement, velocity, acceleration, force and momentum. Vectors are combined or compounded geometrically. They can be completely represented by straight lines, drawn to scale, in the appropriate direction with arrows showing the direction.

Thus we can instantly recognize if a quantity is a vector by looking to see if direction is included in the definition.

The difference between scalar distance and vector displacement is shown in Fig. 2.1. In (a) the distance from A to B is 1m. In (b) the displacement from A to B is 1m in a direction North-East. To show that the direction is from A to B and not B to A the arrow is marked as in the diagram. We denote a vector from A to B as AB.

**FIG. 2.1**

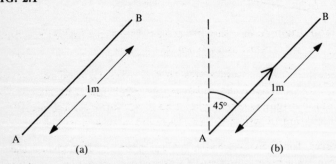

(a)                    (b)

### 2.2 THE COMPOSITION OF VECTORS

The resultant of two or more vectors is the single vector to which they are equivalent. The process of finding this single equivalent vector is known as compounding or composition. Since the process is identical for all vectors we shall consider the case of displacements.

2.2.1   Two vectors in the same direction — the resultant is the sum
of the vectors in the same direction.

2.2.2   Two vectors in opposite directions — the resultant is the
difference between the vectors in the direction of the
greater.

2.2.3   Two vectors in other directions — the resultant is obtained
using the Parallelogram Rule.

Consider Fig. 2.2. A displacement from A to B, denoted by AB, is to
be compounded with a displacement AC. The resultant
displacement is given by AD. Notice that both vectors start at the

**FIG. 2.2**

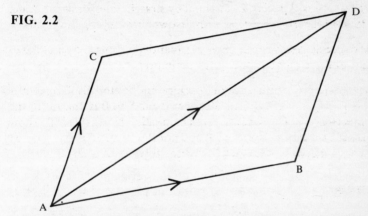

common origin A, and the direction of the arrow on the resultant is
also such as to point away from A.

The Parallelogram Rule states that the resultant of two vectors
represented in magnitude and direction by straight lines, drawn from
a common origin, is given by the line which forms the diagonal of the
parallelogram of which the two original vectors are sides.

However, for accurate results with this rule it is better to use the
diagram as a mere guide and to obtain the answer by resorting to
computational methods involving the cosine and sine rules. This is
shown in Fig. 2.3.

In this diagram

AB is inclined at $\Theta°$ to the horizontal    i.e. $\angle\,BAE = \Theta$

AC is inclined at $\Phi°$ to the horizontal    i.e. $\angle\,CAE = \Phi$

**FIG. 2.3**

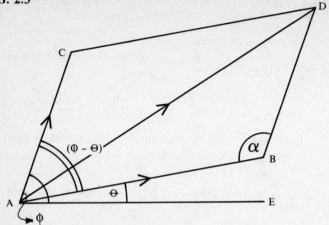

The angle between the vectors is then $(\phi - \theta)$    i.e. $\angle\, CAB = (\phi - \theta)$

Thus, from the geometry of a parallelogram
$$= (180 - (\phi - \theta))°$$

By use of the cosine rule we have
$$AD^2 = AB^2 + BD^2 + 2AB\,BD\,\cos\alpha \qquad (\alpha \text{ is obtuse})$$

In order to find the inclination of the resultant we consider a modified version of Fig. 2.3. as shown in Fig. 2.4.

**FIG. 2.4**

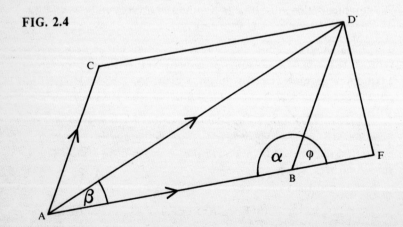

We wish to find $\beta$.

To do this AB is produced to F and DF is drawn perpendicular to BF. By geometry, angle DBF is $\phi$.

In triangle DBF

$$Sin\,\phi = \frac{DF}{DB} = \frac{DF}{AC}$$

$$\therefore \quad DF = AC\,Sin\,\phi$$

Similarly in triangle DAF

$$Sin\,\beta = \frac{DF}{AD} = \frac{AC}{AD}\,Sin\,\phi$$

$$\therefore \quad \beta = \left(Sin^{-1}\left(\frac{AC}{AD}\,sin\,\phi\right)\right)^{\circ}$$

If, of course, the original vectors are perpendicular to each other then the parallelogram becomes a rhombus and the mathematics is simplified.

2.2.4   If more than two vectors are to be compounded then two techniques are available:—

1.   Group the vectors in pairs and repeatedly apply the parallelogram rule.
2.   Represent the vectors diagrammatically by placing the vectors end to end with the resultant being given by the line which completes the polygon, in the direction from the start of the first vector to the end of the last vector. This is shown in Fig 2.5 where the resultant is AH.

**FIG. 2.5**

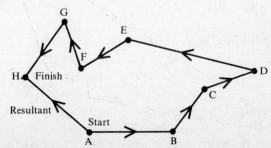

**EXAMPLES**

1) A boat travelling at 3ms⁻¹ from south to north sets course across a stream flowing east to west at 4ms⁻¹. Find the resultant velocity and direction of the boat.

The situation is shown in Fig. 2.6.

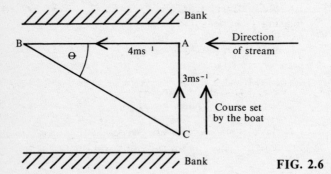

**FIG. 2.6**

The effect of the flowing stream is to cause the boat to be carried downstream whilst it is crossing.

Let AB = velocity of stream
Let CA = course set by boat
Then CB = resultant

By scale drawing.
If we choose a scale of 1cm to represent 1ms⁻¹ then
AB is drawn 4cm long
CA is drawn 3cm long
CB would be found to be 5cm long and $\theta$ = 37°
i.e. Resultant velocity = 5ms⁻¹ at 37° to bank.

By calculation.
$$CB^2 = AB^2 + CA^2$$
$$= 4^2 + 3^2$$
$$= 16 + 9 = 25$$
$$\therefore CB = 5ms^{-1}$$

Now    $\tan \theta = \frac{3}{4}$
$$\therefore \theta = 36° 52' \text{ to bank}$$
Resultant velocity = 5ms⁻¹ at 36° 52' to bank.

2) A car starts at A and travels 10Km due west, 20Km north-east and 30Km due north. Find either graphically or by calculation its distance and bearing from A.

   (a) By diagram : Fig. 2.7.
        Scale chosen : 1cm to represent 10Km.

       AB is measured to be 5cm
           final distance from A = 50Km
        Bearing $\beta$ is measured at 29°

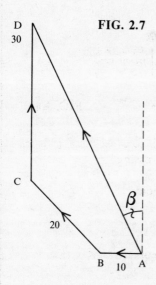

**FIG. 2.7**

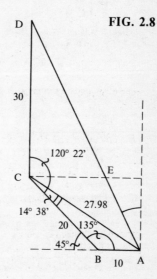

**FIG. 2.8**

(b) By successive combination of vectors — Fig. 2.8

    (1) Compound AB and BC to give AC

$$AC^2 = 10^2 + 20^2 - 2 \times 10 \times 20 \cos 135$$
$$= 10^2 + 20^2 + 2 \times 10 \times 20 \cos 45$$
$$= 782.8$$
$$AC = 27.98 \text{ Km.}$$

(2) Find angle BCA

$$\frac{10}{\sin \angle BCA} = \frac{27.98}{\sin 135°}$$

$$\therefore \sin \angle BCA = \frac{10 \sin 135°}{27.98}$$

$$= 0.2527$$

$$\therefore \angle BCA = 14° \ 38'$$

(3) Find angle DCA

$$\angle, BCE = \angle CBF = 45°$$

$$\angle DCE = 90°$$

$$\angle DCB = 135°$$

But $\angle, DCB = \angle, BCA + \angle DCA$

$$\therefore \angle, DCA = \angle, DCB - \angle BCA = 120° \ 22'$$

$$\therefore \angle DCA = 120° \ 22'$$

(4) Compound AC and CD to give AD, the resultant

$$AD^2 = 30^2 + 27.98^2 - 2 \times 30 \times 27.98 \ Cos \ 120° \ 22'$$
$$= 30^2 + 27.98^2 + 2 \times 30 \times 27.98 \ Cos \ 59° \ 38'$$
$$= 2531.4$$
$$\therefore AD = 50.31 Km.$$

(5) Find angle CDA

$$\frac{27.98}{Sin \angle CDA} = \frac{50.31}{Sin \ 120° \ 22'}$$

$$\therefore Sin \angle CDA = \frac{27.98 \ Sin \ 120° \ 22'}{50.31}$$

$$= \frac{27.98 \ Sin \ 59° \ 38'}{50.31}$$

$$= 0.4799$$

$$\therefore \angle CDA = 28° \ 41' = \text{size of bearing}$$

$\therefore$ Distance and bearing $= 50.31$ Km, N $28° \ 41'$ W

**FIG. 2.9**

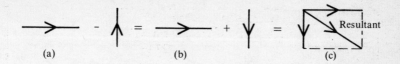

(a)           (b)           (c)

(c) In order to subtract one vector from another, the vector to be subtracted is reversed in direction and added to the other vector. Thus in order to subtract two vectors we use the method in Fig. 2.9. The original vectors are shown in (a), the addition in (b) and the composition in (c).

**FIG. 2.10**

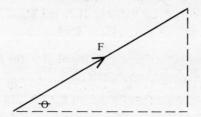

## 2.3  THE RESOLUTION OF VECTORS

The reverse process to the addition of two vectors using the Parallelogram Rule is the splitting or resolution of one vector into two components. The most common case is when the components are taken at right angles, e.g. horizontal and vertical.

Suppose in Fig. 2.10, a force F acts in a direction $\theta$ to the horizontal then

$$\text{horizontal component of F} = F \cos \theta$$
$$\text{vertical component of F} = F \sin \theta$$

Thus a single force F is equivalent to two perpendicular forces $F \cos \theta$ and $F \sin \theta$.

If the force actually acts along the horizontal direction then $\theta = 0$ and

$$\text{horizontal component of F} = F \cos \theta = F$$
$$\text{vertical component of F} = F \sin \theta = 0$$

— thus a force has no component at right angles to it.

Weight is a force which always acts vertically downwards and quite often needs to be resolved into components as shown in the following example.

---

**EXAMPLE**
A mass of 50Kg rests on a plane which is inclined at 30° to the horizontal. Find the components of its weight both parallel and perpendicular to the plane.
(Assume g = 10ms$^{-2}$)

The situation is shown in Fig. 2.11

The weight acts vertically downwards.
The component of weight parallel to the plane is
    mg sin 30 = 50 x 10 x 0.5 = 250N.

The component of weight perpendicular to the plane is
    mg cos 30 = 50 x 10 x 0.866 = 433N.

---

**FIG. 2.11**

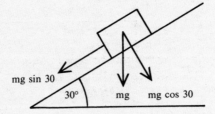

mg sin 30    30°    mg    mg cos 30

**QUESTIONS**
1)  A man walks a distance 12Km due east and then 16Km due south. Show that he is 20Km from his starting point in a direction tan$^{-1}$ ($^4$/$_3$) south of east.

2)  Calculate the component of a force of 10N in a direction making an angle of 60° with it.

3)  Is it possible for the quotient of two vector quantities to be a scalor quantity? Illustrate your answer with an example.

# AREA 2 : MECHANICS

## Chapter 3
## FORCE

### 3.1  DEFINITION

Force is defined as that which changes, or tends to change, a body's state of rest or uniform motion in a straight line. It is a vector. As a result, a force is able to make a stationary body move or to change the velocity of a moving body either by changing its speed or by changing its direction of motion.

We need to include the tendency to change within the definition since a force may have no actual effect on an object which is not free to move.

In practice, a force is interpreted as a push or pull upon a body.

### 3.2  TYPES OF FORCE

FIG 3.1

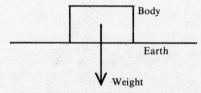

WEIGHT — is the force acting on a body due to gravity. It is always directed vertically downwards or more correctly to the centre of the earth.

FIG. 3.2

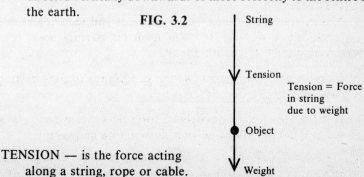

TENSION — is the force acting along a string, rope or cable.

**FIG. 3.3**

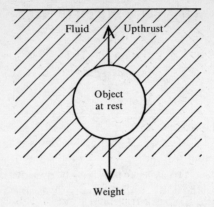

UPTHRUST — is the force acting vertically upwards upon a body whenever it is immersed in a fluid.

**FIG. 3.4**

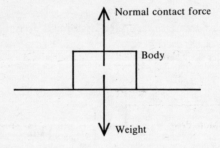

NORMAL CONTACT FORCE — is the force acting vertically upwards on a body due to its weight being in contact with another body.

**FIG 3.5**

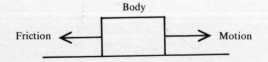

FRICTION — is the force which opposes motion. It is always directed in the opposite direction to the motion.

**FIG. 3.6**

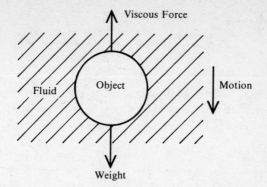

VISCOUS FORCE — is a frictional force in a fluid.

**FIG. 3.7**

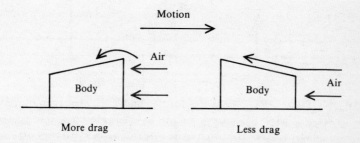

DRAG — is the force opposing the motion of an object due to the flow of displaced medium around the object.

**FIG. 3.8**

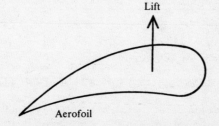

AERODYNAMIC LIFT — is the lifting force generated by the movement of an aerofoil through a medium.

**FIG. 3.9**

ELECTROSTATIC FORCE — is the force which exists between electric charges or electrically charged bodies. It is attractive between unlike charges and repulsive between like charges.

**FIG. 3.10**

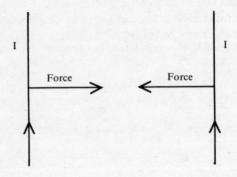

MAGNETIC FORCE — is the force which exists between current carrying wires. Each conductor has a force on it due to the magnetic field of the other. The force is attractive if the currents are in the same direction and repulsive if they are in opposite directions.

### 3.3 WEIGHT

The gravitational pull of the earth on an object is called weight. Mass and weight are related by

WEIGHT = MASS x ACCELERATION DUE TO GRAVITY

Accordingly although the mass of an object is constant, its weight is not because of the variation in the acceleration due to gravity. This varies with height. With the advent of space travel, it is now possible to situate a body on the moon. On the moon, the weight of a body is the gravitational pull of the moon on the object. Since the acceleration due to gravity on the moon is about $\frac{1}{6}$ that on earth, the weight of an object on the moon is also about $\frac{1}{6}$ that on earth.

## 3.4 REPRESENTATION OF FORCE

Force is a vector quantity. It can therefore be represented by a line drawn to scale in the appropriate direction. This line represents the line of action of the force. For a force acting on a particle, the problem is straightforward. For a force acting on a rigid body, we use the fact that such a body behaves as if the whole of its mass were concentrated at a single point called its centre of mass. Since the line of action of its weight always passes through this point, the point is also called the centre of gravity. See Fig. 3.11.

**FIG. 3.11**

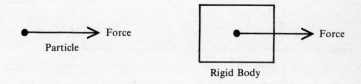

## 3.5 UPTHRUST

When a body is partially or wholly immersed in a fluid, then
(i) the volume of fluid displaced is equal to volume of the body immersed;
(ii) the upthrust, or apparent loss in weight, is equal to the weight of fluid displaced (Archimedes Principle).

If a body floats either partially or wholly immersed in a fluid then it appears to be weightless and therefore

$$\text{Upthrust on body} = \text{weight of body}$$

But by Archimedes Principle

$$\text{Upthrust on body} = \text{weight of fluid displaced}$$

Therefore

$$\text{Weight of body} = \text{weight of fluid displaced}$$

This result, known as the Principle of Floatation can be stated: A floating body displaces its own weight of fluid.

The principle applies equally well to a balloon floating in air as it does to a ship floating in water.

**EXAMPLE**

A string supports a copper block of mass 2Kg which is half-immersed in water. Calculate the tension in the string ($g = 9.81 \text{ms}^{-2}$, density of copper, $\rho_c = 9 \times 10^3 \text{Kgm}^{-3}$, density of water, $\rho_w = 1 \times 10^3 \text{Kg})\,\text{m}^{-3}$)

Volume of block, Vc is given by

$$V_c = \frac{M_c}{\rho_c} \qquad m_c = \text{mass of block}$$

$$= \frac{2}{9 \times 10^3} \quad m^3$$

Since the block is half-immersed, Vw the volume of water displaced is given by

$$V_w = \tfrac{1}{2} V_c$$

$$= \frac{1}{2} \times \frac{2}{9 \times 10^3} \quad m^3$$

Hence, the mass of water displaced Mw is given by

$$M_w = \rho_w V_w$$

$$= 10^3 \times \frac{1}{2} \times \frac{2}{9 \times 10^3} = \frac{1}{9} \quad Kg$$

The weight of water displaced is thus

$$W = M_w g = \frac{9.81}{9} \quad N$$

By Archimedes Principle this is equal to the upthrust.

Now    Tension in string = Weight – Upthrust

$$= 2 \times 9.81 - \frac{9.81}{9}$$

$$= 18.5N$$

Tension in string = 18.5N

**QUESTIONS**

1) Define force.

2) State the nature of the electrostatic force between two electrons.

3) Explain the difference between a viscous force and drag.

4) A uniform cylindrical block of wood floats upright in a layer of oil on the surface of a pond. The bottom 8cm of the block are in the pondwater, the next 10cm of the block are in the oil layer and the top 2cm of the block are above the oil layer. Calculate the density of the wood, given that the density of oil is 800Kgm$^{-3}$ and the density of the pond water is 1000Kgm$^{-3}$.

**FIG. 4.3**

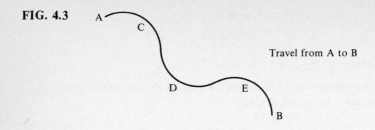

Travel from A to B

**FIG. 4.4**

Travel from A to B

$$\text{The Average Speed} = \frac{\text{total distance travelled}}{\text{total time taken}}$$

$$= \frac{ACDEB}{\text{total time taken}}$$

$$\text{The Average Velocity} = \frac{\text{total displacement}}{\text{total time taken}} \quad \text{in direction AB}$$

$$= \frac{AB}{\text{total time taken}} \quad \text{in direction AB}$$

Now since AB is a straight line it is shorter than the indirect route (since the shortest distance between two points is a straight line in Euclidean space) and so the magnitude of the speed is greater than that of the velocity.

The instantaneous speed is given by $ds/dt$. The instantaneous velocity will be also given by $ds/dt$ and is numerically equal to instantaneous speed with its direction being that of the instantaneous direction of travel. However, the concept of instantaneous velocity for a body moving haphazardly is of so little value that it is not commonly considered in practice.

4.1.4  Average Acceleration is defined as

$$\frac{\text{Change in velocity}}{\text{Time taken}}$$

Its units are ms$^{-2}$ in the given direction.

Instantaneous Velocity is defined as rate of change of velocity moved with time. In terms of calculus

$$\text{Instantaneous} \quad \text{Acceleration} \quad = \quad \frac{dv}{dt} \qquad \begin{array}{l} v = \text{velocity} \\ t = \text{time} \end{array}$$

Its units are ms$^{-2}$

Since velocity is a vector, the velocity of a body may change as a result either of (i) a change in speed or (ii) a change in direction.

In the case of a change in speed, the direction of the average acceleration and the instantaneous acceleration are in the direction of travel. A negative acceleration corresponds to a retardation or deceleration.

The case of a change of direction is more complex. For cases of haphazard motion both average acceleration and instantaneous acceleration have little meaning. However, for the case of a definite change in direction, it may be useful to consider average acceleration as in the following example:—

---

**EXAMPLE**

A car is initially travelling at a velocity of 10ms$^{-1}$ along a road in a direction 20° S of E.

2 minutes later it is still travelling at the same speed but it is now moving in a direction 20° N of E. Calculate the average acceleration.

**FIG. 4.5**

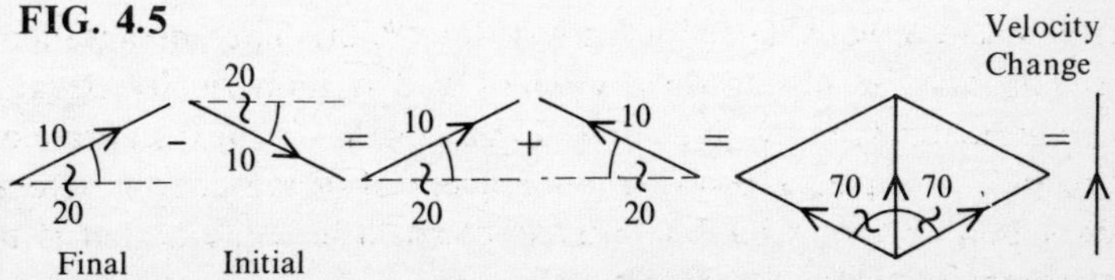

The change of velocity is the final velocity minus the initial velocity. Such a vector subtraction is performed by reversing the initial velocity and adding it to the final velocity vector as shown in Fig. 4.5

From Fig. 4.5

$$\text{Velocity Change} = 2 \times 10 \cos 70°$$
$$= 2 \times 10 \times 0.34$$
$$= 6.8 \text{ ms}^{-1} \text{ due north}$$
$$\therefore \text{Average Acceleration} = \frac{6.8}{120} = 5.7 \times 10^{-2} \text{ ms}^{-2}, \text{ due north}$$

It is useful to use the term acceleration when considering constant changes in direction for a body travelling at a steady speed. In particular, it will be shown in Chapter 7 that for circular motion

$$\text{Acceleration} = \frac{V^2}{r} \qquad \begin{array}{l} V = \text{steady speed} \\ r = \text{radius of circle} \end{array}$$

This acceleration is directed towards the centre of the circular path and is known as centripetal acceleration.

Other steady motions, such as steady speed in an elliptical path, are tractable to calculation but are not the subject of 'A' level studies because of the very difficult mathematics involved.

Note: An alternative representation of acceleration is as follows:—

$$a = \frac{dV}{dt}$$

Now using the 'Chain-Rule' of calculus

$$a = \frac{dV}{dt} = \frac{dV}{ds} \times \frac{ds}{dt}$$
$$\text{But } V = \frac{ds}{dt}$$

$$\therefore \quad a = \frac{dV}{ds} \times V$$

## 4.2  EQUATIONS OF MOTION

A body which covers equal distances in the same straight line in equal time intervals, no matter how short these are, is said to be moving with constant or uniform velocity. Therefore only a body moving in a straight line can have uniform velocity.

The acceleration of a body is uniform if its velocity changes by equal amounts in equal time intervals. The direction of this is that of the direction of travel.

We shall now derive the Equation of Motion for a body moving in a straight line with uniform acceleration.

Suppose the velocity of the body increases steadily from U to V in a time t whilst it covers a distance S in the given direction.

The uniform acceleration a is given by change of velocity/time taken

$$a = \frac{V - U}{t}$$

(i)    $V = U + at$

Since the velocity is increasing steadily then the average velocity is the mean of the initial and final velocities

$$\text{average velocity} = \frac{U + V}{2}$$

But average velocity $= \dfrac{\text{total displacement}}{\text{time taken}} = \dfrac{S}{t}$

hence    $\dfrac{S}{t} = \dfrac{U + V}{2}$

and $V = U + at$

$$\therefore \frac{S}{t} = \frac{U + U + at}{2} = \frac{2U + at}{2}$$

(ii)    $\therefore \quad \underline{S = Ut + \frac{1}{2} at^2}$

We may eliminate t from (ii)

Since $\qquad V = U + at$

then $\qquad \dfrac{V - U}{a} = t \qquad\qquad$ and so by substitution

$$S = U\left(\frac{V-U}{a}\right) + \frac{1}{2}a\left(\frac{V-U}{a}\right)^2$$

$$= \frac{UV}{a} - \frac{U^2}{a} + \frac{a}{2}\left(\frac{V^2 + U^2 - 2VU}{a^2}\right)$$

$$= \frac{UV}{a} - \frac{U^2}{a} + \frac{V^2}{2a} + \frac{U^2}{2a} - \frac{2UV}{2a}$$

$$= \frac{V^2}{2a} - \frac{U^2}{2a}$$

$$2aS = V^2 - U^2$$

or (iii) $\underline{V^2 = U^2 + 2aS}$

In the case of deceleration, in all equations a is replaced by –a.

For bodies falling under gravity, a is replaced by g in all equations.

---

**EXAMPLE**

A car moving with a velocity of $10ms^{-1}$ accelerates uniformly at $1ms^{-2}$ until it reaches a velocity of $15ms^{-1}$. Calculate the time taken and the distance travelled during the acceleration.

Here $\quad U = 10ms^{-1}$

$\qquad\quad V = 15ms^{-1}$

$\qquad\quad a = 1ms^{-1}$

To find the time t, use $V = U + at$

$\therefore 15 = 10 + t$

$\therefore \qquad t = 5s$

To find the distance S, use $S = Ut + \frac{1}{2}at^2$

$\qquad S = 10 \times 5 + \frac{1}{2} \times 1 \times 5^2$

$\qquad\quad = 50 + \frac{1}{2} \times 25$

$\qquad S = 62.5m$

Time taken = 5s, Distance travelled = 62.5m

## 4.3 GRAPHICAL REPRESENTATION OF MOTION IN A STRAIGHT LINE

### 4.3.1 Distance against time graphs

In the case of uniform speed, the graph of distance against time will be a straight line through the origin, the gradient of the line being equal to the uniform speed. This is shown in Fig. 4.6.

**FIG. 4.6**

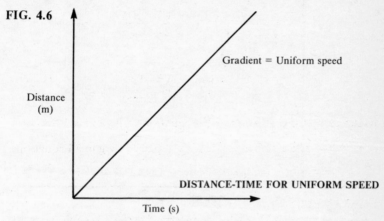

Distance (m)

Gradient = Uniform speed

**DISTANCE-TIME FOR UNIFORM SPEED**

Time (s)

In the case of non-uniform speed, the graph will be a curve. The instantaneous speed is the gradient of the tangent at the point and the average speed is the average gradient of the curve. This is shown in Fig. 4.7.

**FIG. 4.7**

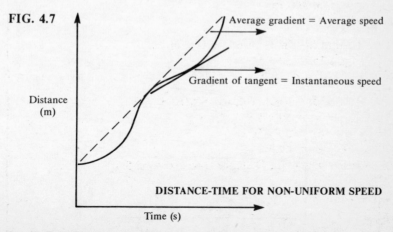

Distance (m)

Average gradient = Average speed

Gradient of tangent = Instantaneous speed

**DISTANCE-TIME FOR NON-UNIFORM SPEED**

Time (s)

In all such graphs, distance must increase as time goes by.

### 4.3.2 Displacement against time graphs

In the case of uniform velocity, the graph of displacement against time will be a straight line through the origin, the gradient of the line being equal to the uniform velocity and the direction of the velocity being that of the displacement. This is shown in Fig. 4.8.

**FIG. 4.8**

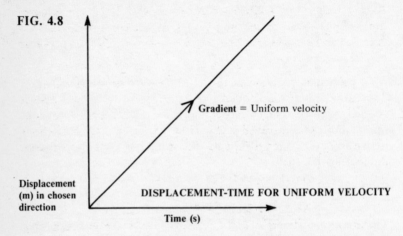

In the case of non uniform velocity, the graph will be a curve. The instantaneous velocity is the gradient of the tangent at the point with the direction being that of the displacement. The average velocity is the total displacement divided by the total time where the total

**FIG. 4.9**

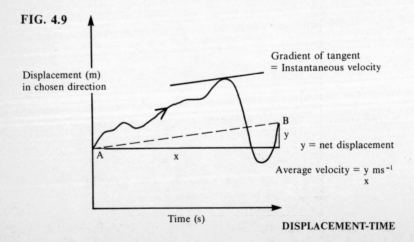

displacement is obtained by directly joining the starting point to the finishing point and subtracting the starting point. Thus in Fig. 4.9, the average velocity may be found by drawing a right angled triangle as shown with

Average Velocity $= \dfrac{y}{x}$ ms$^{-1}$ in the direction of the displacement

A very important difference between distance-time and velocity-time graphs may be seen in Fig. 4.9. Displacement may actually decrease as time goes by. This will happen when the body reverses its direction of travel.

As a particular example of this, consider the following situation. Suppose a body travels from A to B, a distance $x$ and then returns to A and that the journey is carried out at a constant speed. Obviously the total distance travelled is $2x$. However, since it has returned to its starting point, the total displacement is zero. Thus if the time for the journey is t then

$$\text{Average speed} = \frac{2x}{t}$$

$$\text{Average velocity} = 0$$

The situation is shown in Fig. 4.10 with a graphical representation in Figs. 4.11 and 4.12.

**FIG. 4.10**

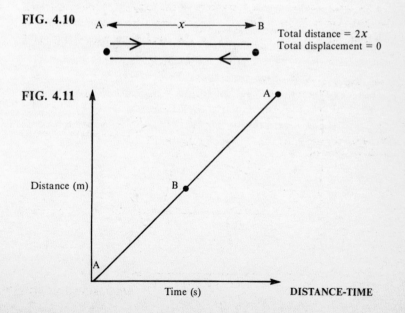

Total distance $= 2x$
Total displacement $= 0$

**FIG. 4.11**

Distance (m)

Time (s)

**DISTANCE-TIME**

**FIG. 4.12**

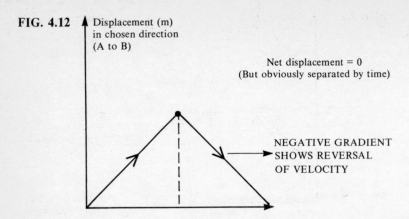

An alternative way of considering the average velocity is to say that for the first part of the journey the uniform velocity $= \frac{x}{2t}$ (since the time for the first part is the same as the time for the second part) and for the second part, the uniform velocity $= -\frac{x}{2t}$ because $x$ is now in the reverse direction.

$$\text{The average is thus} \quad \frac{\frac{x}{2t} + -\frac{x}{2t}}{2} \; = \; 0$$

### 4.3.3 Velocity against time graphs

In the case of uniform acceleration, the graph of velocity against time will be a straight line, the gradient of which is equal to the uniform acceleration. A positive gradient indicates acceleration whilst a negative gradient indicates deceleration. Zero gradient indicates zero acceleration or uniform velocity. These cases are shown in Fig. 4.13. The direction of the acceleration is that of the velocity, or, in the case of a deceleration, in the opposite direction to that of the velocity.

FIG. 4.13

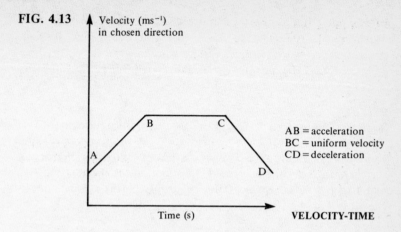

AB = acceleration
BC = uniform velocity
CD = deceleration

VELOCITY-TIME

In the case of non uniform acceleration, the instantaneous acceleration is the gradient of the tangent at the point. The average acceleration is the total velocity change divided by the total time. The total velocity change is as shown in Fig. 4.14.

FIG. 4.14

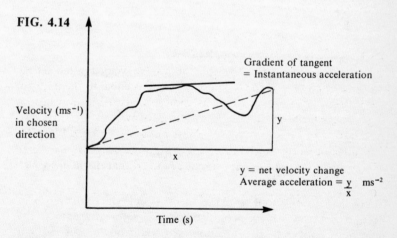

The area under a velocity-time graph is equal to the displacement. In the case of uniform acceleration, such an area may be calculated easily by standard mensuration technique — areas of trapeziums or rectangles and triangles. However, in the case of non-uniform acceleration, the area would have to be evaluated by integration.

Finally, it should be remembered that when dealing with displacement, velocity and acceleration of bodies travelling in straight lines, quite complex situations can arise since all three quantities may be positive or negative. Consider the following cases:—

Case 1:
Suppose a body starts at A and travels at a uniform velocity to B, a distance $x$ away. It then returns to A at the same speed and continues to C, a distance $x$ away on the opposite side of A. Finally it returns to A at the same speed. This motion is shown in Fig. 4.15 and the graphical representation of displacement against time is shown in Fig. 4.16.

**FIG. 4.15**

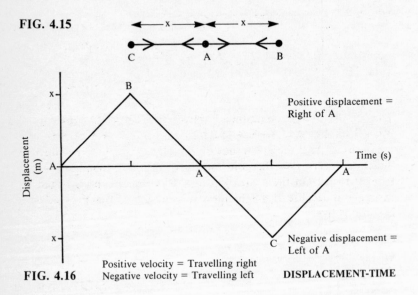

**FIG. 4.16**    Positive velocity = Travelling right
Negative velocity = Travelling left    **DISPLACEMENT-TIME**

In Fig. 4.16, from A to B both displacement and velocity are positive. From B to A, the displacement is still positive since we are still to the right of A. However, the direction of travel is now to the left and therefore negative. From A to C the displacement is right of A, therefore negative, and we are travelling to the left resulting in a negative velocity. Finally from C to A, the displacement is left of A, therefore negative but the direction of travel is to the right giving a positive velocity.

Case 2:

Suppose a body starts from rest at A and accelerates uniformly to B, a distance $x$ away. It then reverses its velocity by reversing its direction and it decelerates uniformly back to A, as in Fig. 4.17

**FIG. 4.17**

**FIG. 4.18**

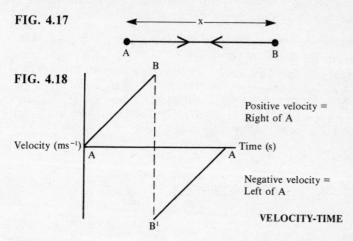

VELOCITY-TIME

The graphical representation of velocity against time is shown in Fig. 4.18 In Fig. 4.18, from A to B both the velocity and acceleration are positive. At B the magnitude of the velocity is maintained but its direction reverses so the point on the graph immediately changes from B to $B^1$. On the return journey to A the velocity is negative throughout because of the change of direction. Note that the gradient is still positive.

**FIG. 4.19**

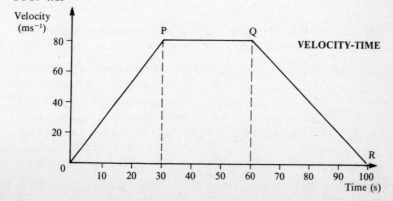

VELOCITY-TIME

**EXAMPLE**

The velocity time graph of a car driving along a straight road is shown below in **Fig. 4.19.** Find the uniform accelerations of the car throughout the journey, the total distance travelled and the average velocity throughout the interval.

For OP, uniform acceleration = gradient = $^{80}/_{30}$ = 2.67ms$^{-2}$
For PQ, the acceleration = 0 ms$^2$
For QR, the acceleration is – $^{80}/_{40}$ = –2.00ms$^{-2}$

$$\begin{aligned}
\text{Total distance} &= \text{Area under graph} \\
&= (\tfrac{1}{2} \times 30 \times 80) + (30 \times 80) + (\tfrac{1}{2} \times 40 \times 80) \\
&= 1200 + 2400 + 1600 \\
&= 5200\text{m}
\end{aligned}$$

$$\text{Average velocity} = \frac{\text{Total distance}}{\text{Total time}} = \frac{5200}{100} =$$
$$= 52\text{ms}^{-1}$$

## 4.4 MEASUREMENT OF THE ACCELERATION OF FREE FALL

Experiments show that at a given place all bodies falling freely under gravity have the same constant acceleration whatever their mass, providing that air resistance is negligible. This acceleration of free fall is the acceleration due to gravity denoted by g. Its value varies slightly with height but is generally taken as 9.81ms$^2$ (or 9.8 or 10 dependent upon the precision quoted).

One method of determining g is to use a pendulum and this will be discussed in Chapter 8. Another method is the free fall method.

In this method the fall of a ball bearing over a measured distance is timed and the values obtained are substituted into an equation of motion. The basic problem is that for all reasonable distances of fall, the time taken is very small and precision methods of timing have to be employed. The solution is to use the apparatus shown in Fig. 4.20.

## FIG. 4.20

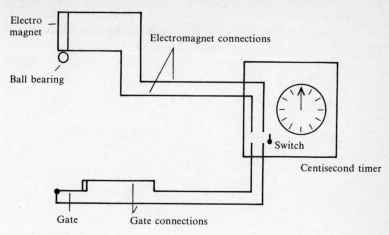

The ball bearing is held by an energised electromagnet. At a suitable distance vertically below the electromagnet is a hinged flap or gate. Electrical connections from the electromagnet and gate are taken to a centisecond timer fitted with a switch. When the switch is opened the electromagnet is de-energised simultaneously releasing the ball bearing and starting the timer. The ball bearing subsequently hits the gate, breaking its circuit and stopping the timer. The experiment is repeated to obtain a series of values of S, the distance fallen (measured from the **bottom** of the ball bearing to the gate) and t, time taken.

Now $S = Ut + \frac{1}{2} at^2$
Here $U = O$ and $a = g$
$\therefore \quad s = \frac{1}{2} gt^2$

Thus if a graph is plotted of S against $t^2$, the result will be a straight line of gradient $g/2$.

## QUESTIONS

1) Find the uniform acceleration of a car which accelerates from the south such that its velocity changes from $10ms^{-1}$ to $20ms^{-1}$ in 5s.

2) A body is projected vertically upwards with a velocity of $20ms^{-1}$. Find the maximum height reached and the time taken to reach this height ($g = 10ms^{-2}$).

3) A sprinter can start with a velocity of $8ms^{-1}$ and run with a uniform acceleration. Use a graph to find his acceleration and his maximum velocity if it takes him 10s to run a distance of 100m.

# Chapter 5
# NEWTON'S LAWS OF MOTION

## 5.1 NEWTON'S FIRST LAW

Newton's First Law states that : Every body continues in a state of rest or uniform velocity unless compelled to do otherwise by a resultant force.

The law follows from the definition of force.

If more than one force acts upon a body then the resultant force must be found using the normal rules for the composition of vectors. (See Chapter 2). A particle which is in equilibrium is obviously acted upon by zero resultant force.

The law also suggests that a body which is at rest has a reluctance to move and, equally, a body moving with uniform velocity has a reluctance to change its velocity. This reluctance is known as inertia and the mass of a body is a measure of its inertia. Indeed the mass of a body as used in Newton's Second Law is more fully referred to as inertial mass.

## 5.2 TERMINAL VELOCITY

When a small object is dropped into a viscous liquid, it is found that the viscous retarding force acting on the object is proportional to its velocity.

**FIG. 5.1**

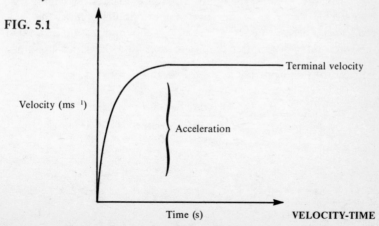

VELOCITY-TIME

The equation describing a force which is proportional to velocity is

$$F = kV$$

   $F = $ force   $V = $ velocity

   $k = $ constant

The downward force = weight.
The upward force = viscous retarding force + upthrust.

A situation is reached when the upward force equals the downward force at which point the velocity of the object reaches a steady maximum known as the terminal velocity.

Fig 5.1 shows how the terminal velocity is reached.

Raindrops fall to earth with a large velocity and so they experience a significant viscous retarding force. This force together with the minute upthrust balances the weight and therefore the raindrops reach their terminal velocity. If this were not the case and raindrops accelerated under gravity, they would acquire such a high velocity upon reaching the earth's surface that great damage would be done.

In the free-fall experiment as described in Chapter 4, the upthrust and viscous retarding force are negligible in comparison to the weight of the ball bearing.

## 5.3  MOMENTUM

5.3.1   Momentum is defined as the product of mass and velocity

   Momentum = Mass x Velocity

It is a vector and its units are $Kgms^{-1}$ in a given direction.

The Principle of Conservation of Momentum states: Providing that no external forces act, when two or more bodies collide, the total momentum before impact measured in a chosen direction is equal to the total momentum after impact measured in the same direction.

A proof of this principle is given in Section 5.4.

**FIG. 5.2**

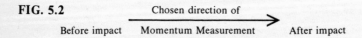

Chosen direction of
Before impact    Momentum Measurement    After impact

In Fig. 5.2
Total momentum before impact $= MV_1 - mv_1$

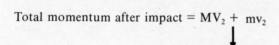

IN DIRECTION OF MOTION       IN OPPOSITE DIRECTION SO SUBTRACT

Total momentum after impact $= MV_2 + mv_2$

Thus   $MV_1 - mv_1 = MV_2 + mv_2$

---

**EXAMPLE**

An object of mass 3Kg moving with a velocity of $3ms^{-1}$ collides head on with an object of mass 2Kg moving with a velocity of $0.75ms^{-1}$ in the opposite direction. Assuming that they coalesce, state their velocity and direction of motion.

Since the 3Kg mass obviously has the greater momentum, its direction is taken as the chosen direction.
Original momentum of 3Kg $= 3 \times 3 = 9Kgms^{-1}$
Original momentum of 2Kg $= 2 \times 0.75 = 1.5Kgms^{-1}$
Total momentum before collision $= 7.5Kgms^{-1}$
Suppose the common velocity after impact is $Vms^{-1}$
Total momentum after collision $= (3 + 2) V = 5V \ Kgms^{-1}$
Using the Principle of Conservation of Momentum
$$5V = 7.5$$
$$V = 1.5ms^{-1}$$
Since this is positive, it is in the chosen direction.

The velocity after impact $= 1.5ms^{-1}$ in the direction of travel of the 3Kg mass.

---

5.3.2   The Principle of Conservation of Momentum applies also to collisions in two dimensions, known as oblique impact. Both before and after impact the momenta must be resolved in the given direction.

**FIG. 5.3**

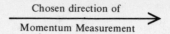

Chosen direction of
Momentum Measurement

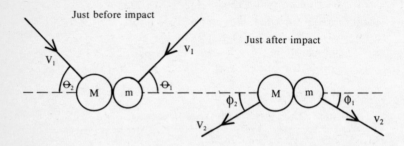

Just before impact

Just after impact

Thus in Fig. 5.3

Total momentum before impact $= MV_1 \cos \Theta_2 - mv_1 \cos \Theta_1$

Total momentum after inpact $= mv_2 \cos \varphi_1 - MV_2 \cos \varphi_2$

Thus $MV_1 \cos \Theta_2 - mv_1 \cos \Theta_1 = mv_2 \cos \varphi_1 - MV_2 \cos \varphi_2$

## 5.4 NEWTON'S SECOND LAW

Newton's Second Law states that: The rate of change of momentum of a body is proportional to the applied force and takes place in the same direction as that of the force.

Consider a force F acts on a mass m initially travelling at a velocity V. Newton's Second Law may then be written

$$F \; \alpha \; \frac{d(mV)}{dt} \qquad\qquad t = \text{time}$$

Since m is constant we may write

$$F \; \alpha \; m \; \frac{dV}{dt}$$

But $dV/dt$ = acceleration, a

Thus $F \; \alpha \;$ ma

This may be written as an equation if we introduce a constant of proportionality, k

$$F = kma$$

We may let $k = 1$ and define our unit of force, the Newton, accordingly.

The Newton (N) is defined as that force which when acting on a mass of 1Kg produces an acceleration of $1ms^{-2}$.

The above equation may then be written

$$F = ma$$
OR FORCE = MASS x ACCELERATION

Use of the above equation (which is NOT a statement of Newton's Second Law but which follows from it) enables the weight of a body to be related to its mass. The weight W of a body is the force of gravity acting on it towards the centre of the earth. If g is the acceleration of the body towards the centre of the earth then

$$F = ma$$

becomes $\quad\quad W = mg$

If $g = 9.8ms^{-2}$ then a mass of 1Kg has a weight of 9.8N

(Also since $a = F/m$, the units of acceleration may also be given as $N\ Kg^{-1}$).

Returning to the statement of the Law we may say that the rate of change of momentum equals the applied force since we have chosen $k = 1$

Thus $$F = \frac{d\ (mV)}{dt}$$

Using the product rule of calculus

$$F = \frac{mdV}{dt} + \frac{Vdm}{dt}$$

$$F = ma + \frac{Vdm}{dt}$$

At 'A' level we are not concerned with simultaneous changes in mass and velocity.

If however the mass rather than the velocity changes then

$$F = \frac{Vdm}{dt}$$
OR FORCE = VELOCITY x RATE OF CHANGE OF MASS

This equation is met in two situations: firstly when material falls from a hopper onto a conveyor belt and secondly when moving particles (e.g. rain) impinge upon a surface.

**EXAMPLE**

Onto a conveyor belt moving at a steady horizontal velocity, falls sand vertically at a rate of $0.8 \text{Kgs}^{-1}$. If the velocity of the belt is $0.25 \text{ms}^{-1}$, calculate the force required to keep the belt moving at the steady velocity.

Here $\quad V = 0.25 \text{ms}^{-1}$

$\quad\quad dm/dt = 0.8 \text{Kgs}^{-1}$

$$F = \frac{Vdm}{dt} = 0.25 \times 0.8 = 0.2\text{N}$$

Force required $= 0.2\text{N}$

## 5.5 IMPULSE

Using $\quad\quad F = \dfrac{d(mV)}{dt}$

we can write

$$Fdt = d(mV)$$

The quantity on the left hand side of this equation, Fdt is known as the impulse of a force and we normally use the term when we consider a large force acting for a very short time.

The quantity on the right hand side of the equation is the change of momentum. Thus

<u>IMPULSE = CHANGE OF MOMENTUM</u>

The notion of impulse is important in ball games such as cricket. The change of momentum of the ball is greater as the impulse increases, i.e. if the force acts for a longer time. This is achieved by keeping the bat in contact with the ball for a longer time by "following through" the hit.

## 5.6 PROOF OF THE CONSERVATION OF MOMENTUM PRINCIPLE

Suppose a bullet is fired from a gun. Since no net force acts upon the system

Forward force on bullet = Backward force on gun.

Writing this algebraically and choosing the direction of the bullet as the given direction

$$F_{\text{ON BULLET}} = -F_{\text{ON GUN}}$$

From Newton's Second Law

Rate of Change of Momentum of Bullet = –Rate of Change of Momentum of Gun

By integration

Change of Momentum of Bullet = –Change of Momentum of Gun

or

Change of Momentum of Bullet + Change of Momentum of Gun = O

∴ Total Change of Momentum = O

Therefore the momentum before the collision — an explosion in this case, is equal to the momentum afterwards and this is the Principle of Conservation of Momentum.

## 5.7 EXPERIMENTAL VERIFICATION OF NEWTON'S SECOND LAW

Newton's Second Law may be verified experimentally by applying varying forces to a known mass and measuring the acceleration produced.

The arrangement used is shown in Fig. 5.4

**FIG. 5.4**

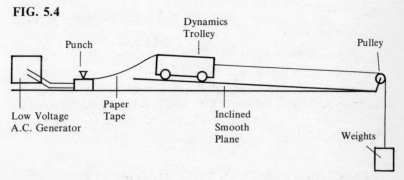

The dynamics trolley is placed on the plane, the inclination of which is adjusted until the trolley rolls down the plane at a uniform velocity. At this point any frictional losses have been compensated for. A known force, provided by weights is applied to the trolley to which a piece of paper tape has been attached. The paper tape passes under a punch (which hits the tape through a piece of carbon paper) vibrating at 50 "punches" every second because it is driven with a low voltage d.c. supply operating at mains frequency. The trolley, which has been restrained until now, is released and it accelerates down the plane until it is stopped at the end. A new piece of paper tape is fitted and the experiment repeated using a different weight. This is repeated four more times.

The observations noted are as follows:

In each case the force used is the weight, W where

$$W = Mg$$

M = Mass attached
g = acc due to gravity

In each case the acceleration produced may be calculated by an examination of the paper tape. On it will be seen a series of dots which become more widely spaced as the time goes by for the application of a given force. An initial velocity is found by measuring the distance between two adjacent dots. Suppose this distance is , the velocity V, will then be given by

$$V_1 = \frac{\text{displacement}}{\text{time}} = \frac{x_1}{1/50} = 50\,x_1$$

(Since the frequency of the punch is 50Hz, the time between successive dots is $1/50$s).

another pair of dots which are a significant way along the tape from the first pair. If the distance between these two dots is $x_2$ the new velocity $V_2$ is given by

$$V_2 = \frac{x_2}{1/50} = 50\,x_2$$

$$\therefore \text{Change in velocity} = V_2 - V_1 = 50(x_2 - x_1)$$

**FIG. 5.5**

MOTION

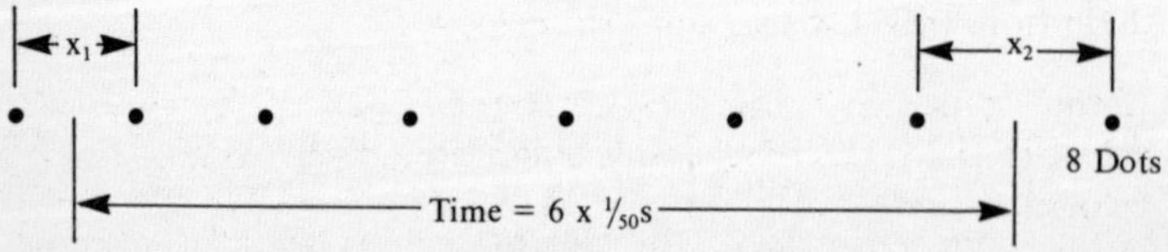

For 8 dots, the time interval elapsed = 6 x $1/50$s
For n dots, the time interval elapsed = (n – 2) $1/50$s

Now suppose the total number of dots punched is n, the time interval over which the velocity changes is given by $(n - 2) \frac{1}{50}$. This is shown in Fig. 5.5.

Thus Uniform Acceleration $= \dfrac{50 (x_2 - x_1)}{\frac{1}{50}(n - 2)} = 2500 \dfrac{(x_2 - x_1)}{n - 2}$

Now if F = ma, a graph of F against a should be a straight line through the origin of gradient equal to m. Thus a graph of the corresponding value of mg against $2500 \dfrac{(x_2 - x_1)}{(n - 2)}$ should be a

straight line through the origin of gradient equal to the mass of the trolley, as in Fig. 5.6.

**FIG. 5.6**

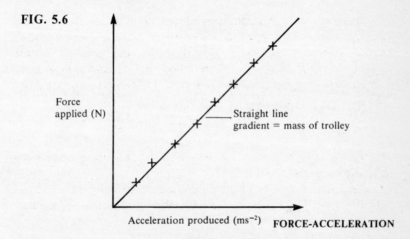

Force applied (N)

Straight line gradient = mass of trolley

Acceleration produced (ms⁻²)    **FORCE-ACCELERATION**

The reason for choosing two widely spaced sets of dots is as follows. In order to calculate a change in velocity we require to subtract two uniform velocities. However, in calculating the two different velocities we are, in effect, calculating two average velocities — since we are concerned with an accelerating body which cannot, by definition, travel with a uniform velocity!

If the change in velocity is great then each of the two average velocities may be more easily considered to be equal to uniform velocities.

In practice therefore a large number of dots must be obtained. This means that a long inclined plane is required together with a high laboratory bench and a long piece of string — in order that the weights will not hit the floor before the trolley completes its journey to the end of the plane.

## 5.8 NEWTON'S THIRD LAW

Suppose two bodies, A and B are in contact as shown in Fig. 5.7. If A exerts a force on B then B also exerts a force on A. These two forces are known as action and reaction forces. Any can be chosen as the action and the other will then be the reaction.

Newton's Third Law states that: Action and reaction are equal in magnitude and opposite in direction.

**FIG. 5.7**

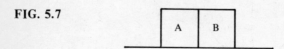

If, in Fig. 5.8, A exerts a force on B of F Newtons to the right then B will exert a force on A of F Newtons to the left. One of these forces is an action force, the other is the reaction force.

**FIG. 5.8**

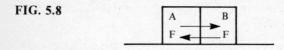

It is very important to note that these two forces act upon two different bodies.

Imagine the situation in Fig. 5.9 where a force F N is applied along a string to a mass of M kg. Since a net force is acting upon the mass, it will be accelerated at a ms$^{-2}$ given by

**FIG. 5.9**

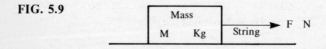

$$F = Ma$$
$$\text{i.e.} \quad a = \frac{F}{M}$$

However, in terms of Newton's Third Law, the force F in the string is an action force acting upon the mass. The equal and opposite reaction force F acting to the left is the force of the mass acting upon the string. Note how this is a two body situation involving the string and the mass. If we were pulling the string with the force F the reaction force would make us aware of the mass!

**FIG. 5.10**

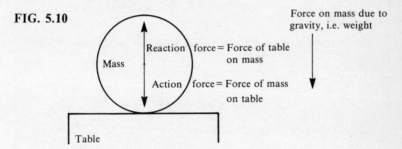

Force on mass due to gravity, i.e. weight

Mass

Reaction force = Force of table on mass

Action force = Force of mass on table

Table

In the case of a mass resting on a table as in Fig. 5.10. Here the action force acts on the table and the reaction force acts on the mass. However, the mass is at equilibrium since the two forces acting up it are equal and opposite.

i.e.  DOWNWARD FORCE ON MASS DUE TO GRAVITY =
(WEIGHT)
UPWARD FORCE ON MASS DUE TO TABLE
(REACTION)

**EXAMPLE**
In Fig. 5.11, a train of mass 15,000Kg pulls a truck of mass 2,000Kg. If they both accelerate at $0.2ms^{-2}$, show using Newton's Third Law that the net force required is 3400N. (Assume they are connected by cable).

**FIG. 5.11**

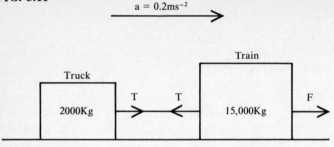

The tension in the cable needed to accelerate the truck is given by

$$T = Ma$$
$$M = 2000\text{Kg} \quad a = 0.2\text{ms}^{-2}$$
$$T = 2000 \times 0.2 = \underline{400\text{N}}$$

Thus 400N acts on the truck to accelerate it. By Newton's Third Law, a force of 400N will act on the train to retard it (the reaction force). The net force required to accelerate the system is

$$F - T \quad = \text{Mass of train} \times \text{acceleration}$$
$$F - 400 = 15,000 \times 0.2$$
$$= 3000$$
$$\underline{F = 3400\text{N}}$$

i.e. 3400N are required of which 3000N are needed to accelerate the train and 400N are needed to accelerate the truck.

N.B. The above example was to show a use of Newton's Third Law. In actual practice it would be much quicker to apply $F = ma$ to the whole system when

$$m = 15,000 + 2,000 = 17,000\text{Kg}$$
$$a = 0.2\text{ms}^{-2}$$
$$F = ma$$
$$= 17000 \times 0.2$$
$$F = 3400\text{N}$$

i.e.   Total force = 3400N

## QUESTIONS

1) Define momentum.

2) A Saturn V rocket has an initial acceleration at lift off, when its mass is 2.8 x $10^6$Kg, of $1.8ms^{-2}$. Assuming $g = 10ms^{-2}$, find the initial thrust.

3) Biscuits, each of mass $10^{-2}$Kg, are fed vertically onto a conveyor belt moving at a steady horizontal velocity of $0.1ms^{-1}$. Assuming that the force required to drive the belt is 0.01N whilst the process occurs, find the number of biscuits per minute fed onto the belt.

# Chapter 6
# WORK, POWER AND ENERGY

## 6.1 ENERGY
Energy is the capacity to do work.

Since it is, in effect, "latent work", its units are those of work — J.

Energy exists in many forms — mechanical, thermal, sound, chemical, electrostatic (due to static charges), magnetic (the magnetic energy due to the passage of an electric current) or electromagnetic (the energy associated with an electromagnetic wave), electrical, nuclear, solar, hydrodynamic (the energy due to fluid motion) and wind. In relativity, we use the fact that mass itself is a form of energy.

## 6.2 WORK
Work is done wherever a force moves its point of application. Work is defined as: The product of force and distance moved in the direction of the force. Examples of work calculations are shown in Fig. 6.1.

The unit of work is the Joule, symbol J.

Work is done at the expense of energy thus when a system does work, its "content" of energy decreases because energy is transferred to do the work.

**FIG. 6.1**

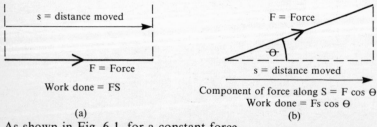

| | |
|---|---|
| s = distance moved | F = Force |
| F = Force | s = distance moved |
| Work done = FS | Component of force along S = F cos Θ |
| | Work done = Fs cos Θ |
| (a) | (b) |

As shown in Fig. 6.1, for a constant force
$$\text{WORK} = \text{FORCE} \times \text{DISTANCE MOVED IN DIRECTION OF FORCE}$$
$$W = FS$$

For a constantly varying force

WORK = AVERAGE FORCE x DISTANCE MOVED IN DIRECTION OF FORCE

For a force which varies non-uniformly

$$dW = FdS$$

and integration is needed to evaluate the total work done in such a process.

In all cases, the work done is equal to the area under a force — time graph as shown in Fig. 6.2

**FIG. 6.2**

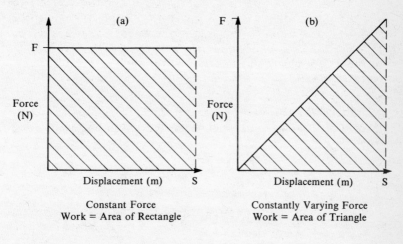

Constant Force
Work = Area of Rectangle

Constantly Varying Force
Work = Area of Triangle

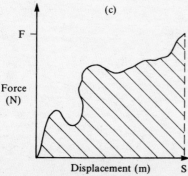

Varying Force
Work = Area under Curve

| | | |
|---|---|---|
| Since | $W = Fs$ | |
| Now | $p = \dfrac{F}{A}$ | $p$ = pressure<br>$A$ area |
| So | $W = PAs$ | |
| Also | $V = As$ | $V$ = volume change |
| So | $W = PV$ | |

Quite often this latter expression is met in the study of gases expanding. However, in these cases P is not constant as volume changes. In these cases

$$W = \int_{V_1}^{V_2} P\,dV$$

*where*  $V_1$ = initial volume
$V_2$ = final volume

In order to evaluate this integral the variation of P with volume must be known.

## 6.3 POWER
Power is defined as: The rate of energy transfer or the rate of doing work.

$$P = \frac{dW}{dt}$$

$p$ = power
$W$ = work
$t$ = time

(For a uniform rate of working $P = W/t$).

The units of power are $Js^{-1}$ or Watts (W). Thus 1 Watt is a rate of working of 1J every second.

Since for a constant force $W = Fs$

$$P = \frac{dW}{dt} = \frac{d(Fs)}{dt} = F\frac{ds}{dt} = Fv$$

Power = Force x Velocity

**EXAMPLE**

A car of mass 1000Kg moves at a constant velocity of 20ms$^{-1}$ along a road. If the tractive force of the engine is 200N, calculate the power which it develops.

Use    P = FV
F = 200N
V = 20ms$^{-1}$
∴  P = 200 x 20
= 4000W or 4Kw
Power developed = 4Kw.

## 6.4   MECHANICAL ENERGY

There are two types of mechanical energy.

### 6.4.1   Kinetic Energy (K.E.)

The kinetic energy of a body is energy which the body possesses because of its motion.

$$K.E. = \tfrac{1}{2}mv^2$$

m = mass of body
v = velocity of body

Since K.E. depends upon $v^2$, this means that doubling the velocity of a body, increases its K.E. by a factor of four. (This equation breaks down at very high velocities — above 75% that of light).

**EXAMPLE**

To calculate the kinetic energy of a bullet of mass 20g travelling at a velocity of 50ms$^{-1}$

Use K.E. = $\tfrac{1}{2}$mV$^2$
Here   m = 20g = 20 x 10$^{-3}$ = 2 x 10$^{-2}$ Kg
V = 50ms$^{-1}$

∴ K.E. = $\tfrac{1}{2}$ x 2 x 10$^{-2}$ x 50
= 0.5J
Kinetic Energy of Bullet = 0.5J

### 6.4.2 Potential Energy (P.E.)

This is energy which a body possesses by virtue of its position or state.

Potential energy of position is exemplified by gravitational potential energy — the potential energy which a body has because it is situated in the earth's gravitational field.

If an object of mass m situated on the surface of the earth is raised by a distance h its increase in P.E. will be given by

$$\text{Increase in P.E.} = mgh \qquad g = \text{acc due to gravity}$$

We usually take the P.E. on the surface of the earth as a zero point of reference and therefore at a distance h above the earth's surface.

$$\text{P.E.} = mgh$$

If a body is initially at a height $h_1$ and is raised to a final height $h_2$ then

$$\text{initial P.E.} = mgh_1$$
$$\text{final P.E.} = mgh_2$$
$$\text{Increase in P.E.} = mg(h_2 - h_1)$$
$$h_2 - h_1 = \text{increase in height} = h, \text{ say}$$
$$\text{Increase in P.E.} = mg \times \text{increase in height}$$

Potential energy of state is exemplified by elastic potential energy — the potential energy which, for example, a spring has when it is stretched beyond its normal length.

If a spring for which Hooke's Constant is k is stretched by an amount $x$ then its P.E. is given by

$$\text{P.E.} = \tfrac{1}{2}kx^2$$

---

**EXAMPLE**

Calculate the P.E. stored in a wire for which Hooke's Constant is $9\,Nm^{-1}$ if it is stretched by 5cm.

$$\text{Use P.E.} = \tfrac{1}{2}kx^2$$
$$k = 9\ Nm^{-1}$$
$$x = 5cm = 5 \times 10^{-2}m$$
$$\text{P.E.} = \tfrac{1}{2} \times 9 \times (5 \times 10^{-2})^2$$
$$= 4.5 \times 25 \times 10^{-4}$$
$$= 1.125 \times 10^{-2}\ J$$

Thus Stored P.E. $= 1.125 \times 10\ 2$ J

(This amount of work had to be done in stretching the spring and is then stored as P.E.)

## 6.5 THE PRINCIPLE OF CONSERVATION OF ENERGY

6.5.1 The Principle of Conservation of Energy states that: Energy can neither be created nor destroyed but may be converted from one form to another.

If we consider an object held above the ground, it will have potential energy.

If it is released, the potential energy will be lost in overcoming air resistance and the rest will be converted into kinetic energy. (Here air resistance is known as a dissipative force). When the object hits the ground its kinetic energy will be converted into P.E. of the ground (deformation energy), thermal energy, sound and depending upon the nature of the ground, light.

**FIG. 6.3**

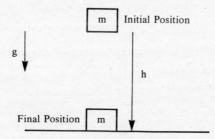

We are often involved in calculations in which dissipative forces are negligible when objects are in free fall and then all the initial P.E. is converted into K.E. Thus in Fig. 6.3

Initial P.E. $= mgh$

Final P.E. $=$ O (immediately before it strikes the ground)

Loss of P.E. $= mgh$

Initial K.E. $=$ O

Final K.E. $= \frac{1}{2}mv^2$ (velocity is v immediately before it
strikes the ground)

Gain of K.E. $= \frac{1}{2}mv^2$

Thus

$$mgh = \tfrac{1}{2}mv^2$$

or

$$V = \sqrt{2gh}$$

---

**EXAMPLE**
A bullet of mass 50g is fired from a rifle and travels horizontally so as to hit a 400g mass hanging from a light string 1m long. The bullet and mass are deflected through an angle of 30°. Find the velocity of the bullet just before impact. You may neglect air resistance and assume g = 10ms⁻².

Using Fig. 6.4

**FIG. 6.4**

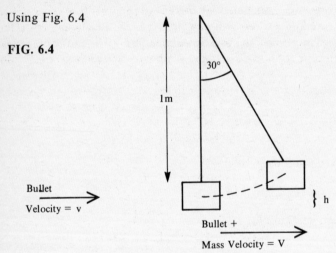

Suppose the velocity of the bullet just before impact is v. After impact the velocity of the bullet and the mass is V.

Applying Conservation of Momentum

$$\frac{50}{1000}\, v = \left(\frac{400 + 50}{1000}\right) V$$

$$v = 9V$$

Applying Conservation of Energy
Loss of K.E. of mass + bullet =
　　　Gain of P.E. of mass + bullet

½ x 0.45 x V² = 0.45 x 10 x h

$$V^2 = 20h$$

But       h  = 1 – cos 30°

               = 0.134m

          V  = $\sqrt{2.68}$

               = 1.637ms⁻¹

and      v  = 9V

               = 9 x 1.637

               = 14.73ms⁻¹

Thus velocity of bullet just before impact = 14.73ms⁻¹

In a collision, momentum as we have seen, is always conserved. Kinetic energy may or may not be conserved depending upon the material from which the colliding objects are made. If it is conserved, the collision is known as elastic. Otherwise it is known as inelastic.

6.5.2   Often work is done at the expense of kinetic energy. For example, when a bullet strikes a surface its kinetic energy is used up in doing work against the resistive force which the surface displays against penetration of the bullet.

In such situations

$$dW = d\ (\tfrac{1}{2}mv^2)$$

or        $$Fds = d\ (\tfrac{1}{2}mv^2)$$

For a constant force

        Force x distance = Loss of K.E.

**EXAMPLE**

A bullet of mass 5g travelling at 100ms⁻¹ hits a target and is brought completely to rest after travelling 5cm into the target. Calculate the constant retarding force acting upon the bullet whilst it is being brought to rest.

Original K.E. of bullet $= \dfrac{1}{2}mv^2 = \dfrac{1}{2} \times \dfrac{5}{1000} \times 100^2$

                             = 25J

Assume all this K.E. is used in overcoming the retarding force

Loss of K.E. = Work done

$$\tfrac{1}{2}mv^2 - O = Fs$$
$$25 = Fs$$
$$= F \times \frac{5}{100}$$
$$F = 500N$$

Retarding Force = 500N

## QUESTIONS

1) A boy climbs a vertical ladder of height 7.5m at a uniform rate in 15s. If he develops 1Kw of power and $g = 10ms^{-2}$, calculate his mass.

2) Define work and power.

3) A stationary nucleus of radium of mass 226 units disintegrates into an alpha particle of mass 4 units and a radon particle of mass 222 units. If the kinetic energy of the alpha particle is E, show that the energy of the radon nucleus is 2E/111.
(Hint: apply Conservation of Momentum to the disintegration and express the velocities of the particle in terms of kinetic energies).

# Chapter 7
# ROTATION

## 7.1  RADIAN MEASURE

In Fig. 7.1, the angle $\Theta$ in radian measure is defined by

$$\frac{\text{arc length}}{\text{radius}}$$

i.e. $\qquad \Theta = \dfrac{x}{r}$

**Fig. 7.1**

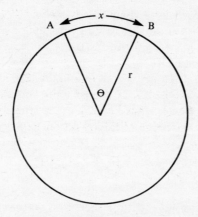

The abbreviation for radian is rad, symbol C in superscript, i.e. $\Theta^c$

The radian may be related to the degree as follows.

Suppose that if instead of starting at A and moving to B, an object continues to move around the circle so that it returns to A. It will then have completed one revolution. $\Theta$ will therefore be equal to 360°. Also $x$ = circumference = $2\pi r$

Thus in radian measure

$$\Theta = \frac{x}{r} = \frac{2\pi r}{r} = 2\pi$$

Thus $\qquad \underline{2\pi^c = 360° = 1 \text{ REVOLUTION}}$

Thus, approximately, a radian is equivalent to 57°

**FIG. 7.2**

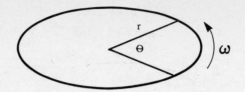

## 7.2 ANGULAR SPEED AND ANGULAR VELOCITY

In Fig. 7.2, consider a disc of radius r rotating at a uniform rate. Suppose that in a time, t, it rotates through an angle Θ radians such that a line on its surface would rotate through this angle.

We define the uniform angular speed as

$$\frac{\text{angle moved through}}{\text{time taken}}$$

We use the symbol $\omega$ (lower case omega) to denote angular speed

Thus $$\omega = \frac{\Theta}{t}$$

Units radians per second (rad s$^{-1}$)

In the case of non-uniform rotation, the instantaneous angular speed is

$$\omega = \frac{d\Theta}{dt}$$

It is important to note that for such a body, $\omega$ is the same for all points and is therefore independent of the distance of a point from the axis of rotation.

**FIG. 7.3**

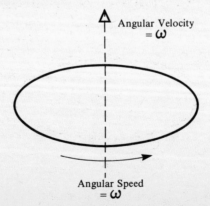

Angular Velocity
= $\omega$

Angular Speed
= $\omega$

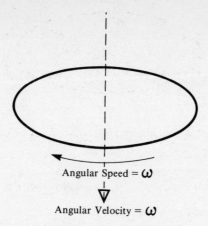

Angular Speed = $\omega$

Angular Velocity = $\omega$

In addition to the disc having an angular speed, it also possesses an angular velocity. Naturally this is a vector quantity and is equivalent to angular speed in a specified direction. The direction chosen is illustrated in Fig. 7.3.

However, this fact is not part of 'A' level physics since it involves mathematics beyond the scope of such a course. Therefore at this level we only really discuss angular speed and refer to it as angular speed or angular velocity, making no reference to direction, i.e. we treat angular speed and angular velocity as identical.

## 7.3 RELATIONSHIP BETWEEN ANGULAR AND LINEAR VELOCITY

Consider a disc rotating at a steady angular speed, $\omega$ rad s$^{-1}$, Fig. 7.4.

**FIG. 7.4.**

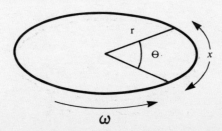

Suppose in a time t it moves through $\Theta$ radians. If the radius of the disc is r then during this motion a point on the circumference of the disc will move through a distance $x$ where

$$x = r\Theta \qquad \text{by definition of radian measure}$$

Hence
$$\frac{x}{t} = \frac{r\Theta}{t}$$

But $x/t$ is the steady speed of the edge of the disc

i.e.
$$v = \frac{x}{t}$$

So
$$v = \frac{r\Theta}{t} = r\omega$$

$$v = r\omega$$

or

Linear Speed = Radius x Angular Speed

Now the numerical value of velocity is identical to that of speed and we often quote the above relationship as

Linear Velocity = Radius x Angular Velocity

---

**EXAMPLE**

A wheel revolves at a steady rate of 120 rev per minute. Calculate (i) its angular velocity in rad $s^{-1}$; (ii) the linear velocity of a point on the wheel 0.5m from the axis of rotation.

$$120 \text{ rev per minute} = 2 \text{ rev } s^{-1}$$
$$1 \text{ rev} = 2\pi \text{ rad}$$
$$\therefore 2 \text{ rev } s^{-1} = 4\pi \text{ rad } s^{-1}$$
$$\therefore \omega = 4\pi \text{ rad } s^{-1}$$

Now
$$v = r\omega$$
$$r = 0.5m$$
$$\omega = 4\pi \text{ rad } s^{-1}$$
$$\therefore v = 0.5 \times 4\pi = 2\pi \text{ ms}^{-1}$$

Angular Velocity = $4\pi$ rad $s^{-1}$
Linear Velocity = $2\pi$ ms$^{-1}$

## 7.4 ANGULAR ACCELERATION

Angular acceleration is defined as rate of change of angular velocity.

$$\text{Angular Acceleration} \quad \alpha = \frac{dw}{dt}$$

Units: rad s$^{-2}$

**FIG. 7.5**

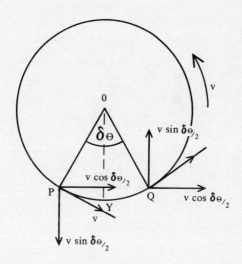

## 7.5 CENTRIPETAL ACCELERATION

In Fig. 7.5 consider a particle describing a circle of radius r at a constant speed v.

The particle will move from P to Q in a time $\delta t$ and the angle moved through is $\delta\theta$ radians.

Resolving the velocities at P and Q into components parallel to OY and perpendicular to OY we have

Perpendicular to OY

|  |  |
|---|---|
| At P | v cos $\delta\theta/2$ |
| At Q | v cos $\delta\theta/2$ |

Change of Velocity = O

Parallel to OY

At P $\quad\quad\quad\quad\quad$ v sin $\delta\theta/2$ away from O

i.e. $\quad\quad\quad\quad$ – v sin $\delta\theta/2$ towards O

At Q $\quad\quad\quad\quad\quad$ v sin $\delta\theta/2$ towards O

Change of Velocity = 2u sin $\delta\theta/2$

Now if SO is very small then sin $\delta\theta/2$ is equal to $\delta\theta/2$

$$\text{Change of Velocity } 2v\frac{\delta\theta}{2}$$

$$= v\,\delta\theta$$

The average acceleration over the interval is then

$$v\,\frac{\delta\theta}{\delta t}$$

Thus the acceleration towards O, along OY, i.e. towards the centre of the circle is

$$v\,\frac{\delta\theta}{\delta t}\quad\quad\quad \text{as } \delta t \longrightarrow O$$

i.e. $\quad a = v\dfrac{d\theta}{dt} = v\omega \quad\quad\quad$ a = acceleration towards centre of circle

Now since $\omega$ = v/r we usually write

$$a = \frac{v^2}{r}$$

Hence a body describing a circle with uniform speed experiences an acceleration towards the centre of the circle of magnitude $v^2/r$ where v is the speed and r the radius of the circle. The acceleration is called centripetal acceleration.

Since the body is moving at a constant speed, it is the change in direction which results in an acceleration.

The time taken for the body to make one complete revolution is known as the periodic time, T.

Now $\quad\quad\quad\quad$ time $= \dfrac{\text{distance}}{\text{speed}}$

Thus $\quad\quad$ T $= \dfrac{\text{circumference}}{\text{speed}} = \dfrac{2\pi r}{v} = \dfrac{2\pi r}{r\omega} = \dfrac{2\pi}{\omega}$

For circular motion
$$T = \frac{2\pi}{\omega}$$

Also since frequency = number of revolutions made per second
$$T = \frac{1}{f}$$

$$\frac{1}{f} = \frac{2\pi}{\omega}$$

or $\quad \omega = 2\pi f$

i.e. $\quad$ Angular Frequency = $2\pi$ x Frequency

## 7.6 CENTRIPETAL FORCE

When a body is describing a circular path at constant speed there must be a net force acting upon it otherwise, in accordance with Newton's First Law, it would continue to move in a straight line (or remain at rest).

The acceleration towards the centre of the circle, a, is given by
$$a = \frac{v^2}{r}$$

The associated force acting upon the body to keep it following a circular path is, from Newton's Second Law
$$F = ma = \frac{mv^2}{r} \qquad m = \text{mass of body}$$

This force acting on the body and directed towards the centre of the circle is known as the centripetal force.

Examples of centripetal force:
— in the case of an object spun round on a string, the centripetal force is provided by the tension in the string;
— in the case of the earth spinning around the sun, the centripetal force is provided by the gravitational attraction;
— in the case of electrons orbiting the nucleus, the centripetal force is provided by the electrostatic attraction.

In the case of an object spun round on a string, if the string is cut, there will be no centripetal force acting and the mass will continue to move in a straight line and it will fly off along the tangent to the circle.

The Newtonian reaction to centripetal force is known as centrifugal force. It should be remembered that this acts upon a different body. In Fig. 7.6, a mass is anchored to a pin by a piece of string and made to rotate at a constant speed.

Centripetal force = $F_1$ — This acts on the mass towards centre of circle.
Centrifugal force = $F_2$ — This is of equal magnitude to F, but it acts on the pin away from centre of circle.

**FIG. 7.6**

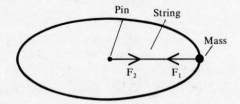

**EXAMPLES**

1) A disc rotates with a steady angular velocity of $4\pi$ rad s$^{-1}$. Calculate its period of rotation.

$$T = \frac{2\pi}{\omega} \qquad\qquad T = \text{period}$$
$$\qquad\qquad\qquad \omega = \text{angular velocity}$$
$$T = \frac{2\pi}{4} = 0.5s$$

Period of Rotation = 0.5s

2) An object of mass 4Kg moves in a circle on a table, at the end of a string 0.7m long. If the breaking strength of the string is 40N calculate the maximum speed of the object.

Let the mass of object = m
radius of circle = r
speed of object = V
tension in string = T

Now the tension in the string provides the necessary centripetal force needed to maintain the object in circular motion.

Thus
$$T = \frac{mV^2}{r}$$

$$V = \sqrt{\frac{Tr}{m}}$$

Maximum value of   T = 40N

$$V = \sqrt{\frac{40 \times 0.7}{4}}$$

$$= \sqrt{7} = 2.646 \text{ ms}^{-1}$$

Thus        Maximum Velocity = 2.646 ms$^{-1}$

3)  An object of mass 0.50Kg on the end of a string is whirled round in a horizontal circle of radius 2m and its period is 0.4 $\pi$ s. Find (i) its angular velocity; (ii) its linear velocity and (iii) the tension in the string.

Now            $T = \dfrac{2\pi}{\omega}$        T = period

$\omega$ = angular velocity

$$\omega = \frac{2\pi}{T} = \frac{2\pi}{0.4\pi} = 5 \text{ rad s}^{-1}$$

Angular Velocity = 5 rad s$^{-1}$

$V = r\omega$            V = linear velocity

so                        r = radius

$$V = 2 \times 5$$
$$= 10 \text{ms}^{-1}$$

Linear Velocity = 10ms$^{-1}$

Tension in string   $T = \dfrac{mV^2}{r}$

$$T = \frac{0.50 \times 10^2}{2}$$

$$= \frac{0.50 \times 100}{2}$$

$$= 25\text{N}$$

Tension in string = 25N

## 7.7 WEIGHTLESSNESS

If we feel no supporting force on our feet, we feel weightless. This force acting on our feet can be zero in two types of situation.

7.7.1 Consider an astronaut in orbit as in Fig. 7.7. An astronaut of mass m is in orbit at a distance r from the centre of a planet at a steady speed v.

**FIG. 7.7**

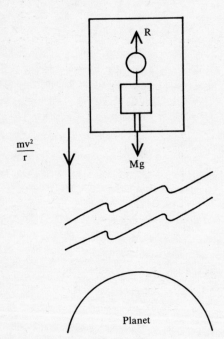

The weight of the astronaut is mg.

The reaction of the floor on the astronaut's feet is R.

The force needed to maintain the orbit is $mv^2/r$ and this is provided by the gravitational attraction between the planet and the orbiting body.

$$\text{Thus} \qquad \frac{mv^2}{r} = mg - R$$

$$R = m\left(\frac{g-v^2}{r}\right)$$

R will be zero when $g = v^2/r$

i.e. $v = \sqrt{gr}$

At this point the astronaut will perceive no reaction on his feet.

An identical situation occurs when water in a bucket is spun around in a vertical circle.

7.7.2  Consider a person in a lift, which is at rest.

$$R = mg$$

R = reaction on feet
m = mass of person
g = acc due to growth

Suppose now that the lift accelerates downwards, at a metre $\sec^{-2}$ as in Fig. 7.8.

**FIG. 7.8**

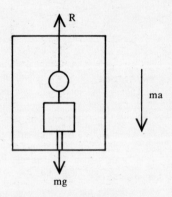

Net force downwards = ma
But net force = mg – R
$$ma = mg - R$$
$$R = mg - ma = m (g - a)$$

If $a = g$ then R is zero. Thus weightlessness would be perceived when the lift accelerates downwards at g metre $\sec^{-2}$. (This situation would arise if the lift cable were to break). When the lift accelerates upwards, we appear to weigh more. These differences in perceived weight explain the strange sensation we sometimes feel in our stomachs when travelling in high speed lifts which rapidly accelerate and decelerate.

## 7.8  MOMENTS
A force applied to a pivoted body causes the body to rotate about the pivot. The turning effect of a force is given in terms of its moment.

The moment of a force is defined as: The product of the force and the perpendicular distance of the line of action of the force to the pivot.

In Fig. 7.9

**FIG. 7.9**

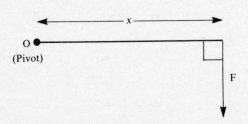

$$\text{Moment of F about O} = Fx$$

Unit: Newton metres (Nm)

Moments can be either positive or negative, depending upon the direction in which they act. They are added algebraically.

Whenever a body is in equilibrium the resultant moment acting on a body is zero. The Principle of Moments states: When a body is in equilibrium the sum of the positive moment is equal to the sum of the negative moment.

Thus in Fig. 7.10 where the plank is in equilibrium

$$F_1 x_1 + F_2 x_2 = F_3 x_3$$

**FIG. 7.10**

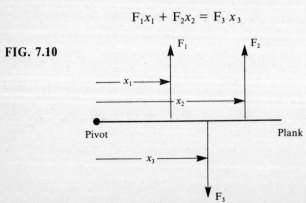

## 7.9 COUPLES AND TORQUE

A pair of equal and opposite parallel forces, not acting in the same line, form a couple.

The two forces have a turning effect upon any body which they act, known as the moment of the couple or torque, defined as

Torque = One force x perpendicular distance between two forces forming the couple

Thus in Fig. 7.11

$$\text{Moment of couple} = Fx$$

Units: Nm

**FIG. 7.11**

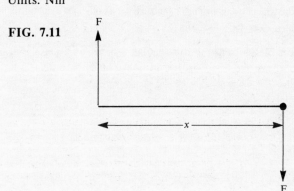

A couple can never be replaced by a single force but can be balanced by an opposite couple, i.e. one of equal torque in the opposite direction. Whenever a couple rotates a body, work is done.

WORK DONE = TORQUE x ANGLE TURNED THROUGH (in radians)

## 7.10 EQUILIBRIUM OF RIGID BODIES

We have seen in Chapter 5 that a body is in equilibrium if it is not acted upon by a resultant force. We may now add the further condition that the sum of the moments must be zero. Thus, for equilibrium

the net force in any direction = 0
the sum of the moments about any axis = 0

In the case of a body which is not a point mass, we regard the mass of the point as being concentrated at one particular point known as the centre of mass.

## QUESTIONS

1) Calculate the angular velocity of the earth, assuming it to be a sphere of radius 6400Km.

2) Calculate the acceleration towards the centre of a centrifuge of radius 0.10m rotating at 200 rad s$^{-1}$.

3) Water is rotated in a bucket in a vertical circle of radius 1m. Calculate the minimum speed of rotation such that the water stays in the bucket (g = 9.8 ms$^{-2}$).

4) The bob of a metre long pendulum has a mass of 2 x 10$^{-2}$Kg. It is made to move in a horizontal circle of radius 0.5m. Calculate the tension in the string and the speed of the bob (g = 10 ms$^{-2}$).

## Chapter 8
# SIMPLE HARMONIC MOTION

### 8.1 DEFINITION
A particle moves with simple harmonic motion (S.H.M.) when its acceleration towards a fixed point in its path varies directly as its distance from that fixed point measured along the path.

Since the acceleration decreases as the distance decreases we say that the acceleration is a restoring acceleration.

The mathematical equation of S.H.M. is

$$a = -\omega^2 x$$

$a$ = acceleration
$\omega$ = constant
$x$ = displacement

The minus sign shows the restoring property of the acceleration.

### 8.2 EQUATIONS OF S.H.M.
Fig. 8.1 shows a point P travelling around a circular path of radius a with a constant linear speed V. The constant angular velocity of P, $\omega$ is given by

$$\omega = \frac{V}{a}$$

**FIG. 8.1**

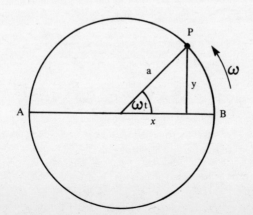

The projection of P onto the diameter of the circle AB moves with S.H.M. The maximum value of $x$, which is a, is the amplitude of the motion. Suppose P starts at B and moves for t seconds.

$$x = a \cos \omega t$$
$$\therefore \quad V = \frac{dx}{dt} = -a\omega \sin \omega t$$

and
$$a = \frac{dV}{dt} = -a\omega^2 \cos \omega t$$

But
$$x = a \cos \omega t$$
$$\therefore \quad a = -\omega^2 x$$

This is the mathematical equation of S.H.M. and it can be seen that $\omega$ = constant.

The equation may be equally well derived by considering a projection on the vertical axis.

From the displacement equation
$$x = a \cos \omega t$$
it is possible to derive a velocity equation as follows:
$$x = a \cos \omega t$$
$$\therefore \quad V = -a\omega \sin \omega t$$

Now from the geometry
$$\frac{y}{a} = \sin \omega t$$

and
$$y^2 = a^2 - x^2$$
$$\therefore \quad y = \pm \sqrt{a^2 - x^2}$$
$$\therefore \quad \sin \omega t = \pm \frac{\sqrt{a^2 - x^2}}{a}$$
$$= \pm \sqrt{\frac{a^2 - x^2}{a^2}}$$
$$\therefore \quad V = -a\omega \sin \omega t = \pm \omega \sqrt{\frac{a^2 (a^2 - x^2)}{a^2}}$$
$$= \pm \omega \sqrt{a^2 - x^2}$$
$$V = \pm \omega \sqrt{a^2 - x^2}$$

The + and − signs tell us that the value of the velocity can be either to the right or left of the rest position.

The maximum velocity, $V_{MAX}$ is
$$V_{MAX} = \pm \omega a$$

when $x = 0$ and the particle is passing through the rest position. The minimum velocity, $V_{MIN}$ is 0 when $x = a$, i.e. when the displacement equals the amplitude.

Since the projection of P, which is moving with S.H.M. has the same period and frequency as P itself, then for a body moving with S.H.M.

$$T = \frac{2\pi}{\omega}$$  T = period
$$\omega = \text{angular velocity}$$
$$f = \frac{1}{T}$$  f = frequency

## 8.3 ENERGY OF A BODY MOVING WITH SIMPLE HARMONIC MOTION

**The kinetic energy of a body is given by**
$$\text{K.E.} = \frac{1}{2} mV^2$$

m = mass of body
V = velocity of body

For a body moving with S.H.M.
$$V = \pm \omega \sqrt{a^2 - x^2}$$

$\omega$ = angular velocity
a = amplitude
x = displacement

$$\therefore \ V^2 = \omega^2 (a^2 - x^2)$$
So   $\text{K.E.} = \frac{1}{2} m \omega^2 (a^2 - x^2)$

Now this equation has a maximum value when $x = 0$
$$\text{K.E.}_{MAX} = \frac{1}{2} m\omega^2 a^2$$

When $x = 0$ the particle is in its equilibrium position and therefore, by definition, cannot have any potential energy
$$\therefore \ \text{P.E.} = 0$$

The total energy is the sum of K.E. and P.E. and hence
$$\text{Total Energy} = \frac{1}{2} m\omega^2 a^2$$

A general expression for P.E. at any instant may thus be found

$$
\begin{aligned}
\text{P.E.} \ &= \ \text{Total Energy} - \text{K.E.} \\
&= \ \frac{1}{2} m\omega^2 a^2 - \frac{1}{2} m\omega^2 (a^2 - x^2) \\
\text{P.E.} \ &= \ \frac{1}{2} m\omega^2 x^2
\end{aligned}
$$

Note that this equation has a maximum value when $x = a$

$$\therefore \text{ P.E.}_{\text{MAX}} = \tfrac{1}{2} \, m\omega^2 a^2$$

In summary

$$\text{K.E.} = \tfrac{1}{2} \, m\omega^2 (a^2 - x^2)$$
$$\text{P.E.} = \tfrac{1}{2} \, m\omega^2 x^2$$
$$\text{TOTAL ENERGY} = \tfrac{1}{2} \, m\omega^2 a^2$$

As the particle goes through its cycle, energy is converted repeatedly from P.E. to K.E. and vice-versa.

## 8.4 GRAPHICAL REPRESENTATION OF S.H.M.

8.4.1 Fig. 8.2 shows a particle P travelling around a circle at a constant speed. The projection is moving along the diameter with S.H.M.

As we have seen

$$x = a \cos \omega t$$
$$V = - a\omega \sin \omega t$$
$$\text{acc} = - a\omega^2 \cos \omega t$$

For the purpose of this analysis, assume $\omega = 1$

$$\therefore \qquad = a \cos t$$
$$V = - a \sin t$$
$$\text{acc} = - a \cos t$$

We choose the positive direction for $x$, V and acc to the right of the rest position and the negative direction to the left.

**FIG. 8.2**

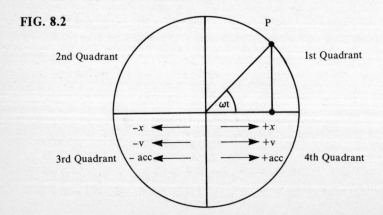

In the first quadrant
  $x$ is positive, sin is positive hence V is negative, cos is positive
  hence acc is negative.
In the second quadrant
  $x$ is negative, sin is positive hence V is negative, cos is negative
  hence acc is positive.
In the third quadrant
  $x$ is negative, sin is negative hence V is positive, cos is negative
  hence acc is positive.
In the fourth quadrant
  $x$ is positive, sin is negative hence V is positive, cos is positive
  hence acc is negative.

We may therefore plot the variation of $x$, V and acc with time
showing the appropriate phase. This is shown in Fig. 8.3

**FIG. 8.3**

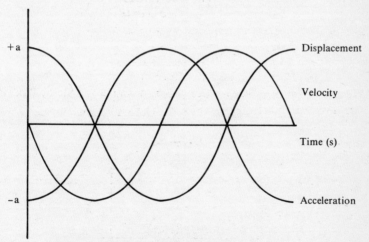

**VARIATION OF DISPLACEMENT, VELOCITY AND
ACCELERATION WITH TIME**

From Fig. 8.3 we may observe how velocity and acceleration both
vary with displacement and this is shown in Figs. 8.4 and 8.5.

**FIG. 8.4**

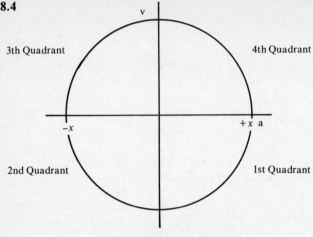

3th Quadrant

4th Quadrant

v

−x    +x a

2nd Quadrant

1st Quadrant

**VARIATION OF VELOCITY WITH
DISPLACEMENT**

**FIG. 8.5**

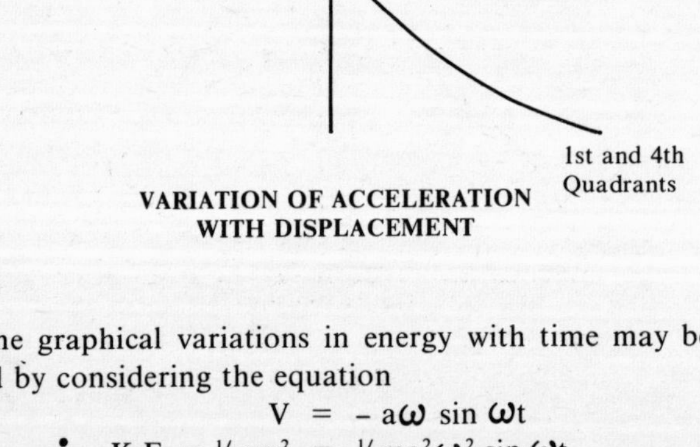

acc

2nd and 3th
Quadrants

acc

−a    +a

1st and 4th
Quadrants

**VARIATION OF ACCELERATION
WITH DISPLACEMENT**

8.4.2 The graphical variations in energy with time may best be displayed by considering the equation

$$V = -a\omega \sin \omega t$$
$$\therefore \; K.E. = \tfrac{1}{2}mv^2 = \tfrac{1}{2}ma^2\omega^2 \sin \omega t$$

The variation of energy with time is shown in Fig. 8.6. The P.E. may be found by subtracting the P.E. from the total energy.

**FIG. 8.6**

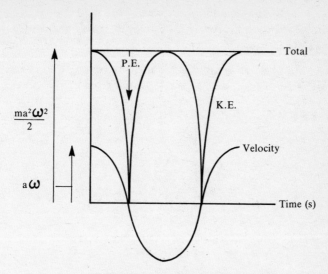

**VARIATION OF ENERGY WITH TIME**

The variation in energy with displacement may be plotted by means of

$$\text{P.E.} = \tfrac{1}{2}m\omega^2 x^2$$

This may be seen in Fig. 8.7

**FIG. 8.7**

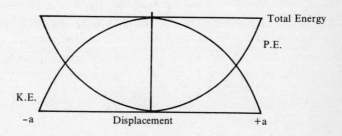

**VARIATION OF ENERGY WITH POSITION**

### 8.5   EXAMPLES OF SYSTEMS MOVING WITH S.H.M.
8.5.1   The Simple Pendulum

A simple pendulum consists of a point mass suspended by a lightweight inextensible string.

Consider a mass of m attached to a string of length $\ell$. The mass is drawn aside through a small angle $\Theta$ and released.

**FIG. 8.8**

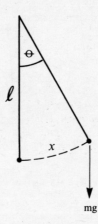

The forces acting on the bob are the tension, T and the weight mg.

The component of the weight along the string is balanced by the tension

$$T = mg \cos \Theta$$

The component of the weight perpendicular to the string acts to decrease $\Theta$ and hence    , the arc of the circle, and it is a restoring force

$$\therefore \quad F = - mg \sin \Theta$$

Now $\qquad F = ma$

$$\therefore \qquad ma = - mg \sin \Theta$$
$$a = - g \sin \Theta$$

Since $\Theta$ is small $\qquad \sin \Theta \approx \Theta \approx \dfrac{x}{\ell}$

$$\therefore \quad a = - g \ \dfrac{x}{\ell}$$

This is of the form

$$a = - \omega^2 x$$

and so the motion is simple harmonic with
$$\omega^2 = \frac{g}{\ell}$$
Hence the period of the motion is
$$T = \frac{2\pi}{\omega} = 2\pi \sqrt{\frac{\ell}{g}}$$
$$T = 2\pi \sqrt{\frac{\ell}{g}}$$

A simple pendulum experiment is often used to determine a value for g.

### 8.5.2 A Mass Attached To A Light Helical Spring

Suppose we have a spring of natural length $\ell$. A mass m is attached to its end causing an extension e. The mass is pulled down from its equilibrium position and caused to extend by an extra amount. This is shown in Fig. 8.9.

**FIG. 8.9**

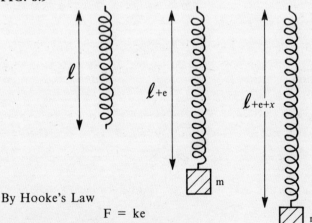

By Hooke's Law
$$F = ke$$
This is the downward force on the spring. By Newton's Third Law this is also the upward force on the mass.

The downward force on the mass is its weight

$$F = mg$$

F = force
k = Hooke's Constant
e = extension

Since the mass is at rest there is no net force acting upon it.
Thus $\qquad\qquad\qquad$ mg = ke

When the mass is now pulled down a further distance $x$ then
$$\text{upward force acting} = k(e + x)$$
$$\text{downward force} = mg = ke \text{ i.e. no change}$$
$$\therefore \ \text{Net upward force} = k(e + x) - ke$$
$$= kx$$

This acts upward to decrease $x$ so it is a restoring force
$$\therefore \quad F = -kx$$
Now $\qquad\qquad\qquad F = ma$
$$\therefore \quad ma = kx$$
$$a = \frac{-kx}{m}$$

This is of the form
$$a = -\omega^2 x$$
and so the motion is simple harmonic with
$$\omega^2 = \frac{k}{m}$$

Hence the period of the motion is
$$T = \frac{2\pi}{\omega} = 2\pi\sqrt{\frac{m}{k}}$$

This equation requires a knowledge of k and so it is often re-written
$$\text{Since} \qquad mg = ke$$
$$\frac{m}{k} = \frac{e}{g}$$
$$T = 2\pi\sqrt{\frac{e}{g}}$$

Thus this experiment may also be used to determine a value for g.

---

**EXAMPLES**
1) A pendulum of length 1m has a bob of mass 100gm. Assuming that the amplitude of the motion is 5cm and $g = 10\text{ms}^{-2}$, calculate the maximum kinetic energy of the bob.

Maximum K.E. $= \frac{1}{2}m\omega^2a^2$ where the symbols have their usual meaning.

For a pendulum

$$\omega = \sqrt{\frac{g}{\ell}}$$

$$\therefore \omega^2 = \frac{g}{\ell}$$

$$\therefore \text{K.E.}_{MAX} = \frac{1}{2}\frac{mg}{\ell}a^2$$

$$m = 100g = 10^{-1}Kg$$
$$\ell = 1m$$
$$a = 5cm = 5 \times 10^{-2}m$$

$$\therefore \text{K.E.}_{MAX} = \frac{1}{2} \times 10^{-1} \times \frac{10}{1} \times (5 \times 10^{-2})^2$$

$$= \frac{1}{2} \times 10^{-1} \times 10 \times 25 \times 10^{-4}$$

$$= 1.25 \times 10^{-3} \text{ J}$$

Maximum kinetic energy $= 1.25 \times 10^{-3}$ J

2) When a mass of 0.2Kg is suspended from a vertical spring of negligible mass it causes an extention of $4 \times 10^{-2}$m. The mass is replaced by one of 0.5Kg and after equilibrium has been reached it is pulled down and released. Find the period of its motion. Assume g = 10ms$^{-2}$.

To find Hooke's Constant for the spring

$$F = ke$$
$$F = mg = 0.2 \times 10 = 2 \text{ N}$$
$$e = 4 \times 10^{-2}m$$

$$\therefore k = \frac{F}{e} = \frac{2}{4 \times 10^{-2}} = 50 \text{ Nm}^{-1}$$

$$m = 0.5Kg$$

To find the period

$$T = 2\pi\sqrt{\frac{m}{k}}$$

$$= 2\pi\sqrt{\frac{0.5}{50}}$$

$$= 2\pi\sqrt{10^{-2}}$$

$$= 0.2\pi \qquad \text{Period} = 0.2\pi\text{ s.}$$

### 8.6 DAMPED S.H.M.

The S.H.M. considered so far is known as undamped or free S.H.M. and its characteristic is that its amplitude is constant with time because no energy is lost to the surroundings.

However, in all practical situations some energy is dissipated due to various factors such as friction, air resistance etc. Accordingly the motion is damped and its amplitude decays or decreases with time.

These motions are compared in Fig. 8.10.

**FIG. 8.10**

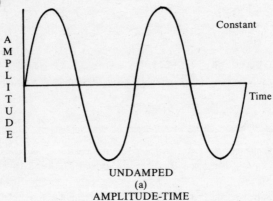

UNDAMPED
(a)
AMPLITUDE-TIME

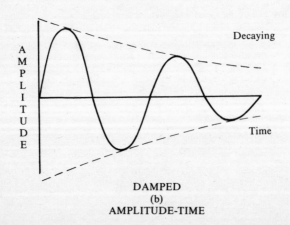

DAMPED
(b)
AMPLITUDE-TIME

The damping may be of three types, depending upon its severity.

Slight damping, as in Fig. 8.10(b), where the amplitude decays reasonably slow.

Critical damping, where the dissipative force is just sufficient to prevent oscillation but not sufficient to prevent a return to the rest position. Thus $\frac{1}{4}$ of an oscillation is completed.

Heavy-damping where the return to the rest position is very slow. In fact a complete return is only achieved after an infinite time. Fig. 8.11 shows critical and heavy damping.

**FIG. 8.11**

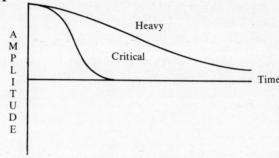

AMPLITUDE-TIME

## 8.7 VIBRATING SYSTEMS

We have seen that the period of a simple pendulum is given by

$$T = 2\pi \sqrt{\frac{\ell}{g}}$$

Its frequency of vibration is thus

$$f = \frac{1}{T} = \frac{1}{2\pi}\sqrt{\frac{g}{\ell}}$$

Also the period of a mass oscillating on a light spring is given by

$$T = 2\pi \sqrt{\frac{e}{g}}$$

Its frequency of vibration is thus

$$f = \frac{1}{T} = \frac{1}{2\pi}\sqrt{\frac{g}{e}}$$

Not only the pendulum and the mass on a spring, but all vibrating systems have their own particular frequency at which they vibrate if they are set in oscillation. This frequency is known as the natural frequency of the system.

If some external agent causes the system to vibrate at some other frequency than the natural frequency then the system is said to be undergoing forced vibration. As energy is required in large amounts for this, the vibrational amplitude is usually small.

If the frequency of the external agent changes until it equals the natural frequency of the system, then the amplitude of vibration begins to increase and reaches a maximum when the natural frequency is reached. Such a body which is being forced to vibrate at its natural frequency, and which therefore vibrates with large amplitude, is said to be in resonance.

Fig. 8.12 shows the variation of amplitude with frequency for lightly and heavily damped systems.

**FIG. 8.12**

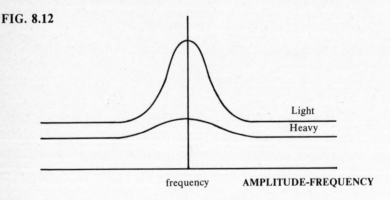

frequency     **AMPLITUDE-FREQUENCY**

Resonance can be sometimes advantageous, e.g. resonance in strings (violins) and resonance in electrical currents (radio tuners). It can also be dis-advantageous and is the reason why shock absorbers are fitted to cars and opera singers should be kept away from empty brandy glasses!

## QUESTIONS

1) A body moves with S.H.M. of amplitude 0.40m. Calculate its maximum acceleration if its maximum velocity is $0.16ms^{-1}$.

2) A particle of mass 2g moves with S.H.M. of amplitude 10cm and period $\pi$ s. Calculate its K.E. when passing through the equilibrium position.

3) Calculate the period of oscillation of a light spring loaded with a mass of 0.2Kg if a mass of $10^{-3}$Kg causes an extension of $10^{-3}$m. Assume g = $10ms^{-2}$.

4) Explain why an empty brandy glass is more likely to break than a full glass when in the presence of a variable frequency high speed drill.

# AREA 3 : ENERGETICS
## (THE MOVEMENT OF HEAT AND ELECTRICITY)

## Chapter 9
## TEMPERATURE

### 9.1 THE CONCEPT OF TEMPERATURE

We all have an intuitive understanding of temperature. We know that a body with a high temperature feels hotter than a body with a lower temperature. However, this idea involves our perception and a more rigorous approach is needed to understand temperature.

The internal energy of a body is the sum of its potential energy — due to intermolecular forces — and its kinetic energy is due to molecular motion which may be translational and/or rotational and/or vibrational. (By molecules we mean atoms or molecules).

The temperature of a body is a measure of its internal energy and we may regard it as: That quantity which increases with the internal energy of a body. Thus, the greater the internal energy, the greater the temperature.

In Fig. 9.1, suppose body A, at temperature $T_2$, is joined to body B, at temperature $T_1$, where $T_2$ is greater than $T_1$.

Since $T_2$ is greater than $T_1$, A will have more internal energy than B. It is common knowledge that if two such bodies are joined, the temperature of the body at the higher temperature will fall while the temperature of the body at the lower temperature will rise. What happens is that the internal energy of A will fall and that of B will rise. This is achieved by the transfer of energy known as heat.

**FIG. 9.1**

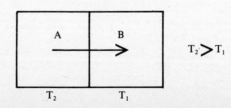

$$T_2 > T_1$$

## 9.2   THE CONCEPT OF HEAT

Heat is energy in transit. It flows from one body to another (or from one part of a body to another) by virtue of a temperature difference only. When this flow has stopped there is no longer any need to use the word 'heat' and it would be incorrect to speak of the "heat in a body", just as it would be incorrect to speak of "the work in a body". The flow of heat is a method whereby the internal energy of a body is changed.

Heat is sometimes referred to as thermal energy.

## 9.3   MEASUREMENT OF TEMPERATURE

9.3.1   The internal energy of a system cannot be measured, although changes in its value can.

However, we can measure temperature. In order to establish a scale of temperature we need two things:—
(i)   Fixed temperatures, known as "fixed points", which can be accurately reproduced in the laboratory;
(ii)  Some physical property of a substance which varies regularly with temperature, over a large range of temperature with the variation being significant.

The devices which we use are called thermometers. The temperature of an object is arbitrary, i.e. it is not a fixed number but it depends upon the type of thermometer used and on the temperature scale adopted. However, we can say that all thermometers use some measurable property of a substance which changes with temperature. Various types of thermometers are listed in Table 9.2.

**TABLE 9.2**

| Type of Thermometer | Change Observed |
|---|---|
| Constant Volume Gas | Pressure at Constant Volume |
| Resistance | Resistance of Pure Metal |
| Thermoelectric | Thermoelectric E.M.F. |
| Mercury-in-Glass | Volume of Mercury |

### 9.3.2 Temperature Scale In Use Before 1954

The scale yielded temperatures in degrees centigrade — °C. It had two fixed points — the ice point and the steam point.

The ice point (the temperature of pure melting ice) was selected to be 0°C and the steam point (the temperature of steam from pure water boiling at 1 atmosphere pressure) chosen as 100°C.

The temperature interval between these two temperatures was divided up into 100 equal parts or "degrees".

Suppose X is the property chosen to measure temperature on this scale. Let $X_0$ be its value at the ice point, $X_\theta$ its value at some temperature $\Theta$ between 0 and 100°C, and $X_{100}$ its value at the steam point.

If the change in X is proportional to temperature then we can say

$$100 \; \alpha \; X_{100} - X_0$$

or
$$100 = k\,(X_{100} - X_0) \qquad (1)$$

where     k is a constant of proportionality

Also
$$\Theta \; \alpha \; X_\theta - X_0$$

or
$$\Theta = k\,(X_\theta - X_0) \qquad (2)$$

Dividing (2) by (1) gives

$$\frac{\Theta}{100} = \frac{X_\theta - X_0}{X_{100} - X_0}$$

or
$$\Theta = 100 \left( \frac{X_\theta - X_0}{X_{100} - X_0} \right) \; °C$$

This equation defines temperature, $\Theta°C$ on the scale on which X is the variable property.

Note: although this definition of temperature has now be abandoned for scientific purposes, it is satisfactory for "ordinary" uses — e.g. calibrated room thermometers.

Applying this scale to particular instruments:

For a mercury-in-glass thermometer, X is the volume of mercury or in effect the length of the mercury column.

So
$$\Theta = 100 \left( \frac{\ell_\theta - l_0}{l_{100} - l_0} \right) \; °C$$

where $l_{100}$ $l_0$ and $\ell_\theta$ denote the length of the mercury column at 100°C, O°C and Θ°C respectively.

For a thermoelectric thermometer (a thermcouple), X is the thermoelectric electromotive force.

$$\text{So} \qquad \Theta = 100 \left( \frac{E_\theta - E_0}{E_{100} - E_0} \right) °C$$

where $E_{100}$, $E_\theta$ and $E_0$ denote the thermoelectric e.m.f. at 100°C, Θ°C and 0°C respectively.

---

**EXAMPLE**

A platinum wire has resistances of 2.000 Ω at 0°C, 2.778 Ω at 100°C and 5.280 Ω at the boiling points of sulphur. A constant mass of gas at constant pressure has volumes of 2.000 x $10^{-4}$, 2.732 x $10^{-4}$ and 5.251 x $10^{-4}$m$^3$ at the same temperatures.

Find the boiling point of sulphur on the two different scales.

In dealing with this question, we assume linear behaviour, i.e. we may extrapolate the scales beyond the upper fixed point of 100°C.

On the constant pressure scale

$$\Theta p = \left( \frac{V_\theta - V_0}{V_{100} - V_0} \right) \times 100 \quad °C$$

$$= \frac{5.251 \times 10^{-4} - 2.000 \times 10^{-4}}{2.778 \times 10^{-4} - 2.000 \times 10^{-4}} \times 100$$

$$\underline{\Theta p = 444.1°C}$$

On the platinum resistance scale

$$\Theta R = \left( \frac{R_\theta - R_0}{R_{100} - R_0} \right) \times 100 \quad °C$$

$$= \frac{5.280 - 2.000}{2.778 - 2.000} \times 100$$

$$\underline{\Theta R = 421.6°C}$$

> The difference is due to the fact that the variation in gas pressure with temperature is different from that of electrical resistance with temperature. They will however agree, by definition, at the fixed points.

### 9.3.3   Temperature Scale In Use After 1954

We use a temperature scale which has only one fixed point, not two. It is based upon work done by the physicist Kelvin in a branch of physics called thermodynamics and is known therefore as the Kelvin or Thermodynamic Scale.

The thermodynamic temperature scale is the standard temperature scale adopted for scientific purposes. It is denoted by the symbol T and is measured in Kelvin, symbol K. Note that since we are not dividing an interval into equal degrees but are just extrapolating from one point we do not refer to degrees Kelvin!

The fixed point is the temperature at which ice, liquid water and water vapour exist in equilibrium known as the triple point of water and defined as 273.16K.

On this scale, absolute zero = OK, ice point = 273.15K and the steam point = 373.15K.

Suppose X is the property we choose to measure temperature

Let $\quad X_{TR}$ = value of X at the triple point

$\quad\quad\quad X_T$ = value of X at an unknown temperature T, then

$$\frac{T}{273.16} = \frac{X_T}{X_{TR}}$$

or $\quad\quad T = 273.16 \; \frac{X_T}{X_{TR}}$

This equation defines temperature, TK on the scale on which X is the variable property.

Applying the scale to particular instruments.

For a mercury-in-glass thermometer, T is defined as

$$T = 273.16 \; \frac{l_T}{l_{TR}} \quad K$$

For a thermoelectric thermometer

$$T = 273.16 \; \frac{E_T}{E_{TR}} \; K$$

---

**EXAMPLE**

The e.m.f. of a copper/nickel thermocouple is 9.02V at the melting point of tin and 2.98V at the triple point. The resistance of a platinum resistance thermometer is 18.56 and 8.83 at the same temperature respectively. Find the melting point of tin on both scales.

$$T = 273.16 \times \frac{18.56}{9.83} = 515.7K$$

On the thermoelectric scale

$$T = 273.16 \times \frac{9.02}{2.98} = 826.8K$$

The scales will only agree — by definition — at the triple point.

---

## 9.4 THE SUBSEQUENT DEFINITION OF THE CENTIGRADE (OR CELSIUS) TEMPERATURE SCALE

Since 1954 the Celsius temperature, $\Theta$, has been defined by

$$\Theta °C = T - 273.15 \qquad T = \text{Kelvin temp.}$$

The temperature change or interval of one degree Celsius is exactly the same as the temperature interval of one Kelvin. So "°C" temperature change may be replaced by "K".

Also, for everyday purposes,

$$0°C = 273K$$
$$100°C = 373K$$

with the absolute zero, OK being –273°C.

It is worthy of note that the absolute zero is **NOT** the temperature at which the molecules of a gas stop moving (i.e. have no kinetic energy). It is the temperature at which the molecules of an ideal gas (with no intermolecular forces and no molecular volume) would have zero pressure and volume.

## 9.5 THE CHOICE OF THERMOMETER

Even using the Kelvin definition of temperature, all thermometers only agree at the triple point.

However, it can be shown that a constant volume gas thermometer containing an ideal gas, the pressure of which varies, give a scale (the ideal gas scale) which is identical with the theoretically based Kelvin scale. In order to realise such a gas scale, corrections are applied to a constant volume thermometer containing low pressure hydrogen. The ideal gas scale is therefore chosen as standard.

However, because the thermometer is complicated and clumsy, it is used to define certain temperature as fixed points (often given in °C by using $\Theta = T-273.15$) between which other secondary thermometers are used. These fixed points constitute the International Practical Temperature Scale (I.P.T.S.). The scale also specifies which secondary thermometers shall be used.

From the boiling point of oxygen, $-182.97$°C to the triple point, a platinum resistance thermometer is used.

The variation in resistance is given by

$$R_\Theta = R_0 (1 + A\Theta + B\Theta^2 + C (\Theta - 100) \Theta^3)$$

where

$R_\Theta$ = resistance at $\Theta$°C
$R_0$ = resistance at 0°C
$\Theta$ = temperature, in degrees centigrade, on the ideal gas scale
$A, B$ and $C$ = constants.

Thus by measuring $R_0$ and $R_\Theta$ and a knowledge of $A$, $B$ and $C$ we may determine the gas scale temperature, $\Theta$, in degrees centigrade. We may then convert this to Kelvin using

$$T = \Theta + 273.15$$

From the triple point to the melting point of antimony, 635.50°C we use the platinum resistance thermometer with the variation in resistance being given by a quadratic equation

$$R_\Theta = R_0 (1 + A\Theta + B\Theta^2) \qquad \text{symbols as before}$$

From the melting point of antimony to the melting point of gold, 1064.5°C, a thermocouple of platinum and platinum/rhodium is used with one junction being maintained at the triple point.

The variation in thermoelectric e.m.f., E, is given by

$$E = a + b\Theta + c\Theta_2$$

when

$a, b$ and $c$ = constants (NOT A, B and C!)

$\Theta$ = temperature, in degrees centigrade, on the ideal gas scale.

The important point to realize is that any property of a substance which varies measurably and reasonably uniformly, may be used to measure temperature on a chosen scale. We chose a certain temperature scale and to allow for the fact that various thermometers would not necessarily agree except at a fixed point, we select a particular thermometer. However, there is nothing sacrosanct in this — it is merely an agreed convention.

## QUESTIONS

1) Define $\Theta°C$ on the constant volume scale.

2) Define TK on the constant volume scale.

3) A mercury thread in a mercury in glass thermometer has a length of 5.0cm at the ice point and 20cm at the steam point. What will be the centigrade temperature on the mercury-in-glass scale when the column is 8.0cm long?

4) The resistance of a platinum resistance thermometer is $2.000\,\Omega$ as the ice point and $2.760\,\Omega$ at the steam point. Calculate the temperature in degrees centigrade on the platinum resistance scale when the resistance is $2.480\,\Omega$.

## Chapter 10
## ENERGY TRANSFER

### 10.1  ENERGY CONVERSION

#### 10.1.1  THERMAL ENERGY

When thermal energy enters a body, it increases the internal energy of that body and consequently there is a rise in temperature.

The rise in temperature produced by a given amount of heat depends upon the nature of the body and its mass.

The relationship between the heat entering a body and the resultant rise in temperature is given by

$$\Delta Q = mc\,\Delta T$$

$\Delta T$ = rise in temperature produced by an amount of heat $\Delta Q$

We use $\Delta Q$ to indicate that we are not speaking of the heat content **of** a body but the amount of heat **flowing** into a body.

m = mass of body
c = constant called Specific Heat Capacity

#### 10.1.2  ELECTRICAL ENERGY

When an electric current flows, electrical energy is converted into other forms of energy such as mechanical and thermal energy.

The relationship between electrical current and energy is given by

$$\Delta W = IV\Delta t$$

I = steady current through device
V = steady p.d. across device
W = electrical energy converted by it in time $\Delta t$

We use $\Delta W$ to signify a change in electrical energy in the given time.

## 10.2   THE FIRST LAW OF THERMODYNAMICS

Thermodynamics concerns the relationship between thermal energy and work. The First Law is really a statement of the Conservation of Energy (i.e. energy can neither be created nor destroyed but may be converted from one form to another) for a given amount of work.

A given amount of work can be transformed completely into heat. However, the reverse is not true and a given amount of heat can never be converted completely into work.

Suppose a substance takes in heat. Its internal energy will increase. Also the substance may change its dimension and in doing so it will do work against its surroundings — known as external work.

**FIG. 10.1**

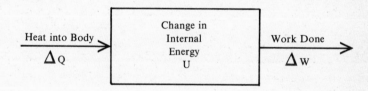

The First Law states

Heat supplied to system = Change in internal energy + External work done.

i.e. $\qquad \Delta Q = \Delta U + \Delta W$

$\Delta Q =$ heat supplied
$\Delta U =$ change in internal energy
$\Delta W =$ external work done.

Consider an application of the equation to an ideal gas undergoing an expansion. Suppose a small amount of heat, $\Delta Q$, is supplied to an ideal gas which expands by a small amount $\Delta V$, with there being no dissipative forces such as friction.

It may be shown that

$$\Delta W = p \, \Delta V$$

$p =$ gas pressure
$\Delta V =$ change in volume

thus $\qquad \Delta Q = \Delta U + p \Delta V$

If the volume of the gas is kept constant when it is warmed then $V = 0$ and no external work is done. All the heat supplied goes in raising the internal energy and so

$$\Delta Q = \Delta U$$

For a process which occurs at constant heat, or adiabatically,

$$\Delta Q = 0$$

So

$$- \Delta U = \Delta W$$

Therefore if the system does work, the internal energy will fall resulting in a fall in temperature.

In the case of an ideal gas expanding adiabatically by an amount $\Delta V$ then we have

$$- \Delta U = p\Delta V$$

# Chapter 11
# THE EFFECT OF HEAT UPON MATTER

## 11.1 DEFINITIONS OF HEAT CAPACITY AND SPECIFIC HEAT CAPACITY

The heat capacity of a body is the amount of heat required to raise its temperature by 1K (or 1°C).

Its units are joules per Kelvin, $JK^{-1}$, which is, of course, identical to $J°C^{-1}$.

The specific heat capacity of a substance is the amount of heat required to raise the temperature of 1Kg by 1K (or 1°C).

Its units are joules per kilogram Kelvin, $J(KgK)^{-1}$ which, of course, is identical to $J(Kg°C)^{-1}$. We use the symbol C.

Typical values of C are for water 4200 $J(KgK)^{-1}$ and for copper 400 $J(KgK^{-1})$.

It follows from the above
Heat Capacity = **Mass of Body x Specific Heat Capacity**

**Additionally, it follows from the definition of specific heat capacity**
$$\Delta Q = mC\Delta T$$
$\Delta T$ = change in temperature produced by an input of heat, $\Delta Q$
m = mass of body

## 11.2 DEFINITIONS OF LATENT HEAT AND SPECIFIC LATENT HEAT

Suppose ice, initially below its freezing point is heated. The heat supplied will cause the temperature of the ice to increase. The rise in temperature will continue until the ice begins to melt. During this melting process the temperature of the ice and water formed will stay constant until all the ice has melted. When this has occured, the temperature of the water will begin to increase if further heat is supplied.

During the melting process, heat is being absorbed and yet no increase in temperature results. Instead of change of phase results — the water changes from solid to liquid. Accordingly the heat absorbed is known as latent (or hidden) heat. The latent heat supplied to a solid is supplying energy to overcome the forces between molecules which exist whilst the molecules are arranged on the crystal lattice. The result is that the order breaks down because molecules are no longer constrained to vibrate upon the lattice. Such a lack of order characterises a liquid.

A similar constant temperature phenomenon occurs when a liquid changes to a vapour. The thermal energy supplied during a vaporization process is used in separating the molecules in order to allow them to move around independently as gas molecules. Also, when a liquid changes to a vapour there is a significant increase in volume and this expansion must be done against atmosphere pressure. Some of the thermal energy supplied is used in enabling this to occur.

Latent heat of fusion is the quantity of heat required to change a substance from solid to liquid with no change in temperature.

The Specific Latent Heat of Fusion is defined as: The quantity of heat required to change 1Kg of a substance from solid to liquid with no change in temperature.

Its units are J Kg$^{-1}$ and it is denoted by the symbol $\ell$.
Thus $\Delta Q = \ell \Delta m$ $\Delta Q$= heat needed to melt $\Delta m$
For ice the accepted value for $\ell$ is 334 KJ Kg$^{-1}$.

Latent heat of vaporization is the quantity of heat required to change a substance from liquid to vapour with no change in temperature.

The Specific Latent Heat of Vaporization is defined as: The quantity of heat required to change 1Kg of a substance from liquid to vapour with no change in temperature.

Its units are J Kg$^{-1}$ and it is denoted by the symbol $\ell$
Thus $\Delta Q = \ell \Delta m$ $\Delta Q$ = heat need to vaporize $\Delta m$
For water the accepted value for $\ell$ is 2300 KJ Kg$^{-1}$.

**EXAMPLES**

1) 9600J of heat are supplied to a 1.2Kg block of aluminium. If the temperature rises by 8K, calculate the specific heat capacity of aluminium.

Using
$$\Delta Q = mC \, \Delta T$$
$$c = \frac{\Delta Q}{m \, \Delta T}$$

here
$$\Delta Q = 9600J$$
$$m = 1.2Kg$$
$$\Delta T = 9K$$

$$C = \frac{9600}{1.2 \times 9} = 890$$

Specific Heat Capacity of Aluminium = 890J $(KgK)^{-1}$

2) A piece of copper of mass 100g at 100°C is quickly transferred to a copper can of mass 50.0g containing 200g of water at 10.0°C. Assuming no heat losses, find the final temperature of the water.
(Assume specific heat capacities of water and copper are 4200 J$(KgK)^{-1}$ and 400 J$(KgK^{-1})$ respectively.)

There are no heat losses to the surroundings. In these circumstances, heat flows from the hot body to the cold body until they both acquire the same final temperature, i.e. thermal equilibrium is reached.
Thus
$$\text{Heat lost} = \text{Heat gained}$$
i.e. Heat lost by copper = Heat gained by water + Heat gained by copper can.

Let the final steady temperature be $\Theta$ °C.
Thus
Fall in temperature of copper = $(100 - \Theta)$°C
Rise in temperature of can and water = $(\Theta - 10)$°C

Heat lost by copper = 0.1 x 400 x $(100 - \Theta)$ J
Heat gained by copper can = 0.05 x 400 x $(\Theta - 10)$ J
Heat gained by water = 0.2 x 4200 x $(\Theta - 10)$ J

Hence

$$0.1 \times 400 \times (100 - \Theta) = 0.05 \times 400 \times (\Theta - 10) + 0.2 \times 4200 \times (\Theta - 10)$$
$$4000 - 40\Theta = (20 + 840)(\Theta - 10)$$
$$4000 - 40\Theta = 860\Theta - 8600$$
$$900\Theta = 12600$$
$$\Theta = 14.0°C$$

Final temperature = 14.0°C

3) An electric kettle supplies 3KW to 1.7Kg at 100°C. How long will it take for all the water to boil away? Assume specific latent heat of vaporization of water is $2.3 \times 10^6$ J Kg$^{-1}$.

Now $\qquad \Delta Q = \ell \Delta m$

In 1 second $\qquad \Delta Q$ = heat supplied per second

$\Delta m$ = mass vaporized per second

Hence $\qquad \Delta Q = 3KW = 3000$ J s$^{-1}$

$\ell = 2.3 \times 10^6$ J Kg$^{-1}$

thus

$$\Delta m = \frac{\Delta Q}{\ell} = \frac{3000}{2.3 \times 10^6} = \frac{3 \times 10^3}{2.3 \times 10^6} = \underline{1.30 \times 10^{-3} \, s}$$

So, time taken for all the water to boil away

$$= \frac{\text{total mass of water}}{\text{mass vaporized per second}}$$

$$= \frac{1.7}{1.30 \times 10^{-3}} = 1.3 \times 10^3 \, s$$

Time taken = $1.3 \times 10^3$ s

4) Calculate the work done in pushing back the atmosphere when 1Kg of water vaporizes. Explain why the work done is less than the specific latent heat of vaporization of water.

Assume atmosphere pressure = $1.0 \times 10^5$ Pa, specific latent heat of vaporization of water = $2.3 \times 10^6$ J Kg$^{-1}$ density of water = 1000Kg m$^{-3}$, density of steam at 100°C = 0.60Kgm$^{-3}$.

The work done, $\Delta W$, when a gas expands, is

$$\Delta W = p\Delta V \qquad \text{(see earlier)}$$

Normally this only applies for a small change in volume since any such change in volume leads to a change in pressure as in accordance with Boyle's Law.

However, here it applies to the total change because such a change has no effect on atmospheric pressure.

$$\therefore \Delta W = p(V_2 - V_1) \qquad \begin{aligned} V_2 &= \text{final volume} \\ V_1 &= \text{original volume} \end{aligned}$$

Since

$$\text{density} = \frac{\text{mass}}{\text{volume}}$$

$$\text{original volume, } V_1 = \frac{1}{1000} = 10^{-3} m^3$$

$$\text{final volume, } V_2 = \frac{1}{0.60} = 1.666 m^3$$

$$\therefore \text{ increase in volume, } V_2 - V_1 = 1.665 m^3$$

$$\therefore \Delta W = 1.0 \times 10^5 \times 1.665$$
$$= 0.1665 \text{ mJ}$$

The total work done, i.e. the total amount of energy needed, must also include the work done in increasing the separation of the molecules.

(This problem also shows how most of the energy supplied goes to increase molecular separation rather than doing external work).

Note: One often sees confusion between the terms vapour and gas. The difference is that a vapour can be liquified by the application of pressure alone, whereas a gas must first be cooled before it can be liquified. Thus, when a boiling liquid changes phase it becomes a vapour. Once the temperature of the vapour increases above the boiling point, the vapour is known as a gas.

## 11.3 THE DETERMINATION OF SPECIFIC HEAT CAPACITIES AND SPECIFIC LATENT HEATS

### 11.3.1 SPECIFIC HEAT CAPACITIES
Classically, the method of mixtures was used. In the case of a solid, a known mass of solid at a known temperature was added to a mass of

water at a known temperature. In the case of a liquid, a solid of known mass, specific heat capacity and temperature was added to a known mass of liquid at a known temperature.

These methods have now been superceded by electrical methods.

For a solid, the apparatus is shown in Fig. 11.1.

**FIG. 11.1**

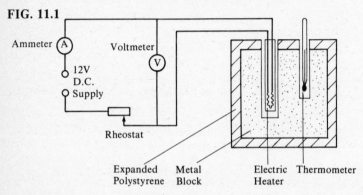

A cylindrical block of the substance is used. It is lagged with expanded polystyrene. Suppose the mass of the block is m and its initial temperature is $\Theta_1$. The block is drilled and an electric heater and a mercury-in-glass thermometer inserted in the drilled holes. In order to ensure good thermal contact, both the heater and thermometer should be greased. The current is switched on and a stop clock is started. The voltmeter reading, V and the ammeter reading I are both noted. When the temperature has risen appreciably, about 10 to 15K, the current is switched off and time t seconds is noted. The final temperature is noted, $\Theta_2$.

Assuming no energy loss then
electrical energy supplied by heater = thermal energy received by block
$$VIt = mC (\Theta_2 - \Theta_1)$$
where C = specific heat capacity of the metal

hence

$$C = \frac{VIt}{m (\Theta_2 - \Theta_1)}$$

For a liquid, the apparatus is shown in Fig. 11.2. The liquid is contained in a copper can known as a calorimeter. The procedure is

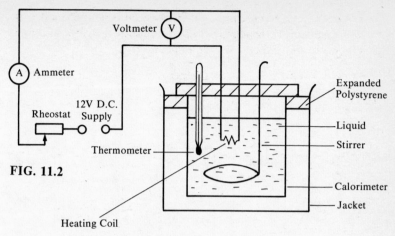

Voltmeter V

A Ammeter

Rheostat

12V D.C.
Supply

Thermometer

**FIG. 11.2**

Heating Coil

Expanded
Polystyrene

Liquid

Stirrer

Calorimeter

Jacket

identical to that for solids with the exception that the liquid is stirred continuously with the stirrer.

Assuming no heat losses then
electrical energy supplied by heater
= thermal energy received by liquid
+ thermal energy received by calorimeter and stirrer.
(Both made from copper)

Now
$V$ = p.d. across heater
$I$ = current in heater
$t$ = time of heating
$\Theta_1$ = initial temperature
$\Theta_2$ = final temperature
$m$ = mass of liquid
$m_c$ = mass of calorimeter and stirrer
$C$ = specific heat capacity of liquid
$C_c$ = specific heat capacity of copper

$$VIt = mc(\Theta_2 - \Theta_1) + m_cC_c(\Theta_2 - \Theta_1)$$
$$= (mC + m_cC_c)(\Theta_2 - \Theta_1)$$

thus
$$\frac{VIt}{(\Theta_2 - \Theta_1)} = mC + m_cC_c$$

$$C = \frac{\dfrac{VIt}{(\Theta_2 - \Theta_1)} - m_cC_c}{m}$$

In both methods heat losses to the surroundings are reduced by using expanded polystyrene (to reduce conduction and convection) and in the second experiment the calorimeter is polished (to reduce radiation).

Also, in both methods we ignore the small amount of heat received by the heater and the thermometer.

### 11.3.2  SPECIFIC LATENT HEATS

Classically, the method of mixtures was also used here. However, electrical methods are now used extensively.

For a solid to liquid phase change, when finding the specific latent heat of fusion, apparatus as shown in Fig. 11.3 is used.

**FIG. 11.3**

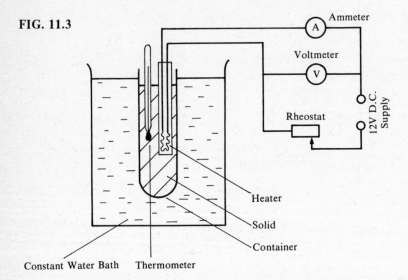

A mass, m, of the substance under investigation is melted in a container and a heater and thermometer is inserted into the melted solid. The liquid is allowed to solidify obviously with the heater switched off.

A constant temperature bath at the melting point of the substance, $\Theta_m$, is placed around the container. The heater is switched on and the voltmeter and ammeter readings noted. Simultaneously the stop clock is started and the temperature read at regular intervals during the time that the solid warms up, melts and then the molten solid warms up. The circuit is switched off.

A graph is then plotted of temperature against time as in Fig. 11.4

**FIG. 11.4**

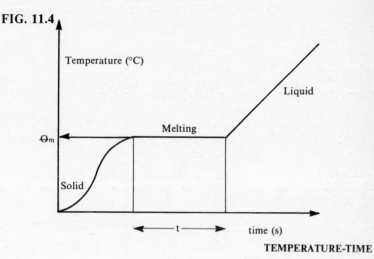

TEMPERATURE-TIME

Now at the melting point the substance is at the same temperature as that of the thermometer, heater, container and external surroundings (the water in the bath). Thus all the electrical energy supplied is used in melting the substance.

If
$V$ = p.d. across heater
$I$ = current in heater
$t$ = time during which solid melts
$\ell$ = specific latent heat of fusion

and
$$VIt = Ml$$
$$\therefore \ell = \frac{VIt}{m}$$

For a liquid to vapour phase change, when finding the specific latent heat of vaporization, the apparatus as shown in Fig. 11.5 is used.

**FIG. 11.5**

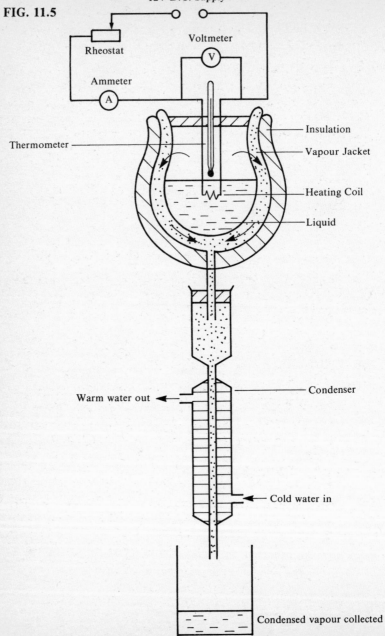

12V D.C. Supply

Rheostat

Voltmeter

Ammeter

Thermometer

Insulation

Vapour Jacket

Heating Coil

Liquid

Warm water out

Condenser

Cold water in

Condensed vapour collected

The liquid is heated by a coil carrying a steady current I across which is a p.d. V. Vapour passes down a condenser where cold water flowing through the outer tube condenses it back to a liquid.

After the liquid has been boiling for a little while, it reaches a stage when it is surrounded by a jacket of vapour at its boiling point. A steady state is reached when the rate of vaporization equals the rate of condensation. At this stage all the electrical energy supplied to the liquid by the coil is used to supply latent heat to the liquid.

If

$m$ = mass of liquid collected in time t
$\ell$ = specific latent heat of vaporization of liquid

then

$$VIt = m\ell$$
$$\therefore \ell = \frac{VIt}{m}$$

The insulation reduces heat losses by conduction and convection. Radiation losses are reduced by silvering the inside of the outer wall of the container.

## QUESTIONS

1) Define specific heat capacity.

2) An electric kettle has a heat capacity of 530 $JK^{-1}$. When 1.7Kg of water is placed in it, it takes 223s for the temperature of the water and kettle to rise from 20°C to 100°C. If the specific heat capacity of water is 4200J $(KgK)^{-1}$, calculate the wattage of the kettle.

3) Define specific latent heat of vaporization.

4) Define specific latent heat of fusion.

# Chapter 12
# THERMAL ENERGY TRANSFER

## 12.1 METHODS OF ENERGY TRANSFER
There are three ways in which thermal energy may be transferred.

### 12.1.1 Conduction
In conduction, heat moves bodily through a substance from a point at a high temperature to a point at a lower temperature.

Two mechanisms are involved: 1) electrons at a higher temperature migrate through the substance towards the lower temperature. In doing this they convey heat along the bar; 2) the atoms themselves transmit heat along the substance from high temperatures to low temperatures.

The first mechanism is the most important since it conveys most heat and it is known as electronic conduction. The latter mechanism is known as phonon conduction. In good conductors, both mechanisms occur. Metals are good conductors because they contain free electrons which are able to make electronic conduction occur. Whilst phonon conduction occurs in both good and bad conduction, it is the only mechanism occurring in bad conductors. Thus non metals which contain no free electrons are poor conductors. Indeed, since electrons are responsible for electronic conduction (of heat) and electrical current conduction, it is the fact that good thermal conductors are good electrical conductors and vice-versa.

Conduction occurs in solids, liquids and gases.

### 12.1.2 Convection
In convection, heat is transferred by bodily movement of a substance. The effect occurs because of density differences. If a beaker of water is heated at the bottom, the volume of liquid nearest the heat supply increases, leading to a reduction in density. Accordingly the less dense liquid rises with its place being taken by cooler more dense water. Consequently a convection current is established. It should be noted that for convection to occur, a substance should be heated at the bottom, thus enabling the less dense substance to rise.

Convection can only occur in fluids, i.e. liquids and gases, because they do not possess a rigid shape.

### 12.1.3   Radiation

Thermal radiation is the electromagnetic radiation emitted by solids, liquids and gases by virtue of their temperature. Since it is an electromagnetic wave it does not require a solid, liquid or gas to transmit it because electromagnetic waves can travel through a vacuum. It is, of course, the way in which the earth receives heat from the sun.

The power radiated per m² of a substance depends upon the fourth power of its Kelvin temperature and therefore very hot bodies dissipate most of their thermal energy in this way.

## 12.2   THERMAL CONDUCTIVITY

If the temperature of one end of a bar is raised above that of the other, then heat passes along the bar from the hot to the cold end, the temperature of which rises.

Such a process is known as conduction or, more properly, thermal conduction. Different substances conduct heat at different rates and we characterise the ability of a particular substance by specifying a constant quantity for a given material known as the Coefficient of Thermal Conductivity.

### 12.2.1   Coefficient of Thermal Conductivity

Suppose we have a bar of material as shown in Fig. 12.1. It is surrounded by a layer of expanded polystyrene which is a very poor conductor of heat and prevents any loss of heat through the sides of the bar, i.e. it acts as lagging.

**FIG. 12.1**

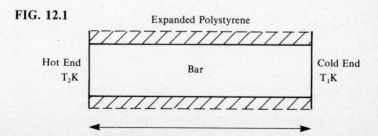

Expanded Polystyrene

Hot End
$T_2$K

Bar

Cold End
$T_1$K

Suppose the temperatures of the hot and cold ends are $T_2$ and T, K respectively. Additionally, the length of the bar is $\ell$ and its cross sectional area normally to the direction of heat flow is A.

It is found that the rate of flow of heat along the bar, Q/t depends upon

1) the cross-sectional area, A
2) the temperature gradient, $\dfrac{T_2 - T_1}{\ell}$

Expressed mathematically

$$\frac{Q}{t} \quad \alpha \quad \frac{A(T_2 - T_1)}{\ell}$$

We may convert this to an equation by the introduction of a constant of proportionality, K. Thus

$$\frac{Q}{t} \quad = \quad \frac{KA(T_2 - T_1)}{\ell}$$

The constant, K, is known as the Coefficient of Thermal Conductivity.

In order to define K, we make all quantities in the above equation equal to unity then K is numerically equal to $\dfrac{Q}{t}$

Thus, the coefficient of thermal conductivity of a material is defined as: That amount of thermal energy conducted every second between opposite faces of a unit cube ($1m^3$) when a temperature difference of 1K is maintained between the opposite faces.

By re-arranging the equation we find the units of K to be Watts per metre Kelvin, i.e. $W(MK)^{-1}$.

Some values of K are given in Table 12.2, from which it can be seen, quite naturally, that poor conduction of heat are non metals which all have low values of K.

**TABLE 12.2**

| SUBSTANCE | K (W(mK)$^{-1}$) |
|-----------|-------------------|
| Cotton wool | $2.5 \times 10^{-2}$ |
| Asbestos | $1.1 \times 10^{-1}$ |
| Cardboard | $2.1 \times 10^{-1}$ |
| Glass | 1.1 |
| Lead | $3.6 \times 10$ |
| Iron | $8.4 \times 10$ |
| Aluminium | $2.36 \times 10^{2}$ |
| Copper | $4.03 \times 10^{2}$ |

Note: The mathematically rigorous equation for thermal conductivity is:—

$$\frac{dQ}{dt} = -KA\frac{dT}{d\ell}$$

1) $\dfrac{dT}{d\ell}$ covers the case where the temperature gradient is non-uniform. This happens when the bar is unlagged.

2) $\dfrac{dQ}{dt}$ allows for the fact that when heat flows along the bar, the hot end cools and the cool end warms. Thus temperature gradient would change leading to a change in the rate of flow of heat which would no longer be steady.

3) The minus sign indicates that as $\ell$ increases, T decreases thus making $\dfrac{dT}{d\ell}$ negative. This is very important if the equation needs to be integrated.

The above three points do not arise in problems at 'A' level and we use the simpler equation.

Also, for building applications the U value is defined as $K/\ell$

**EXAMPLE**

Calculate the quantity of heat conducted per second through a copper block of dimensions 0.10m x 0.05m x 0.05m if a temperature difference of 10K exists between the two square faces and the four long faces are perfectly lagged. K for copper is 403 $W(mK)^{-1}$.

Use

$$\frac{Q}{t} = \frac{KA(T_2 - T_1)}{\ell}$$

Here

$$K = 4.03 \times 10^2 \ W(mK)^{-1}$$
$$A = 0.05 \times 0.05 = 2.5 \times 10^{-3} m^2$$
$$T_2 - T_1 = 10K$$
$$\ell = 0.10m = 10^{-1}m$$

So

$$\frac{Q}{t} = \frac{4.03 \times 10^2 \times 2.5 \times 10^{-3} \times 10}{10^{-1}}$$

$$= 101 \ Js^{-1} = 101W$$

Heat conducted per second = 101W

## 12.3 GOOD AND POOR CONDUCTORS

The fact that some substances are better conductors than others is of great importance.

Substances through which heat is required to be conducted should be good conductors. Thus pans should be made of material with a high coefficient of thermal conductivity.

Substances through which heat is not required to be conducted should be poor conductors and have a low coefficient of thermal conductivity. In thermal insulation, cotton (or glass) wool, foam and air are all used extensively.

Cotton or (glass) wool is used in roof insulation. Not only is this material a poor conductor but also the air pockets trapped within it have a poor conductivity. Thus heat is prevented from escaping through the roof of a house.

Foam is used in cavity wall insulation. The space between the inner and outer wall of a building is filled with such foam under high pressure. The foam solidifies and since both it and the air trapped within it are poor conductors, heat loss through the walls is prevented.

Air is used in double glazing. A layer of air is trapped between two layers of glass. The glass-air-glass sandwich so formed is a poor conductor of heat and heat loss is prevented.

In practice, most heat loss in a house is through the roof and therefore roof insulation is of vital importance.

## QUESTIONS

1) Define coefficient of thermal conductivity and show that the equation defining it is dimensionally correct.

2) In a steel boiler the plates are 8mm thick and 0.5Kg of water is evaporated per second per square metre of boiler surface. If the temperature drop across the boiler plates is 195K, calculate the thermal conductivity of steel. Assume that the specific latent heat of vaporization of water is $2.25 \times 10^6$ J Kg$^{-1}$.

3) A copper kettle has a base of area $4 \times 10^{-2}$m$^2$ and thickness $2 \times 10^{-3}$m. Calculate the steady temperature difference between the inner and outer surfaces of the base needed to increase the temperature of 2Kg of water in the kettle at the rate of 12K per minute. You may assume no heat losses and K for copper = $3.8 \times 10^2$ W(mk)$^{-1}$ , specific heat capacity of water = $4.2 \times 10^3$ J(KgK)$^{-1}$.

# Chapter 13
# ELECTRICAL ENERGY

## 13.1  ELECTRIC CURRENT

The flow of electric current in a conductor is due to a movement of negatively charged electrons.

In order to make the electrons flow, they must be situated in an electric field and the application of a potential difference across the ends of a conductor provides such an electric field.

Fig. 13.1 shows the flow of an electric current. The electrons flow from B to A because A is at a positive voltage with respect to B.

**FIG. 13.1**

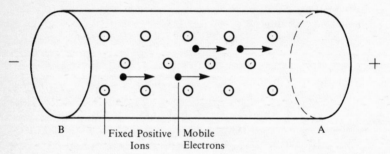

Fixed Positive Ions    Mobile Electrons

In a given amount of time, t seconds, a certain amount of charge, Q coulombs will move through the wire. The current flowing is defined as: The Rate of Flow of Charge.

The current is measured in Amperes (or Amps), symbol A. Thus the current I is given by

$$I = \frac{dQ}{dt}$$

In the case of a steady flow of charge we can write

$$I = \frac{Q}{t}$$

The ampere is defined in terms of the magnetic effect of a current and from this we can define the coulomb, symbol C, as the quantity of electric charge carried past a given point in an electric circuit when a steady current of one ampere flows for one second.

## 13.2 ELECTRICAL POTENTIAL ENERGY

In any electric circuit, electrical energy is converted into other forms of energy — in a wire the electrical energy is converted into heat whereas in a lamp it is converted into heat and light. In order to be able to calculate such energy conversions we define the term potential difference. The potential difference between two points in a circuit is the amount of electrical energy changed into other forms of energy when unit charge, one coulomb, passes from one point to the other.

Thus

$$\text{Potential Difference} = \frac{\text{Energy Transfer}}{\text{Charge}}$$

The unit of potential difference (P.D.) is the volt, symbol V. The potential difference between two points is one volt if one joule of electrical energy is converted when one coulomb passes between the two points. From this definition, it is evidence that we may write

$$1V = 1JC^{-1}$$

i.e.     1 volt = 1 Joule per coulomb

From the definition of potential difference

$$V = \frac{W}{Q}$$

or     $W = QV$

V = P.D.
W = energy transfer
Q = charge

Now for a steady current

$$Q = It$$

Hence

$$W = VIt$$

In order that an electric current can flow between two points, energy is needed to push the electrons along. Thus electrical energy has to be supplied to provide the energy. In other words, a potential difference is needed between, or we usually say across, two points in order that a current should flow between the two points.

Thus in the same way that a temperature difference causes heat to flow, a potential difference causes electricity to flow.

**EXAMPLE**

9J of energy are converted in moving a charge of 3C between two points. Calculate the p.d. between the points.

$$\text{Use} \qquad W = QV$$
$$\therefore \quad \frac{W}{Q} = V$$
$$\therefore \quad V = \frac{9}{3} = 3V$$
$$\text{P.D. is } 3V.$$

We sometimes use the term voltage instead of potential difference.

### 13.3 ELECTROMOTIVE FORCE OF A CELL OR GENERATOR

In order that an electric current should flow between two points in a wire, a potential difference is needed between those two points, i.e. electrical energy must be transformed into heat as the current flows. Such electrical energy must be provided by devices known as cells and generators.

We define the electromotive force (e.m.f.) of a cell or generator as the energy converted into electrical energy when unit charge passes through it, i.e. the energy supplied per coulomb by the cell.

The unit of e.m.f. is the same as p.d. — the volt and it equals the e.m.f. of a source which changes 1J of energy into electrical energy when 1C passes through it. Thus a car battery with an e.m.f. of 12V supplies 12J per coulomb passing through it.

E.M.F. applies to a source supplying electrical energy whereas p.d. refers to the conversion of electrical energy within a circuit.

Let us consider the energy change involved when a battery drives current around a wire. The chemistry of a battery is such that one terminal, the positive terminal is deficient in electrons whilst the other terminal, the negative, has a surplus of electrons. When the terminals are joined with a wire, the chemical energy is changed into electrical energy as electrons leave the negative terminal and migrate to the positive. As they move through the wire, they collide with metal atoms, transferring their kinetic energy and increasing the temperature of the wire. The electrons are accelerated by the electric field (see Chapter 20) in the wire and continue their journey along the wire, colliding with more metal atoms as they do so.

## 13.4   CURRENT — POTENTIAL DIFFERENCE RELATIONSHIPS

The application of a potential difference between two points in a conductor will cause an electric current to move between the two points. This electron movement will be hindered by the ions on the lattice of the conductor because the electrons will repeatedly collide with them. This opposition is a measure of the resistance of a conductor.

Ohm's Law states that: The current through a conductor is proportional to the potential difference between its ends provided that the temperature remains constant.

Thus at constant temperature

$$\frac{\text{Potential Difference}}{\text{Current}} = \text{Constant}$$

The constant is known as the resistance of the conductor. In symbols

$$\frac{V}{I} = R$$

The unit of resistance is the Ohm, symbol $\Omega$ and it may be defined by making the quantities in the above equation equal to unity.

One ohm is defined as: The resistance of a conductor such that a current of 1 amp flows through it when a potential difference of 1 volt is applied between its ends.

Ohm's Law is obeyed by metals which are the most important class of conductors. These are therefore known as ohmic conductors. In this type of conductor the current is proportional to the potential difference and if the potential difference is reversed (for example by interchanging the connections to battery terminals) the magnitude of the current remains the same but the direction is reversed. An electrolyte of copper sulphate solution between copper electrodes also behaves ohmically.

Current against voltage graphs for ohmic materials are shown in Fig. 13.2 and Fig. 13.3.

The reciprocal gradient is equal to resistance.

**FIG. 13.2**

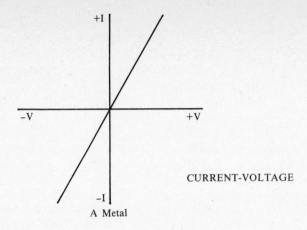

CURRENT-VOLTAGE

A Metal

**FIG. 13.3**

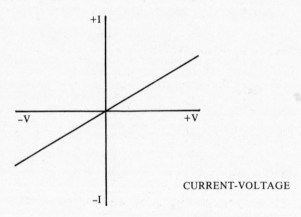

CURRENT-VOLTAGE

COPPER SULPHATE SOLUTION WITH COPPER ELECTRODES

Non-ohmic conductors are those which do not obey Ohm's Law. A metal can behave non-ohmically under certain conditions, e.g. when it is in the form of a fine filament as in an electric light bulb. Because it is so fine, it has a very high resistance. Accordingly when a current passes through it, its temperature is increased thereby increasing the resistance. Effectively it is this change in temperature which causes the variation in resistance. A current against voltage graph is shown in Fig. 13.4. (See also Chapter 16).

The reciprocal gradient at any point is equal to the resistance at that point.

**FIG. 13.4**

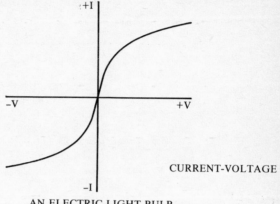

CURRENT-VOLTAGE

AN ELECTRIC LIGHT BULB
NON-UNIFORM RESISTANCE

Many electronic components are truly non-ohmic in that their resistance changes with voltage even at constant temperature. They are useful precisely because they possess this important quality.

Fig. 13.5 shows the current against voltage graph for a thermistor. This is made from semi-conducting material and its resistance decreases as temperature rises.

**FIG. 13.5**

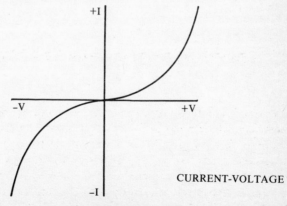

CURRENT-VOLTAGE

A THERMISTOR
NON-UNIFORM RESISTANCE

Fig. 13.6 shows the current voltage graph for a junction diode. This is made of two pieces of semi-conducting material each doped with different impurities. For one voltage direction the resistance is non uniform. For a voltage in the reverse direction the resistance is almost constant and very high.

**FIG. 13.6**

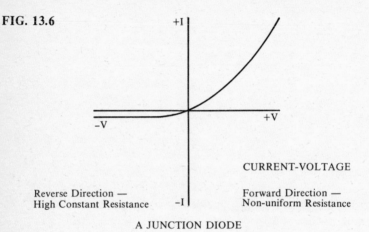

CURRENT-VOLTAGE

Reverse Direction —
High Constant Resistance

Forward Direction —
Non-uniform Resistance

A JUNCTION DIODE

## 13.5  RESISTIVITY AND CONDUCTIVITY

The resistance of a piece of wire depends not only on the material from which it is made but also the length and its cross sectional area.

We find that
$$R \alpha \frac{\ell}{A}$$

R = resistance
$\ell$ = length
A = area

This may be converted into an equation by introducing a constant of proportionality, $\rho$

Thus
$$R = \frac{\rho \ell}{A}$$

$\rho$ is known as the resistivity of the material.

From the above equation
$$\rho = \frac{RA}{\ell}$$

Thus the units of $\rho$ are ohm metre, symbol $\Omega$ m.

Accordingly we define resistivity as the resistance across opposite faces of a unit cube ($1m^3$) of a material.

The reciprocal of resistivity is conductivity, denoted by $\sigma$

Thus $\qquad \sigma = \dfrac{\ell}{RA}$

The units of conductivity are Siemanns, symbol S.

The analogy between thermal conductivity and electrical conductivity is as follows:—

For thermal conduction $\qquad \dfrac{Q}{t} = \dfrac{KAT}{\ell}$

For electrical conduction

$$V = IR$$

$$I = \dfrac{V}{R}$$

But $\qquad\qquad I = \dfrac{Q}{t}$

Thus $\qquad \dfrac{Q}{t} = \dfrac{V}{R} = \dfrac{\sigma AV}{\ell}$

Thus the electrical equivalent of temperature is voltage.

---

**EXAMPLE**

Calculate the resistance of a piece of iron wire of diameter 0.15mm and length 0.80m, given that the resistivity of iron at 0°C is $8.9 \times 10^{-8}$ $\Omega$ m.

So $\qquad \rho = 8.9 \times 10^{-8}$ $\Omega$ m

$\qquad\qquad \ell = 0.80$m

$\qquad\qquad A = \pi r^2 = \pi \times (0.075 \times 10^{-3})^2 \, m^2$

Hence $\qquad R = \dfrac{8.9 \times 10^{-8} \times 0.80}{\pi \times 0.075^2 \times 10^{-6}}$

$\qquad\qquad\quad = 4.03\,\Omega$

Resistance of Wire $= 4.03\,\Omega$ .

---

## 13.6 INTERNAL RESISTANCE OF A CELL

A battery resists the flow of an electric current through it. In other words, it behaves as if it contained a resistance. This resistance is known as the internal resistance of the cell.

As a result the e.m.f. provided by the cell is never able to be fully utilised as some of the voltage is used in driving the current through the cell.

The size of the internal resistance of a cell depends upon its size, the nature of the electrodes and the electrolyte and also its age. Dry cells in good condition have a resistance of about 0.5 $\Omega$ but this increases to one or two ohms as the cell runs down.

So called "high power" cells have a lower internal resistance. The measurement of internal resistance is discussed in 13.9.2.

## 13.7 THE COMBINATION OF RESISTORS
(The circuit symbol for a resistor is as shown in Fig. 13.7)

**FIG. 13.7**

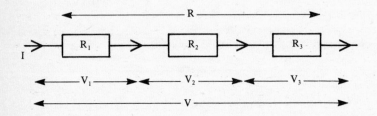

### 13.7.1 SERIES COMBINATION
Resistors connected as in Fig. 13.7 are said to be connected in series.

The same current flows through each resistor. Let the value of this current be I and suppose that the voltage across $R_1$, $R_2$ and $R_3$ are $V_1$, $V_2$ and $V_3$. Let the total voltage be V and the combined resistance be R

$$\text{Thus} \qquad V = IR$$
$$\text{But} \qquad V = V_1 + V_2 + V_3$$
$$\therefore \quad IR = IR_1 + IR_2 + IR_3$$
$$\text{So} \qquad R = R_1 + R_2 + R_3$$

When resistors are connected in series, the effective resistance is the sum of the separate resistances.

**FIG. 13.8**

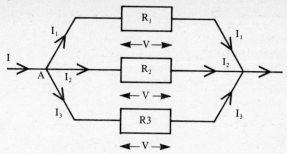

## 13.7.2 PARALLEL COMBINATION

Resistors connected as in Fig. 13.8 are said to be connected in parallel.

Suppose the values of the resistances are $R_1$, $R_2$ and $R_3$. The voltage across each is identical, V. The current entering the network will subdivide into $I_1$, $I_2$ and $I_3$. Let the effective resistance be R.

Current entering point A $= I$
Current leaving point A $= I_1 + I_2 + I_3$
Since charge is conserved
$$I = I_1 + I_2 + I_3$$
or
$$\frac{V}{R} = \frac{V}{R_1} + \frac{V}{R_2} + \frac{V}{R_3}$$
So
$$\frac{1}{R} = \frac{1}{R_1} + \frac{1}{R_2} + \frac{1}{R_3}$$

When resistors are connected in parallel, the reciprocal of the effective resistance is the sum of the separate reciprocal resistances.

---

**EXAMPLE**

Four identical resistors, $R_1$, $R_2$, $R_3$ and $R_4$ each $1\,\Omega$ are connected as shown in Fig. 13.9. Calculate the effective resistance of the network between points A and B.

**FIG. 13.9**

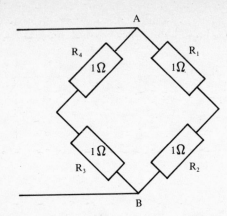

The network effectively consists of $R_1$ in series with $R_2$ and $R_3$ in series with $R_4$ with each of these arrangements being in parallel with the other.

The effective resistance of $R_1$ and $R_2$ is given by $R_5$

$$\text{where} \qquad R_5 = R_1 + R_2$$
$$= 1 + 1 \quad = 2\Omega$$
$$R_5 = 2\Omega$$

The effective resistance of $R_3$ and $R_4$ is given by $R_6$

$$\text{where} \qquad R_6 = R_3 + R_4$$
$$= 1 + 1 \quad = 2\Omega$$
$$R_6 = 2\Omega$$

The total effective resistance, R, is given by

$$\frac{1}{R} = \frac{1}{R_5} + \frac{1}{R_6}$$
$$= \frac{1}{2} + \frac{1}{2} = 1\Omega$$
$$\therefore \qquad R = 1\Omega$$

Total resistance $= 1\Omega$

## 13.8 RHEOSTATS AND POTENTIAL DIVIDERS

The resistors used in electronic circuits are usually variable resistors and they can be used in two ways. Common properties of all variable resistors is that they have three electrical contacts — fixed ones at either end and a variable contact, the position of which can be moved from one end of the resistor to the other.

### 13.8.1 Rheostats

A variable resistor is used as a rheostat when it is used to control the current flowing in a circuit. In this use, only one end contact together with the variable contact are used. The further the distance from the fixed to the sliding contact, the greater the resistance which is included in the circuit and the smaller is the current flowing in the circuit. See Fig. 13.10.

**FIG. 13.10**

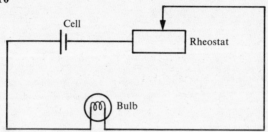

### 13.8.2  Potential Dividers

Here all three contacts are used, as in Fig. 13.11.

**FIG. 13.11**

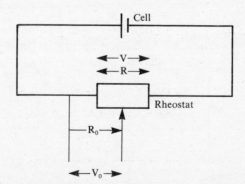

The voltage, V, across the resistor, R, is constant. The variable contact "taps off" a fraction of this voltage dependent upon its position from the end. The voltage is given as follows:—

$$\text{Current through resistance} = \frac{V}{R} = I$$

$$\text{thus} \qquad V_0 = I\,R_0 = \frac{V\,R_0}{R}$$

$$\text{i.e.} \qquad V_0 = \frac{R_0}{R}\,V$$

$\dfrac{R_0}{R}$ is known as the tapping fraction of a potential divider.

## 13.9   OHM'S LAW FOR A COMPLETE CIRCUIT

13.9.1   We now know that an electric current consists of a flow of negatively charged electrons, flowing from negative terminal to positive terminal when they are joined by a wire. In fact when electric currents were first observed, they were thought to consist of a flow of positive charges flowing from positive to negative terminals. This direction is taken as the direction of conventional current flow and is shown by the arrow on Fig. 13.12. In all circuit diagrams we show this conventional current direction, since most of the theories relating current direction to other phenomena were formulated before it was discovered that currents actually consisted of electrons in motion.

**FIG. 13.12**

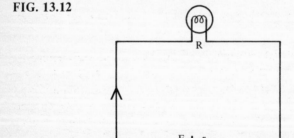

Suppose then a bulb of resistance R is connected across a cell of e.m.f. E and internal resistance r.

Ohm's Law applied to the complete circuit gives

$$\text{Current} = \frac{\text{Total voltage}}{\text{Total resistance}}$$

Now the total voltage in the current is the amount of electrical energy converted when one coulomb passes round the circuit. But this, of course, must equal the energy supplied, per coulomb, by the cell — i.e. the E.M.F.

$$\text{Total Voltage} = \text{E.M.F.}$$

Thus Current, I, is given by

$$I = \frac{E}{R + r}$$

This current flows through the circuit resistance, R, and the internal resistance r.

The p.d. across R is thus

$$V = IR = \frac{E}{R + r} R$$

The p.d. across r is thus

$$v = Ir = \frac{E}{R + r} r$$

The sum of v and V is, of course, E.

$$E = V + v \quad \left( \begin{array}{l} \text{i.e. E.M.F.} = \text{Sum of all p.d.'s in circuit} \\ \text{THIS IS ALWAYS TRUE} \end{array} \right)$$

V is often called useful volts and v the lost volts.

**13.9.2** The above may be used in order to find the internal resistance of a cell.

We connect a very high resistance voltmeter across the cell terminals. Because it has a high resistance, no current (or very, very little!) flows in the circuit so formed. There are therefore no lost volts and the meter records the e.m.f. of the cell, E, sometimes known as the terminal voltage. We now connect a bulb or other resistor across the battery terminals and measure the voltage across it, V. We also connect an ammeter OF VERY LOW RESISTANCE in the bulb circuit in order to determine the current, I, flowing in the circuit. Suppose the internal resistance of the cell ir r and that of the bulb is R. See Fig. 13.13.

**FIG. 13.13**

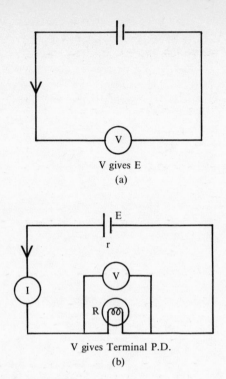

V gives E

(a)

V gives Terminal P.D.

(b)

In (b) V = IR. (Since the voltmeter has a very high resistance, all the current, I, passes through R).

$$\therefore \quad \text{Lost volts} \quad v \ = \ E - V$$
$$= \ E - IR$$
$$\text{But} \quad v \ = \ Ir$$
$$\therefore \quad Ir \ = \ E - IR$$
$$r \ = \ \frac{E - R}{I}$$

Hence r is found.

---

**EXAMPLE**
A cell of E.M.F. 1.SV is connected across a resistance of 4.0 Ω . The current flowing through the bulb is 0.3A and the p.d. across the bulb is 1.2V. Determine the internal resistance of the cell. See Fig. 13.14.

**FIG. 13.14**

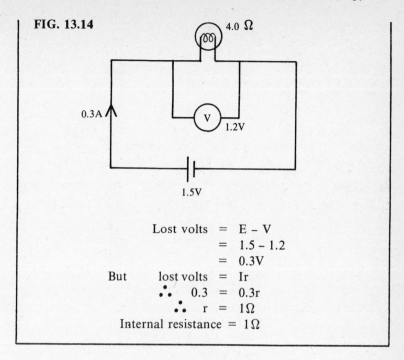

$$
\begin{aligned}
\text{Lost volts} &= \text{E} - \text{V} \\
&= 1.5 - 1.2 \\
&= 0.3\text{V}
\end{aligned}
$$

$$
\begin{aligned}
\text{But} \quad \text{lost volts} &= \text{Ir} \\
\therefore \quad 0.3 &= 0.3\text{r} \\
\therefore \quad \text{r} &= 1\Omega \\
\text{Internal resistance} &= 1\Omega
\end{aligned}
$$

## 13.10   VOLTMETERS AND AMMETERS

13.10.1   Most ammeters and voltmeters are essentially moving coil galvanometers which measure small currents and are calibrated with voltage or current scales. By connecting suitable resistors in series of parallel with them (internally) they may be used to measure voltages or currents. The construction of a moving coil galvanometer will be considered in Chapter 23.

An ammeter is used by connecting it in series in a circuit. Its resistance must therefore be small compared with the rest of the circuit in order that it should cause minimum change to the circuit current which it is attempting to measure. The perfect ammeter would have zero resistance so as not to disturb the circuit current.

A voltmeter is used by connecting it in parallel with the device across which it is measuring the p.d. Its resistance must therefore be very high compared to the resistance of the device so that most of the current entering the parallel arrangement passes through the device.

The perfect voltmeter would have infinite resistance and therefore take no current.

A device capable of measuring current and voltage over different ranges is called a multimeter. It is a galvanometer containing shunts and multipliers.

### 13.10.2  Shunts
The range of an ammeter may be extended by connecting a very low resistor in parallel with the meter. This is known as a shunt.

Suppose a meter of full scale deflection 0.0001A has a resistance of 1000 $\Omega$ . We wish to convert it into a meter of full scale deflection 1A.

$$\text{Thus current to go through shunt} = 1 - 0.0001$$
$$= 0.9999A$$

Since we have a parallel arrangement
$$\text{p.d. across meter} = \text{p.d. across shunt}$$

If r = resistance of shunt
$$0.0001 \times 1000 = 0.9999r$$
$$\therefore \quad r = \frac{0.0001 \times 1000}{0.9999} = 0.1\,\Omega$$

Thus a shunt of 0.1 $\Omega$  is needed.

The new scale will be "linear" with half full scale deflection now reading 0.5A.

### 13.10.3  Multipliers
The range of an ammeter may be converted to a large range voltmeter, a very high resistor should be connected in series with it. This is known as a multiplier.

Suppose a meter of full scale deflection 0.0001A has a resistance of 1000 $\Omega$ . We wish to convert it into a voltmeter of full scale deflection 1V.

$$\text{Voltage across meter and multiplier} = 1V$$

Since we have a series arrangement

Voltage across meter and   = Voltage across meter + Voltage
multiplier                            across multiplier

$$\text{Voltage across meter} = 0.0001 \times 1000 = 0.1$$
$$\therefore \quad \text{Voltage across multiplier} = 1 - 0.1 = 0.9V$$

If the resistance of the multiplier is r

$$\text{thus} \quad\quad 0.9 = 0.0001 \, r$$
$$\therefore \quad r = 9000 \, \Omega \,.$$

Thus a multiplier of $9000 \, \Omega$ is needed.

The new scale will be linear with half full scale deflection now reading 0.5V.

## 13.11   THE POTENTIOMETER

A potentiometer is a device which accurately measures p.d. because no current flows in meters connected to the device when readings are taken.

In its basic form it consists of a length of resistance wire, XY, of constant cross sectional area. A current is maintained through it by a driver cell. The voltage is tapped off at various points — in other words the primary circuit, as it is called, acts as a potential divider. If we wish to measure an unknown p.d. we merely balance it against the potential divider voltage. See Fig. 13.15

**FIG. 13.15**

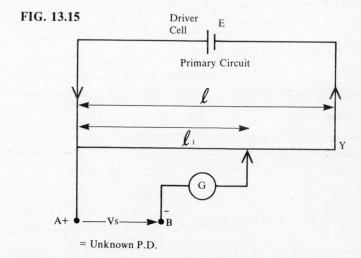

= Unknown P.D.

Thus, suppose no current flows through the galvanometer when we tap the primary circuit at $\ell_1$.

Let $\ell$ = length of potentiometer wire, E = e.m.f. of driver, $V_s$ = Unknown voltage.
The voltage along $\ell_1$ due to the driver cell = $\dfrac{\ell_1 E}{\ell}$.

because the wire is uniform so the voltage drop per cm is identical along the wire.

When there is no current through the galvanometer the unknown voltage equals the voltage due to the driver cell and the circuit is balanced.

$$\text{Thus} \qquad V_s = \frac{\ell_1}{\ell} E$$

and a knowledge of E enables $V_s$ to be found.

Quite often we do not know E and instead we use a standard cell — a Weston Cell — with an e.m.f. of 1.08V to obtain another balance point $\ell_2$. If the e.m.f. of 1.08V is denoted by $V_w$

$$\text{then} \qquad V_s = \frac{\ell_1}{\ell} E$$

$$V_w = \frac{\ell_2}{\ell} E$$

$$\therefore \quad \frac{V_s}{V_w} = \frac{\ell_1}{\ell} \qquad \text{or} \qquad V_s = \frac{\ell_1}{\ell} V_w$$

It should be noted that no current flows through the galvanometer and thus there is no p.d. across the meter. A current does still flow around the primary circuit.

Suppose now that the tapping off point were moved nearer to X. The voltage due to the driver would decrease and would be less than the unknown voltage. The difference in voltage would act to cause a current to flow. The driver voltage acts to drive current anti-clockwise whilst the unknown voltage acts to drive current clockwise. The resultant voltage due to the unknown voltage would cause a net clockwise current which would travel from A through E, Y and through the galvanometer back to B. The galvanometer would therefore deflect. (Current would not travel from X along $\ell_1$ because of the high resistance). If the tapping off point were now nearer to Y than the balance point, the driver voltage would exceed the unknown voltage and the galvanometer would deflect in the opposite direction.

NOTES:
1) In practice, a large protective resistance is placed in series with the galvanometer only to be removed as a position of balance is approached.
2) If no balance point is found, then either one of the voltages is too small or the voltages are the wrong way round so that they both act to drive current in the same direction.

The instrument is usually used to compare the e.m.f. of cells and by ensuring that only minute current flows in the primary circuit it may also be used to measure thermoelectric e.m.fs.

It may be used to compare resistances as follows. (See Fig. 13.16)

**FIG. 13.16**

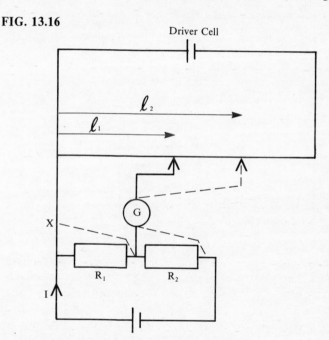

The unknown resistors $R_1$ and $R_2$ are connected to a cell. Accordingly a current flows through each and there will be a p.d. across each.

Suppose the galvanometer is connected across $R_1$ and a balance point obtained at $\ell_1$ (see solid lines)

Voltage across $R_1$ = $IR_1$ is balanced by $\ell_1$.

We now measure the voltage across $R_2$ by connecting it to X and connecting the galvo across it. A new balance point is obtained at $\ell_2$ (see dotted lines).

Voltage across $R_2$ = $IR_2$ is balanced by $\ell_2$

Thus
$$\frac{R_1}{R_2} = \frac{\ell_1}{\ell_2}$$

It may be used to determine internal resistance as follows. See Fig. 13.17.

**FIG. 13.17**

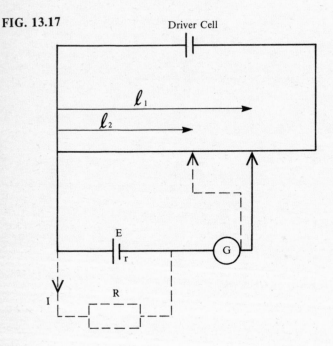

Driver Cell

The circuit is first balanced to find the e.m.f. of the cell E (solid lines). The balance point is $\ell_1$.

∴    This e.m.f. E balanced by $\ell_1$

A known resistance is then connected across this cell (dotted lines) and the p.d. across the cell, V, is balanced at a new point, $\ell_2$ (dotted lines).

$$\therefore \quad \frac{E}{V} = \frac{\ell_1}{\ell_2}$$

Now $\quad E = IR + Ir = I(R + r)$

and $\quad V = IR$

$$\therefore \quad \frac{E}{V} = \frac{I(R + r)}{IR} = \frac{R + r}{R} = \frac{\ell_1}{\ell_2}$$

Re-arranging this equation gives

$$r = R\left(\frac{\ell_1 - \ell_2}{\ell_2}\right)$$

Hence r is found.

---

**EXAMPLE**

In the experiment described above the e.m.f. is balanced on the potentiometer at 90.6cm. When a resistor of 10.0 Ω is connected in series with the cell, the new balance length is found to be 75.5cm. Determine the internal resistance of the cell.

Thus
$$k = 10.0\,\Omega$$
$$\ell_1 = 90.6\text{cm}$$
$$\ell_2 = 75.5\text{cm}$$

$$\therefore \quad r = 10.0\left(\frac{90.6 - 75.5}{75.5}\right)$$

$$= 10.0 \times \frac{15.1}{755} = \frac{151}{75.5} = 2.00\,\Omega$$

Internal Resistance $= 2.00\,\Omega$

---

## 13.12  KIRCHHOFF'S LAWS

At any point in a circuit, charge is conserved. Thus the current must also be conserved, i.e. the total current entering a point must equal the total current leaving it.

Also we have seen that the e.m.f. in a circuit is the sum of all the separate voltages (or sum of all the IR).

The above two points are formalized in Kirchhoff's Laws:

Law 1:   The algebraic sum of the currents at a junction is zero.

Law 2:   The algebraic sum of the e.m.fs. in a closed electrical circuit is equal to the algebraic sum of all the IR products in that circuit.

Thus in Fig. 13.18, Kirchhoff's First Law gives
$$I_1 = I_2 + I_3$$

**FIG. 13.18**

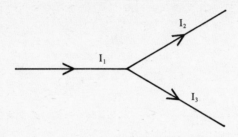

Thus in Fig. 13.19, Kirchhoff's Second Law gives
$$I_2R_1 + I_2R_2 - I_3R_3 = 0$$

(The minus sign is used because $I_3$ flows in the opposite direction to the chosen direction).

**FIG. 13.19**

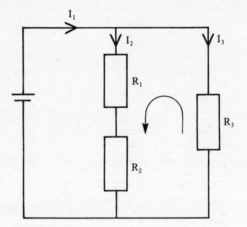

**ARROW INDICATES CHOSEN DIRECTION**

**EXAMPLE**
In the circuit shown in Fig. 13.20, calculate the p.d. across cell A, the p.d. across cell B, the p.d. across cell C and the p.d. across XY.

**FIG. 13.20**

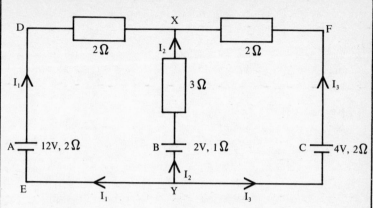

Applying Kirchhoff's First Law to junction Y
$$I_1 + I_2 + I_3 = 0$$

Applying Kirchhoff's Second Law to closed network DXYE
$$12 - 2 = 2I_1 + 2I_1 - 3I_2 - I_2$$
$$10 = 4I_1 - 4I_2$$

Applying Kirchhoff's Second Law to closed network FXYG
$$4 - 2 = 2I_3 + 2I_3 - 3I_2 - I_2$$
$$2 = 4I_3 - 4I_2$$

Solving these three simultaneous equations we obtain
$I_1 = 1.75A$
$I_2 = -0.75A$ } MEANS B AND C ARE NOT SUPPLYING
$I_3 = -2.50A$ } CURRENTS, BUT RECEIVING THEM.

Thus

P.D. across cell A = 1.75 x 2 = 3.50V
P.D. across cell B = 0.75 x 1 = 0.75V
P.D. across cell C = 2.50 x 2 = 5.00V
P.D. across XY = 0.75 x 4 = 3.00V

## QUESTIONS

1) Calculate the amount of charge passed by a steady current of 5A for 2s.

2) Calculate the energy transferred by a current of 5A flowing between 2 points between which there is a P.D. of 2V volts. The current flows for 0.5 minute.

3) Calculate the resistance of a 1Km length of steel bar if the cross-sectional area is 50cm² and $\rho = 1.0 \times 10^{-7} \Omega$ m.

4) A galvanometer of resistance 20 $\Omega$ is connected in series with a 4.0V accumulator and a resistance box, P. When the galvanometer is shunted with 80 $\Omega$ and P = 384 $\Omega$ the galvanometer gives a full scale deflection. The shunt is then removed. Calculate the new value of P needed to limit the reading to full-scale deflection.

# AREA 4 : MATTER

## Chapter 14
## THE NUCLEAR ATOM

### 14.1   EVIDENCE FOR THE EXISTENCE OF ATOMIC NUCLEI

Rutherford, in 1911, proposed a nuclear theory for the structure of the atom. He was led to this by the results of experiments performed by his assistants, Geiger and Marsden.

They investigated the scattering of alpha particles by a thin gold foil using the apparatus shown in Fig. 14.1.

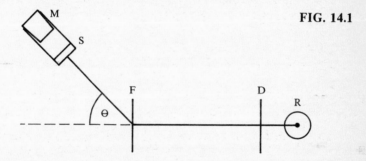

FIG. 14.1

Alpha particles from a radon source, R, passed through a diaphran, D. This provided a narrow parallel beam of alpha particles which were then scattered by a thin gold foil, F, through an angle Θ. Subsequently they impinged upon a zinc sulphide screen, S, attached to a microscope M. When the alpha particles struck S they caused scintillations (bright emissions of light) and these were observed through M.

The microscope and screen were rotated about an axis perpendicular to the plane of the paper and passing through the centre of F and the number of particles striking the screen were measured at different angles over a range of 5 to 150°.

Geiger and Marsden observed that some of the alpha particles were scattered through angles greater than 90°, that is, they were reflected along the side of incidence.

In order to explain such large angle scattering of fast moving alpha particles, Rutherford postulated that the alpha particle was deflected by a single atom and that the positive charge of the atom was concentrated in a very small nucleus and that the electrons occupied the space outside the nucleus.

The scattering mechanism is shown in Fig. 14.2.

**FIG. 14.2**

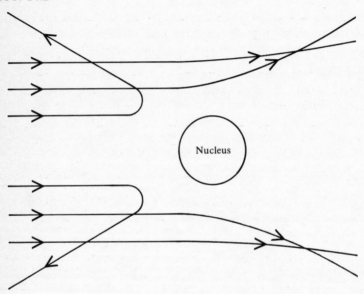

Those alpha particles passing closest to the nucleus will experience the largest repulsive electrostatic force and will be deflected most along the radial field due to the nuclear charge. (See Chapter 20). Those passing mid-way between the nuclei will obviously experience no net deflecting force and will pass straight through.

In his theory, Rutherford proposed that the number of alpha particles falling on the screen would be proportioned to
1)  the reciprocal of $\sin^4 (\theta/2)$.
2)  the reciprocal of the square of the initial kinetic energy of the alpha particles.
3)  the square of the nuclear charge.
4)  the square of the thickness of the scattering foil.

Experiments to confirm these proposals were performed by Geiger and Marsden in 1913 and repeated with greater accuracy by Chadwick in 1920. They verified completely Rutherford's nuclear theory of the structure of the atom.

## 14.2 ATOMIC PARTICLES

The atom consists of a central nucleus surrounded by extra-nuclear electrons carrying negative charge.

Inside the nucleus are particles known as nucleons and they may be of two types: protons, which carry a positive charge and neutrons which are uncharged. Protons must be present and neutrons usually are.

The electrons travel in paths known as Bohr orbitals — the one nearest to the nucleus being known as the first Bohr orbital with the next being known as the second, etc. These orbitals are shown in Fig. 14.3 and are not sharply defined but are blurred as shown in this figure. The electrons will definitely be found at a radius within the orbital although they may be anywhere within the "thickness" of the orbital. A simple analogy is that of a stone whirled in a horizontal circle on a piece of elastic. If this elastic has

**FIG. 14.3**

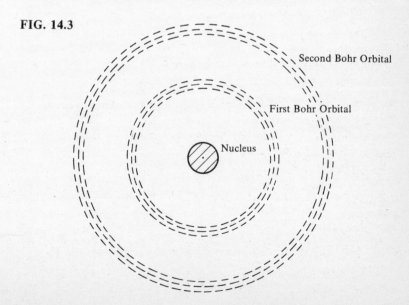

Second Bohr Orbital

First Bohr Orbital

Nucleus

an unstretched length of 1m and will stretch by a maximum of 1mm before it breaks, then we can say with certainty that the stone will be travelling in a circle of radius between 1m and 1.001m.

The maximum number of electrons in a given orbital is given by $N = 2n^2$      $n$ = number of orbital

$N$ = maximum capacity

Thus the first orbital can hold

$$N = 2(1)^2 = 2 \text{ electrons}$$

In any atom, the orbitals (or shells) are filled from the lowest to the highest, thus after the first shell the second is filled, then the third etc. The reason for this will be discussed in 14.3.

In any neutral atom the number of orbiting electrons is equal to the number of protons in the nucleus. If an atom loses an electron it will have a net positive charge and is known as a positive ion. If an atom gains an electron it will have a net negative charge and accordingly is known as a negative ion. The formation of ions can be explained in terms of electron movement only.

For any nucleus we define the following:

the nucleon number is the number of nucleons in the nucleus, i.e. the sum of the protons and neutrons. It is denoted by A. (an alternative name is mass number).

the proton number is the number of protons in the nucleus. It is denoted by Z. (an alternative name is atomic number).

Thus if      $A$ = No. of protons + No. of neutrons

and      $Z$ = No. opf protons

then      No. of neutrons = $A - Z$

It follows from the definition of proton number that since a neutral atom contains equal numbers of protons and electrons, the proton number is also equal to the number of electrons in the uncharged atom.

An atom is fully represented by its chemical element, with the nucleon number written in superscript and the proton number in subscript. Thus for an element X we have

$$_{z}^{A}X$$

---

**EXAMPLE**

Calculate the number of electrons, protons and neutrons in an atom of chlorine, $_{17}^{35}Cl$

Thus

No. of protons = No. of electrons = 17
No. of neutrons = 35 – 17 = 18

17 protons, 17 electrons and 18 neutrons

---

Atoms of an element need not have identical nucleon numbers. Consider chlorine. It exists in the form $_{17}^{35}Cl$ as described above and also $_{17}^{37}Cl$, which contains 20 neutrons instead of 18. Both forms of chlorine have identical physical and chemical properties and therefore occupy the same place in the periodic table of chemical elements. They are known as isotopes (derived from the Greek, iso = same, topos = place). Thus isotopes of a given element contain the same number of protons but different numbers of neutrons.

The number of naturally occurring isotopes per element varies from one for elements fluorine and gold, to ten for the element tin. About 280 different isotopes occur in nature.

The fundamental particles — electrons, protons and neutrons may be represented in nucleon/proton representation as

$$_{-1}^{0}e, \quad _{0}^{1}n, \quad _{1}^{1}p$$

(The electron is denoted with a proton number –1 since it has a charge of –1 rather than +1 !).

Relative atomic mass is defined as

$$\frac{\text{Mass of any atom}}{^{1}/_{12} \text{ Mass of } _{6}^{12}C \text{ atom}}$$

The units are Atomic Mass Units (A.M.U.s)

$$1 \text{ A.M.U.} = 1.66 \times 10^{-27} \text{Kg}$$

The mass of the proton = 1.007595 A.M.U.
The mass of the neutron = 1.008987 A.M.U.

The original definition of nucleon number, or mass number, was the whole number nearest to the mass of a nucleus.

This definition fell into dis-use and to re-inforce this fact the term was superceded by the term nucleon number.

## 14.3 THE EXTRA-NUCLEAR ELECTRONS

14.3.1   The nuclear radius is given by the relationship

$$\text{Nuclear radius} = 1.2 \times 10^{-15} A^{\frac{1}{2}} \text{ metre}$$

where A = nucleon number.

For helium

$$\text{Nuclear radius} = 2.4 \times 10^{-15} \text{m}.$$

The radius of the first Bohr orbital is

$$5.29 \times 10^{-11} \text{m}$$

It can be seen that in the helium atom, the atomic radius is approx. $2 \times 10^4$ times greater than the nuclear radius.

Consider also $^{238}_{92}U$ which has the largest naturally occurring nucleon number.

$$\text{Its nuclear radius} = 1.2 \times 10^{-15} \times (238)^{\frac{1}{2}}$$
$$\approx 2 \times 10^{14} \text{m}.$$

Now the radius, $r_n$, of the $n^{th}$ Bohr orbital is given by

$$r_n = n^2 r_1 \qquad r_1 = \text{radius of first Bohr orbital}$$

$^{238}_{92}U$ has 92 electrons, meaning that some electrons occupy the fifth Bohr orbital, the radius of which is

$$r_5 = 5^2 \times 5.29 \times 10^{-11} \text{m}$$
$$\approx 10^{-9} \text{m}.$$

It can be seen that in the uranium atom, the radius of the atom is approx. $5 \times 10^4$ times greater than the nuclear radius.

In general, the atomic radius is at least 10,000 times greater than the nuclear radius and it can be seen that most atoms are, in fact, full of empty space!

14.3.2   An electron in a Bohr orbital has kinetic energy, since it is motion, and potential energy since it is electrostatically attracted to the positively charged nucleus.

In the case of the hydrogen atom, the energy of the electron, E, is given by

$$E = \frac{-e^2}{8\pi\epsilon_0 r}$$

e = charge in electron
$\epsilon_0$ = permittivity of free space
r = Bohr orbital radius

The situation is more complex in atoms containing more than one electron because electrostatic interactions occur between the electrons themselves. Nevertheless, the energy equation is of the form

$$E = -\frac{K^4}{r} \qquad \text{where K is a constant}$$

It may be seen that $E = 0$ when $r = \infty$ ; that is, the zero level of energy is taken as that of the ionized atom. The minus sign shows that the energy of the atom is decreased as the electron comes closer to the nucleus.

This explains why orbitals always fill from the innermost to the outermost thereby decreasing the energy of the atom. Atoms, just like any other system, always tend to the lowest energy state possible.

An electron may be made to increase its energy by moving to a larger Bohr orbital. In order for it to do this the ground state atom, as it is called, must be excited by some external agency. Such transitions may take place because of the transfer of energy during collisions between atoms in a gas at high temperature or because of the supply of electrical energy as, for example, in a discharge tube.

Such an excited atom may then relax spontaneously. The electron falls back into a vacancy in a Bohr orbital nearer to the nucleus. In doing so the energy of the atom decreases and the lost energy is radiated in the form of electromagnetic waves. The frequency of this radiation, v, is given by

$$E_i - E_f = hv$$

$E_i$ = energy of excited atom
$E_f$ = energy of ground state atom
h = Planck's Constant

Now the energies associated with particular Bohr orbitals have particular values and thus $E_i - E_f$ has only fixed values resulting only in definite values of frequency. The actual frequency radiated will depend upon the initial and final Bohr orbital. Associated with each atom will be a line spectrum — a series of lines drawn horizontally (or sometimes vertically) at the specific wavelength of radiation. These may be misleading since they are not graphs but merely visual presentation of the wavelength at which atoms radiate.

The above analysis applies for a monatomic gas. In polyatomic gases, many more energy levels exist because of the interactions between the atoms in a molecule. Accordingly, many energy transitions are possible, resulting in a greater number of possible wavelengths of emitted electromagnetic radiation. The line spectrum will now contain many more lines.

The situation is much more complex in a solid. Even more energy levels are present, as are the number of possible energy transitions. Many more wavelengths of emitted radiation occur and the line spectrum becomes a band spectrum.

## QUESTIONS

1) How many electrons, protons and neutrons are there in an atom of $^{27}_{13}Al$?

2) Write down the electronic configuration of rhodium which has 45 electrons per atom (i.e. how many electrons in each Bohr orbital?)

3) Show that the nuclear radius of an atom of zinc ($^{64}_{30}Zn$) is 9.6 x 10$^{-15}$m.

4) An atom relaxes and emits electromagnetic radiation of frequency 6 x 10$^{14}$Hz. Calculate the difference in energy levels of the atom. (h = 6.6 x 10$^{-34}$ Js).

# Chapter 15
# RADIOACTIVITY

## 15.1 NATURAL AND INDUCED RADIOACTIVITY

There are three types of radioactivity — alpha, beta and gamma. Certain isotopes are said to be radioactive since they emit such radiation.

An isotope that is naturally radioactive usually is found to emit either alpha or beta radiation with gamma emission sometimes accompanying this. Practically all the elements with proton numbers from 81 to 92 are naturally radioactive.

The naturally occurring radioactive isotopes provided alpha radiation which was used for a direct attack on the nucleus (see Chapter 14), but which was also used for transmutation of elements, i.e. changing one element into another. Initially M and Mme Curie-Joliot in 1934 bombarded boron and aluminium targets with alpha radiation and observed that the bombarded substances continued to emit radiation even after the sources of radioactivity had been removed. This was because the new nucleus so formed was an unstable isotope which decayed by radioactive emission. The phenomenon is known as induced radioactivity and it occurs in all the so-called transuranic elements — those with a proton number greater than 92. Important examples are neptunium (Z = 93) and plutonium (Z = 94). Plutonium plays an important part in nuclear bombs because when its nucleus is hit by neutrons it splits into fragments with the release of large amounts of energy.

All around us, naturally occuring radioactivity is present. Cosmic rays come to earth from all directions in space. They consist of particles known as positrons and they interact with nuclei in the atmosphere to produce delta rays which are similar in composition to beta radiation. On earth itself there are supplies of uranium and granite — both of which are radioactive. Because of all of these sources, there is a large amount of natural radioactivity present on earth. It is known as background radiation. The background radiation is high in such places as Aberdeen where there are large quantities of granite.

At a particular location, extra radioactivity may be present, in addition to background. These include such places as high energy nuclear physics establishments and nuclear reactor sites. In these reactors naturally occuring uranium and transmutted plutonium may be present.

## 15.2 ALPHA, BETA AND GAMMA RADIATION
There are three types of radioactive emission:

15.2.1   Alpha radiation is particulate, comprising of helium nuclei. Such nuclei contain 2 protons and 2 neutrons and so

$$\alpha = \ _{2}^{4}\text{He}$$

It carries a positive charge and therefore may be deflected by a magnetic field.

Not all $\alpha$ particles travel with the same velocity but an average value of emission is $10^{7}$ ms$^{-1}$ with an associated kinetic energy of around $1.2 \times 10^{-12}$J.

For any nucleus emitting alpha radiation, the remaining nucleus has a proton number 2 less than originally (in the "parent" nucleus) and a mass number reduced by 4. Suppose a nucleus X, decays into a nucleus Y by the emission of an alpha particle. We may write

$$_{Z}X \longrightarrow\ _{2}^{4}\alpha\ +\ _{Z-2}^{A-4}Y$$

i.e. Z and A are conserved on each side of the equation.

15.2.2   Beta radiation is particulate, comprising of electrons. It may therefore be represented as

$$\beta = \ _{-1}^{0}\text{e}$$

It carries a negative charge and is therefore deflected by a magnetic field but in the opposite direction to that of alpha radiation particles are emitted with a range of velocities with an average value being $10^{9}$ ms$^{-1}$ with an associated kinetic energy of around $10^{-13}$J.

For any nucleus emitting beta radiation, the remaining nucleus has an unchanged mass number and a proton number increased by 1. Thus, if a nucleus X decays to nucleus Y with beta emission we may write

$$_{Z}^{A}X \longrightarrow {}_{1}^{0}\beta + {}_{Z+1}^{A}Y$$

i.e. Z and A are conserved on each side of the equation.

15.2.3 Gamma radiation consists of electromagnetic waves of high energy and short wavelength — typical values being $10^{-9}$J and 0.026nm respectively. It is represented by the symbol $\gamma$.

Since it does not carry a charge, it is undeviated by a magnetic field. The deviation of $\alpha$, $\beta$ and $\gamma$ by such a field is shown in Fig. 15.1. The direction is given by Fleming's Left Hand Rule.

**FIG. 15.1**

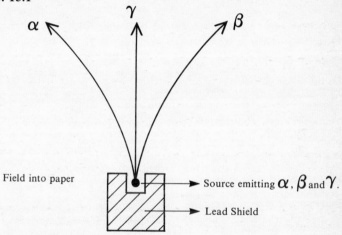

Field into paper

Source emitting $\alpha$, $\beta$ and $\gamma$.

Lead Shield

Any nucleus emitting gamma radiation suffers no change in proton or mass number and therefore does not change its constitution. However, the energy level of the nucleus changes. We may write

EXCITED NUCLEUS ⟶ GAMMA RADIATION + GROUND STATE NUCLEUS

---

**EXAMPLE**

$_{92}^{237}$U decays by beta emission. Show by means of a nuclear equation that the new nucleus formed is $_{93}^{237}$Np.

Thus, here $_{Z}^{A}X = {}_{92}^{237}$U

Let the new nucleus be Y. We have

$$^{237}_{92}U \longrightarrow ^{0}_{-1}e + ^{A}_{Z}Y$$

Now $\qquad$ 237 = O + A

$\qquad\qquad\qquad\therefore$ A = 237

and $\qquad$ 92 = -1 + Z

$\qquad\qquad\qquad\therefore$ Z = 93

$$\therefore {^{A}_{Z}}V = {^{237}_{93}}Y \quad \text{which is neptunium}$$

## 15.3 THE ABSORPTION OF RADIATION IN MATTER

15.3.1 Alpha radiation consists of moving positive charges. As it passes through matter it meets the atomic electrons and "collides" with them. The collision is not a physical impact but an electrostatic interaction. Because of the electrostatic attraction between itself and these electrons, it removes them from their orbitals thereby causing ionisation. In so doing, it loses energy through two mechanisms:

(i) energy is needed to remove the electron from its orbital thereby increasing its potential energy.

(ii) energy is needed to cause the electron to move thereby increasing its kinetic energy.

As a result, the kinetic energy of the alpha particle is reduced. If the material through which it passes is thick enough, the radiation is eventually brought to rest, i.e. it is absorbed.

Typical ranges of alpha particles are up to 12cm in air and 1mm in paper.

15.3.2 A similar situation arises when beta radiation passes through matter. Again, the radiation loses energy by "collision" with the electrostatic force being repulsive rather than attractive. In addition to energy losses by collision, another less important phenomenon known as BREMSSTRAHLUNG is involved in which the decelerating beta particles emit electromagnetic radiation.

However, the ionising effect is less with beta than alpha radiation because the charge on beta is less and also it is moving with a greater velocity thereby having less time to influence the electrons in a particular atom.

Beta particles are not stopped by air but need a layer of material to bring them to rest. Typically, a few mm of aluminium or about $\frac{1}{2}$mm of lead.

15.3.3 Gamma radiation is uncharged and suffers no electrostatic forces when it passes through matter. However, it interacts with the atomic electrons by several processes to produce high energy electrons. These processes are:

(1) the photoelectric effect — gamma radiation is absorbed to liberate electrons from the surface of the material. Energy, known as the "work function" is needed to remove an electron from its orbital and take it to the surface of the material and then kinetic energy must be supplied in order that it may escape.

(2) the Compton effect — the gamma radiation physically collides with the atomic electrons removing them and itself being scattered in the process. Here the energy loss if of a similar nature to that in alpha and beta "collisions" with electrons.

(3) pair production — the gamma radiation changes into electrical particles — an electron and a positron — and these move off with kinetic energy.

However, because gamma radiation has to physically collide with electrons, its ionising properties are very much less than those of alpha and beta radiations and its range is much greater. A few cms of lead are required in order to bring it to rest.

It can be seen from the above that

$$\text{Range} \quad \alpha \quad \frac{1}{\text{Ionisation}}$$

## 15.4 THE DETECTION OF RADIOACTIVE EMISSIONS
Devices for the detection of radioactive emissions make use of their ionising properties. The types available are known as cloud chambers, bubble chambers and Geiger counters.

A Geiger counter is shown in Fig. 15.2. Essentially it consists of a cylinder C and a fine wire W mounted parallel to the axis of the cylinder and insulated from it. The cylinder contains a low pressure gas such as air or argon. A voltage less than that needed to ionise the atoms of this gas is maintained between the wire and the tube, with the wire being at a positive voltage compared to the cylinder. This voltage sets up an electric field (see Chapter 20) between the wire and the cylinder. Ionising radiation enters the counter through aperture A, which is usually covered with a thin sheet of mica, glass or aluminium. It then ionises the gas along its path. These ions are accelerated by the electric field and produce more ions by collision with neutral atoms and molecules so that the ionisation current builds up very rapidly. A very high resistance, R, is connected between the wire and ground to prevent current flowing so that the energy due to the ionisation current is rapidly dissipated. The effect is the production of a very large current lasting for a very short period of time. This momentary current registers as a "kick" in a device connected at G. The device connected may register a count (i.e. the total number of ionising particles entering the aperture) when it is known as a scaler or it may register the number of ionising particles entering the aperture every minute when it is known as a ratemeter. Also the kick may be amplified to operate a loudspeaker thus giving an audible signal. A suitable choice of R ensures that each ionising particle entering the chamber produces its own electrical surge.

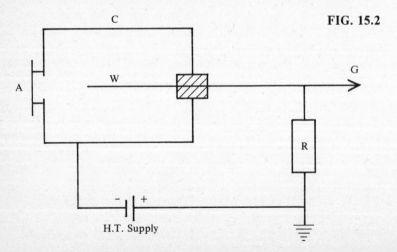

**FIG. 15.2**

By placing suitable material over the aperture, either alpha or alpha and beta radiations can be filtered out of any incident radiations.

The counting rate of a Geiger counter depends upon the voltage applied to the tube as shown in Fig. 15.3, which shows the variation in count rate, in counts per minute, against voltage. The counter operates at a minimum voltage, the threshold voltage, which is needed to accelerate the ions to the wire. It very rapidly reaches the threshold knee which identifies the start of a flat almost horizontal portion known as the geiger plateau along which the count rate is virtually independent of voltage. When the racing voltage is reached the count rate increases dramatically because ions rapidly ionise atoms with which they collide producing an avalanche effect. By operating the counter at the centre of the plateau, the count rate will be almost independent of the applied voltage and the effects of small drifts in voltage will therefore be minimised. A good counter should have a plateau at least 200V in length with a plateau slope less than 0.05% per volt. As the counter ages, the plateau decreases in length and increases in slope as shown by the dotted line.

**FIG. 15.3**

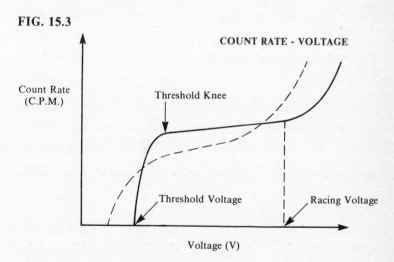

COUNT RATE - VOLTAGE

Count Rate (C.P.M.)

Threshold Knee

Threshold Voltage

Racing Voltage

Voltage (V)

## 15.5 THE EQUATIONS OF RADIOACTIVE DECAY
15.5.1 The rate at which a particular radioactive material disintegrates or decays, is a constant that is almost completely independent of any physical and chemical conditions.

The activity of a sample of radioactive material is defined as the number of disintegrations per second. Its unit is the Bequerel — symbol Bq — with 1Bq being equal to 1 disintegration per second. The activity is found to be proportional to the number of radioactive nuclei present and therefore if N radioactive nuclei are present at a time t, the activity is given by dN/dt. We must use a calculus definition in order that the change in N is negligible compared to N.

Since activity is proportional to the number of radioactive nuclei present, we may write

$$\frac{dN}{dt} \quad \alpha \quad N$$

This relationship may be changed into an equation by the introduction of a constant, $\lambda$ . Further, as time goes by the number of radioactive nuclei decreases and hence so does the activity. We allow for this by the inclusion of a minus sign

$$\text{Thus} \qquad \frac{dN}{dt} \quad = \quad -\lambda N$$

$\lambda$ is a constant for all nuclei of a particular isotope but differs for different isotopes of the same element and for different elements. It is called the decay constant of the isotope. Its units are $\sec^{-1}$ and it represents the constant probability of decay per unit time.

15.5.2    Now

$$\frac{dN}{dt} \quad = \quad -\lambda N$$

This equation may be re-arranged and integrated. Suppose that at time $t = 0$ there are $N_0$ radioactive nuclei present with there being N at time t.
Then

$$\int_{N_0}^{N} \frac{dN}{N} \quad = \quad -\lambda \int_{0}^{t} dt$$

$$[\log_e N]_{N_0}^{N} \quad = \quad -\lambda \, [t]_0^t$$

$$\log_e \left( \frac{N}{N_0} \right) \quad = \quad -\lambda t$$

Hence from the theory of logarithms

$$\frac{N}{N_0} = e^{-\lambda t}$$

or
$$\underline{N = N_0 e^{-\lambda t}}$$

This equation shows that the number of nuclei of a given radioactive substance decays exponentially with time, provided that no new nuclei are introduced.

Half of the material will have decayed at the end of a certain time interval T, which can be found by setting $N = N_0/2$ and $t = T$ in the above equation

$$\frac{N_0}{2} = N_0 e^{-\lambda T}$$

Taking logarithms and re-arranging

$$\lambda T = \log_e 2$$
$$\therefore \quad T = \frac{\log_e 2}{\lambda}$$

thus
$$T = \frac{0.693}{\lambda}$$

T is called the half-life of the isotope. It is defined as the time for the number of radioactive nuclei of a particular isotope to half. Therefore it is the time taken for the mass of the radioactive nuclei to half.

It is, however, important to avoid the misconception that the half-life is the time taken for the physical mass of the substance to half, as if half of a block had suddenly vanished! The radioactive substance will decay into another substance and the only physical mass which will be lost will be that due to any alpha emission during this decay.

Half-life is measured in units of time, i.e. seconds, but some values are large and it is standard practice rather than to quote large numbers as seconds, using standard form, to use hours, days or even years. Values range from 0.88s for $^8_3$Li to 24,000 years for $^{239}_{94}$Pu with the shortest being thorium C', $3 \times 10^{-7}$s and the longest being thorium, $1.39 \times 10^{10}$years — notice that these are isotopes of the same element. The exponential decay of a radioactive element with time in half-life periods is shown in Fig. 15.4.

FIG. 15.4

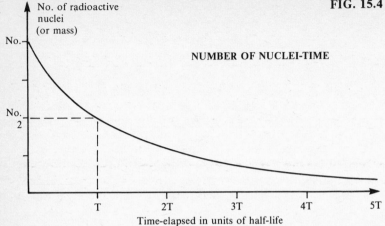

Time-elapsed in units of half-life

After one half-life, one half of the original material remains. After two half-lives, one half of this half remains — i.e. one quarter of the original material remains.

Thus after     1 half-life,     $\frac{1}{2}$ remains
              2 half-lives,    $\frac{1}{4} = \frac{1}{2^2}$ remains

In general, after  $n$  half-lives
          Amount remaining    $=$    $\frac{1}{2^n}$  x Original

   or
          Fraction remaining    $=$    $\frac{1}{2^n}$

---

**EXAMPLE**

After two hours, $\frac{1}{16}$th of the initial amount of a certain radioisotope remains undecayed. Calculate the half-life of the isotope.

$$\text{Now fraction remaining} \; = \; \frac{1}{2^n}$$

$$\text{thus} \qquad \frac{1}{16} \; = \; \frac{1}{2^n}$$

$$\therefore \qquad 2^n \; = 16$$

$$n \; = 4$$

Hence

$$4 \text{ half-lives} = 2 \text{ hours}$$
$$1 \text{ half-life} = 30 \text{ minutes}$$

Although it is possible to quantify radioactive decay in terms of half-life it is, however, impossible to tell just when one particular nucleus will decay because radioactive disintegrations follow the laws of chance or probability.

15.5.3   In experiments on radioactivity, we do not monitor the number of radioactive nuclei present but rather the activity. In the way that a radioactive substance decays exponentially, so does its activity. This may be shown as follows.

Suppose we consider $N_0$ nuclei at time 0 and $N$ at t.
Then at $t = 0$

$$\frac{dN_0}{dt} = - \lambda N_0 \qquad \text{(i)}$$

At t

$$\frac{dN}{dt} = - \lambda N \qquad \text{(ii)}$$

Now

$$N = N_0 \, e^{-\lambda t} \qquad \text{(iii)}$$

Substituting for $N$ from (iii) into (ii)

$$\frac{dN}{dt} = - \lambda N_0 \, e^{-\lambda t}$$

and substituting for $N_0$ from (i) into the above equation

$$\frac{dN}{dt} = - \lambda \left( \frac{-1}{\lambda} \frac{dN_0}{dt} \right) e^{-\lambda t}$$

or

$$\underline{\frac{dN}{dt} = \frac{dN_0}{dt} \, e^{-\lambda t}}$$

Thus, the activity decays exponentially with time.

The equation has the same form as the decay equation

$$N = N_0 \, e^{-\lambda t}$$

and in view of this we may also define the half-life of a radioactive substance as the time taken for the activity of the substance to decay by half.

Similarly

After n half-lives

$$\text{Activity remaining} = \frac{1}{2^n} \times \text{Original activity}$$

or   $$\text{Fractional activity} = \frac{1}{2^n}$$

---

**EXAMPLE**

The original activity of phosphorous 32 is 2 MBq. If the half-life is 14.3 days, calculate the activity after 49 days.

$$\text{Now Final Activity} = \text{Original Activity} \times \frac{1}{2^n}$$

Here

$$\text{number of half-lives elapsed} = \frac{49}{14.3}$$

$$\text{Final Activity} = 2 \times \frac{1}{2^{49/14.3}}$$

$$= 2 \times \frac{1}{2^{3.4}}$$

$$= 0.19 \text{ MBq}$$

---

**QUESTIONS**

1) Identify the nucleus formed when $^{238}_{94}$Pu decays by alpha emission.

2) Identify the nucleus formed when $^{237}_{92}$U decays by beta emission.

3) Calculate the decay constant of potassium given that its half-life is $12.5 \times 10^8$ years.

4) Find the activity of 1g of Thorium C[1], given that its decay constant is $1.31 \times 10^6$ s$^{-1}$.

5) The half-life of Rhenium is $5 \times 10^{16}$ years. Calculate the fraction of a given sample which will remain after $2.25 \times 10^{11}$ years.

# Chapter 16
# ELECTRONS

## 16.1 THERMIONIC EMISSION

16.1.1   When a piece of metal is heated to a high temperature, electrons escape from its surface. This effect is known as thermionic emission.

The effect may be demonstrated with the apparatus shown in Fig. 16.1. A tungsten wire, F, is enclosed in an evacuated glass bulb. It can be heated by means of the low voltage supply. Opposite the wire is a metal plate, T. When the wire is heated and the plate is at a positive voltage with respect to the wire, there is a current across the gap between F and T and this can be measured by means of the meter in the circuit, M. The direction of this current shows that the charge emitted is indeed negative. If the heater is switched off, the current no longer flows, because the thermionic emission ceases.

**FIG. 16.1**

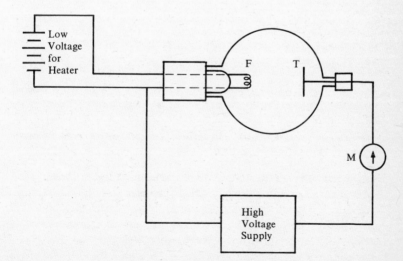

The purpose of the high voltage supply across F and T is to provide an intense electric field which acts on the electrons to accelerate them to T and so complete the circuit. If the voltage across F and T is reversed, the direction of the electric field is also reversed and it draws any negative charge back into F and thus no current flows.

Thus, in order for a current to flow, the heater must be switched on in order that thermionic emission should occur and T must be at a positive voltage with respect to F in order that the emitted electrons should reach T.

The system is maintained at a low pressure in order that there should be fewer gas molecules between the filament and the target. The number of electron-gas molecule collisions will then be reduced and energy losses of the electrons kept to a minimum.

The electrode of such an electron tube from which the electrons are emitted, F, is known as the cathode whilst the electrode to which the electrons travel, T, is known as the anode. No chemical change takes place in either electrode and the electrons which are needed in the process are supplied by the high voltage supply.

Such an arrangement of a heater cathode in an evacuated enclosure is known as an electron gun. It is a fundamental component of devices such as fine beam tubes, used for finding the ratio of charge to mass of electrons, cathode ray oscilloscopes, used for investigations of voltage and frequency and, of course, television tubes.

In a fine beam tube horizontal metal plates, across which a voltage is maintained, are placed between the cathode and anode. These cause deflection of the electrons and measurements of this and other physical quantities enable the ratio of charge to mass of the electrons to be determined.

In cathode ray oscilloscopes and television tubes, the target is removed and the anodes, which are placed nearer to the cathode, are cylindrical. They help to accelerate and focus the electrons onto a glass screen. This is coated with zinc sulphide which emits visible radiation when it is struck by electrons. Vertical and horizontal deflections of the electrons are achieved by horizontal and vertical plates of metal, across which varying voltages may be maintained.

16.1.2 The velocity and acceleration of electrons liberated in this process may be calculated as follows.

Suppose an electron of mass m carrying a charge e is accelerated by a potential difference V.

The electrical energy supplied = electrical force x distance moved by electron

$$\text{Now} \qquad \text{electrical force} = E\,e$$

$$E = \text{electric field strength}$$
$$e = \text{charge on electron}$$

and also $\qquad E = \dfrac{\text{Voltage across cathode-anode}}{\text{distance between them}}$

thus $\qquad E = \dfrac{V}{x}$

$$V = \text{voltage between cathode-anode}$$
$$x = \text{distance between them}$$

Thus electrical energy supplied $\quad = \quad F\,x$
$$= \quad E\,e\,x$$
$$= \quad \dfrac{V}{x}e\,x$$

$$= \quad e\,V$$

This is converted into kinetic energy and thus

$$\dfrac{1}{2}\,m\,v^2 = e\,V$$

when $v$ = final velocity of electron as it strikes the anode.

and thus

$$v = \sqrt{\dfrac{2\,e\,V}{m}}$$

When the electron strikes the anode it is brought to rest and most of its energy is converted into internal energy of the anode.

Since $\qquad\qquad E = \dfrac{V}{x}$

and $\qquad E = \dfrac{\text{Force}}{\text{Charge}} = \dfrac{\text{Mass x Acceleration}}{\text{Charge}} = \dfrac{Ma}{e}$

$$m = \text{mass}$$
$$a = \text{acceleration}$$
$$e = \text{charge}$$

then

$$\frac{Ma}{e} = \frac{V}{x}$$

So $\qquad a = \dfrac{e\,V}{m\,x}$

Now e and m are, of course, constants. Also in any given device, $x$ is also a constant. Consequently both the acceleration and final velocity acquired by the electrons depend upon the variable voltage.

## 16.2 ELECTRON FLOW IN METALS

Consider Fig. 16.2. This shows a conductor of length $x$ and cross sectional area A, having n free electrons per unit volume, each carrying a charge e .

**FIG. 16.2**

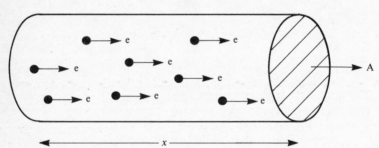

Volume of conductor $= A\,x$
No. of free electrons $= n\,A\,x$
∴ Total charge, Q, of free electrons $= n\,A\,x\,e$

These free electrons will drift around at random, colliding with the atom of the conductor, and passing from one atom to the next. If a voltage is applied across the ends of the conductor, the electrons will be caused to pass along the conductor from the – to the + voltage at a given average drift velocity, V.

The resulting steady current, I, is given by

$$I = \frac{Q}{t}$$

$$\therefore \quad I = \frac{nAxe}{t}$$

Now
$$V = \frac{x}{t}$$

where t = time to pass through length $x$

$$\therefore \quad t = x/V$$

Hence
$$I = \frac{nAxe}{\frac{x}{V}} = nAeV$$

$$I = nAeV$$

This equation is sometimes called the Drude Equation and is written as

$$J = \frac{I}{A} = neV$$

$$J = \text{current density, in Am}^{-2}.$$

The average drift velocity, V, is given by

$$V = \frac{I}{nAe}$$

When a voltage is applied across the ends of a conductor, the free electrons will drift along it with this average drift velocity. They will pass to the positive terminal of the cell, providing the voltage. At the same time more electrons will flow from the negative terminal to enter the conductor and continue the process.

**FIG. 16.3**

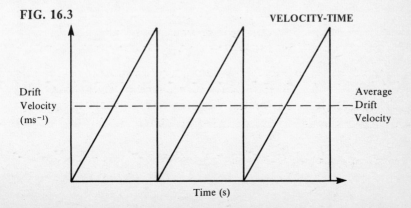

VELOCITY-TIME

Drift Velocity (ms$^{-1}$)

Average Drift Velocity

Time (s)

The increase in velocity with time is shown in Fig. 16.3. The electrons are accelerated uniformly by the electric field in the conductor.

The acceleration, a, is given by

$$a = \frac{E e}{m}$$

E = electric field strength
e = electronic charge
m = mass of electron

The electrons then collide with the atoms of the conductor and are brought to rest. They then accelerate again and repeat the process. Thus the graph is a "triangular wave" as shown. The average drift velocity is, therefore, given by the dotted line.

---

**EXAMPLE**

Calculate the average drift velocity of electrons in SWG28 copper wire of cross sectional area $1.1 \times 10^{-7}$ m$^2$ when a current of 1A flows. Assume each copper atom contributes one free electron and there are $10^{29}$ electrons per m$^3$. Charge on electron = $1.6 \times 10^{-19}$C.

Use
$$V = \frac{I}{n A e}$$

here
$$I = 1A$$
$$n = 10^{29} \text{ m}^{-3}$$
$$A = 1.1 \times 10^{-17} \text{ m}^2$$
$$e = 1.6 \times 10^{-19} \text{ C}$$

thus
$$V = \frac{1}{10^{29} \times 1.1 \times 10^{-17} \times 1.6 \times 10^{-19}}$$
$$= \frac{1}{1.76 \times 10^3}$$
$$= 0.57 \times 10^{-3} \text{ ms}^{-1}$$

$\therefore$ Average drift velocity = $5.7 \times 10^{-2}$ ms$^{-1}$

It will be noted that this is a remarkably small velocity, particularly when it is compared to the random velocity upon which it is superimposed. This random velocity is about $\frac{1}{1000}$ the velocity of light.

When a current flows in a conductor, the flow begins immediately at all points in the circuit. Now electrons would only leave the conductor at the low velocity as calculated and so it would be quite a time before they arrived at the other parts of the circuit. However, whenever a circuit is "made", an electric field travels along the circuit at almost the speed of light. This field causes the current to start to flow simultaneously at all points in the circuit.

## 16.3 CONDUCTION MECHANISMS IN SEMICONDUCTORS

16.3.1 These substances are in between conductors and insulators as regards their conductivity. They include silicon, germanium, and tellurium. The important points about their electrical behaviour are:—
1) their resistivity decreases with temperature.
2) they are sensitive to light.
3) their electrical properties change when placed in a magnetic field.
4) they are affected by the presence of other atoms — impurity atoms.

16.3.2 Pure or intrinsic semiconductors include the very important ones of silicon and germanium. Both have a valency of four and are known as tetravalent elements. Each of the silicon valence electrons is shared by one of four nearest neighbour atoms, as in Fig. 16.4. [The silicon atom contains 14 electrons — 2 in the first orbital, 8 in the second and 4 valence electrons in the third orbital. These four are the valence electrons.] With all four valence electrons used in the covalent bonds there are no free electrons. Consequently at low temperatures, around absolute zero, silicon is an insulator.

**FIG. 16.4**

2D REPRESENTATION OF A 3D LATTICE — THE CURVED
LINES REPRESENT BONDS

These electrons are weakly bound and if the temperature of a silicon crystal is raised, electrons gain energy and some will gain enough to break free from the covalent bonds and become available as current carriers. Only a very tiny number break free below 300K. An electron which escapes from a lattice site leaves behind a vacancy in the lattice known as a hole. Each electron leaves behind a positive hole and together they constitute an electron-hole pair. The hole will attract an electron from a surrounding atom so that the hole will be filled. This results in the vacancy or hole being transferred to the surrounding atom. Accordingly the hole is mobile but its motion is in the opposite direction to that of the electrons. The hole therefore has the property of a positive charge and is fully known as a positive hole.

In Fig. 16.5, a hole is situated at A. The electric field causes an electron at B to move to the hole. This electron leaves a hole behind. The electron moves from B to A whilst the hole moves from A to B.

**FIG. 16.5**

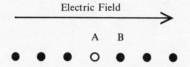

Whereas the conduction mechanism in a conductor is solely due to electrons, in semiconductors it is due to electron-hole pairs.

Silicon therefore shows electrical conductivity at elevated temperatures because of the generation within its lattice of electron-hole pairs where the electron is freed from covalent bonds and leaves behind it a hole. The resulting conductivity is known as intrinsic conductivity.

As the temperature increases, more electrons break free from covalent bonds, generating more electron-hole pairs. The current given by the Drude Equation is

$$I = n e A (V_e + V_H)$$

$V_e$ = velocity of electron

$V_H$ = velocity of holes

$n$ = no. of electrons = no. of holes per unit volume

So as the temperature increases, $n$ increases and so does $I$. Accordingly the conductivity increases also.

16.3.3 The conducting properties of silicon may be increased by the addition of certain impurities, a process known as doping. The most useful impurities to add are elements which are pentavalent (valency = 5) or trivalent (valency = 3), i.e. either one more or one less than the silicon.

Consider the addition of pentavalent phosphorus. Four of the five valence electrons will take part in the covalent bonds as shown in Fig. 16.6. The fifth valence electron is bound only very weakly to its parent atom and only a minute amount of energy will be needed to free it. Before the temperature is high enough for significant intrinsic conductivity of the silicon to occur, all the impurity atoms will have donated a free electron and become ionised. The pentavalent phosphorus donates conduction electrons to the silicon and so it is known as a donor impurity. The doped silicon is known as n type because negative charges, i.e. electrons, are responsible for the increased conductivity.

**FIG. 16.6**

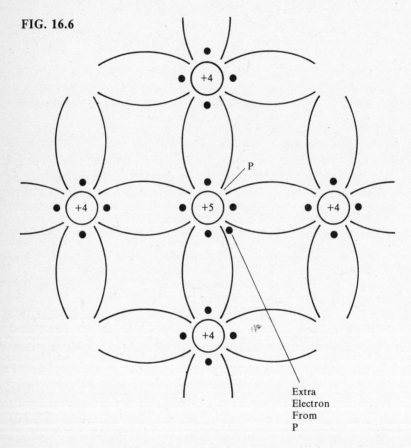

Extra
Electron
From
P

At all temperatures above 0K there will be electron-hole pairs leading to intrinsic conductivity. The few electrons add to the large number of conduction electrons donated by the phosphorus. Electrons are, therefore, known as the majority carrier. The holes are known as the minority carriers.

Consider now the addition of trivalent boron as shown in Fig. 16.7. Boron has one too few valence electrons to provide the four necessary for the four bonds in silicon. There is, therefore, a vacancy or positive hole left in the lattice. This hole readily captures a thermally energised electron from a neighbouring atom and again this transfer needs less energy than that needed for an electron to break free from the silicon bond as an intrinsic conductivity process. The trivalent phosphorus is known as an acceptor because it accepts an electron to fill the vacancy and complete the bonding. The doped silicon is known as p type because conduction is due to positive holes. Once again there will be intrinsically generated electron-hole pairs. The few holes add to the large number generated by the donor. Holes are therefore the majority carrier. The electrons are here known as the minority carriers.

**FIG. 16.7**

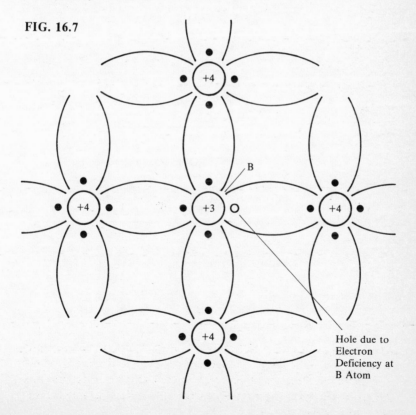

Hole due to Electron Deficiency at B Atom

In both n and p type semiconductors, the conductivity due to the impurities is known as extrinsic conductivity.

In both cases, the current is given by

$$I = e A ( n_e V_e + n_H V_H)$$

$n_e$ = number of electrons per unit volume
$n_H$ = number of holes per unit volume
$V$ = velocity of electrons
$V$ = velocity of holes

The variation in the number of carriers per unit volume with temperature is shown in Fig. 16.8. The situation is identical for both p and n type semiconductors.

**FIG. 16.8**

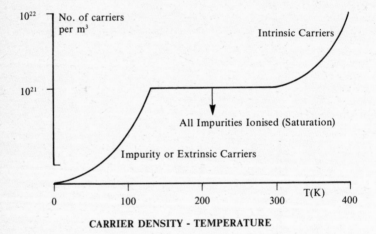

CARRIER DENSITY - TEMPERATURE

Above 0K, conduction is due to extrinsic carriers, i.e. electrons or holes supplied by the impurity atoms. Eventually, at around 130K all the impurity atoms will have been ionised and saturation is said to occur. At about 300K, just a little above room temperature, intrinsic electron-hole pairs are generated and the carrier concentration begins to increase exponentially.

The resulting conductivity is rather complex and will be discussed in the next section, 16.4.

## 16.4   TEMPERATURE COEFFICIENT OF RESISTANCE

16.4.1   Suppose the resistance of a substance is Ro at 0°C and Rt at t°C. It is found that the fractional change in resistance at 0°C is proportional to the temperature change.

Thus
$$\frac{Rt - Ro}{Ro} \; \alpha \;\; t$$

Introducing a constant of proportionality, a, we have
$$\frac{Rt - Ro}{Ro} \;\; = \;\; at$$

hence
$$a \;\; = \;\; \frac{Rt - Ro}{Rot}$$

The constant, a, is known as the temperature coefficient of resistance and its unit is $K^{-1}$.

It should be noted that the above analysis yields the equation Rt = Ro (1 + at).

Such a linear equation is not exactly correct — certainly not when the variation of resistance with temperature is used as a thermometric property. However, it is reasonably accurate over small temperature ranges.

**FIG. 16.9**

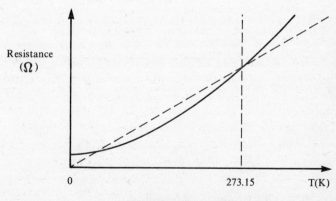

**RESISTANCE-TEMPERATURE**

16.4.2 In the case of a metal, its resistance increases with temperature, i.e. Rt $>$ Ro. Accordingly a is positive for all metals. The temperature coefficients of all metals are fairly close to the value $3.7 \times 10^{-3} \, K^{-1}$. If we plot a graph of resistance against temperature, in K, we obtain a curve that lies close to a straight line through the origin as in Fig. 16.9. Since this is very close to a straight line we say that a is a constant for a metal or we quote an average value for a particular temperature range.

A few metals behave rather strangely in that at a temperature close to absolute zero their resistance suddenly drops to zero. The temperature is called the transition temperature. For Niobium it is 9K and it is as low as 0.01K for tungsten. The phenomenon is known as superconductivity.

For metallic alloys, the temperature coefficients of resistance are generally lower than for pure metals.

The reason for the increase in resistance of a metal is as follows. When the temperature of a metal is increased, the increase in internal energy is due to an increase in kinetic energy of the metal atoms on their lattice. This increased kinetic energy causes the amplitude of vibration of the lattice atoms to increase. As a result, the number of collisions between the current carrying electrons and the lattice increase. The electrons find it harder to travel through the metal — in other words the resistance of the metal increases.

16.4.3 In the case of a pure semiconductor, there are very few carriers, in the form of electron-hole pairs, until a temperature of around 300K is reached. The number of carriers then begins to increase almost exponentially, causing a very rapid rise in current, I (since I = n AV e ). Accordingly the resistance decreases. The very large increase in the number of carriers greatly outweighs the fact that the amplitude of vibration of the lattice atoms increases.

As a result the temperature coefficient of resistance is negative, large and non-constant for a pure semiconductor and the resistance variation against temperature is as shown in Fig. 16.10. Below around 300K the resistance is too high to represent on the axis.

**FIG. 16.10**

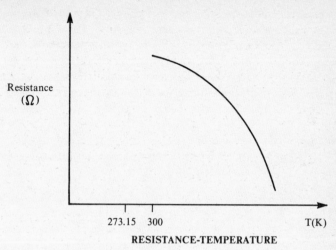

**RESISTANCE-TEMPERATURE**

16.4.4.    In the case of a p or  n  type semiconductor, the situation is very complex. The fact that carrier concentration increases (as shown in Fig. 16.8) is an important factor in determining resistance but the effect of lattice vibration is also another factor. The resultant variation in resistance with temperature is of the form as shown in Fig. 16.11.

**FIG. 16.11**

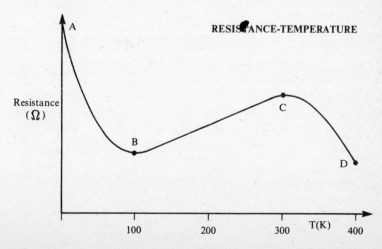

In this graph from A to B, the resistance decreases. This is due to the large increase in extrinsic carriers leading to a rapid rise in current ($I = n\,AVe$) and a reduction in resistance. At such low temperatures the effects of any lattice vibration are insignificant. At B, saturation is just reached. From B to C no more carriers are available. However, the lattice vibration increases and causes a rise in resistance. From C to D, the carrier concentration is increased by the intrinsic electron-hole pairs and this effect outweighs the increase in lattice vibration causing a reduction in resistance. Thus, along A to B, the temperature coefficient of resistance is negative, large and non-uniform. Along B to C, it is positive, not as large but almost constant in value. Along C to D, it is negative once again, large and non-uniform.

It should be noted that the details of this resistance against temperature curve will depend significantly upon the amount of doping. However, what is vital is that the temperature coefficient of resistance of a doped semiconductor can be either positive or negative, depending upon its temperature.

---

**EXAMPLE**

The resistance of a metal wire is 10.0 $\Omega$ at 20°C and 13.1 $\Omega$ at 100°C. Find the temperature coefficient of resistance of the wire.

$$\text{Thus} \qquad Ro = 10.0 \ \Omega$$
$$Rt = 13.1 \ \Omega$$
$$t = 100 - 20 = 80°C = 80K$$

$$\text{Now} \qquad a = \frac{Rt - Ro}{Rot}$$

Hence

$$a = \frac{13.1 - 10.0}{10.0 \times 80}$$
$$= \frac{3.1}{800} = 3.9 \times 10^{-3} \ K^{-1}$$

$\therefore$ Temperature Coefficient of Resistance $= 3.9 \times 10^{-3} \ K^{-1}$

Note: In this problem the starting temperature is 20°C rather than 0°C. Here, a is defined as the fractional increase of the resistance at 20°C per unit rise in temperature and we implicity assume that a is constant over the range from 0°C to 100°C.

## QUESTIONS

1) Sketch a graph showing the variation in resistance with temperature of a doped semiconductor in the range 0 to 400K. Superimpose upon the graph that of a pure semiconductor and explain the differences between the two graphs.

2) A current of 3.2A flows in a wire. Calculate the velocity of the electrons if there are $10^{28}$ per $m^3$ and the cross-sectional area of the wire is $1mm^2$. Assume each electron carries a charge of $1.6 \times 10^{-19}C$.

3) Calculate the resistance of a platinum wire at 100°C if its resistance of 0°C is $8.0\,\Omega$ and its average temperature coefficient of resistance over the range is $4 \times 10^{-3}K$.

# Chapter 17
# GASES

## 17.1 BROWNIAN MOTION

If fine particles suspended in a fluid are examined by a microscope, it will be observed that they are in constant haphazard motion. This random motion continues indefinitely and is found to depend upon the fluid in which they are immersed, the size of the particles and the temperature of the system. The motion of these particles was first observed by Brown in 1827. The explanation of the Brownian motion, first given by Einstein in 1905 and later extended by Smoluchowski, is based on the assumption that the particles in suspension are continually bombarded by the molecules of the fluid and this bombardment produces an unbalanced force which accelerates the particles.

In 1909, Ehrenhaft reported the first results on the Brownian motion of particles suspended in gases. He found that there was a much greater activity in gases than in liquids, as predicted by theory.

The most important experiment on Brownian motion in gases was carried out by Millikan in 1911 — his so-called oil-drop experiment. He found that the mean value of the squared displacements for all the particles considered in a given time period were much greater than those observed by Perrin in the case of liquids.

## 17.2 THE IDEAL GAS EQUATION

17.2.1  It is often useful to measure the amount of a substance in terms of the number of individual particles it contains. The unit of amount of substance reckoned in this way is called the mole, abbreviated to mol. The mole is the amount of substances of a system which contains as many elementary particles as there are atoms in 0.012Kg of carbon 12.

Obviously, the mass-per-mole, or molar mass M, of carbon is $0.012 \text{Kg mol}^{-1}$.

In order to calculate the molar mass of hydrogen, we use the fact that the mass of a hydrogen atom is almost $\frac{1}{12}$ the mass of a carbon atom.

Since a mol of any substance always contains the same number of particles, it follows that the molar mass of hydrogen is $\frac{1}{12}$ that of carbon which gives $0.001 \text{Kg mol}^{-1}$. In the case of hydrogen molecules, we use the fact that the mass of such a molecule is twice that of the atom and hence the molar mass of hydrogen molecules is $0.002 \text{Kg mol}^{-1}$.

It is possible to find out how many atoms there are in a mole of substance.

Since

No. of atoms per mole $=$ $\dfrac{\text{Molar mass}}{\text{Mass of a single atom}}$

Now for carbon

Molar mass $= 0.012 \text{Kg mol}^{-1}$

Mass of a single atom $= 1.992 \times 10^{-26} \text{Kg}$

$\therefore$ No. of atoms per mole $=$ $\dfrac{0.012}{1.992 \times 10^{-26}}$ $= 6.02 \times 10^{23} \text{ mole}^{-1}$

This quantity is called the Avagadro Constant. It is the same for all substances.

$N_A =$ Avagadro Constant $= 6.02 \times 10^{23} \text{ mole}^{-1}$

A knowledge of this constant is useful in finding the mass of a given number of moles because

Mass of n moles $=$ n x Avagadro's Constant x Mass per atom

---

**EXAMPLE**

Calculate the mass of 2 moles of hydrogen atoms if the mass of a hydrogen atom is $1.6729 \times 10^{-27} \text{Kg}$.

Using the above equation

Mass $= 2 \times 6.02 \times 10^{23} \times 1.6729 \times 10^{-27} \text{ Kg}$

$= 2.01 \times 10^{-3} \text{Kg}$

Mass of 2 mole of hydrogen atoms $= 2.01 \times 10^{-3} \text{Kg}$

---

Also, a given number of moles, n, can be expressed slightly differently.

$$\text{number of moles} = \frac{\text{mass}}{\text{molar mass}}$$

If the mass is m and the molar mass is M then

$$n = \frac{m}{M}$$

17.2.2  Robert Boyle, in 1660, found that the pressure of a fixed mass of gas at constant temperature was inversely proportional to volume.

$$\text{Thus} \qquad p \; \alpha \; \frac{1}{V}$$

$$\text{where} \qquad p = \text{pressure}$$
$$V = \text{volume}$$

Introducing a constant of proportionality, k, then

$$p = \frac{k}{V}$$

$$\text{or} \qquad pV = \text{constant}$$

This relationship is known as Boyle's law.

**FIG. 17.1**

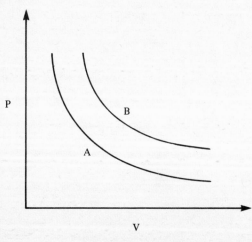

**PRESSURE-VOLUME**

If we plot a graph of p against V, a rectangular hyperbola is obtained as in Fig. 17.1. It is more convenient to plot p against 1/V in order to obtain a straight line, the gradient of which is equal to the constant in Boyle's law. This is shown in Fig. 17.2. For a particular amount of gas, in mole, the graphs would be the plots shown in A for each case. Similar results would be obtained for identical amounts of any other gas.

**FIG. 17.2**

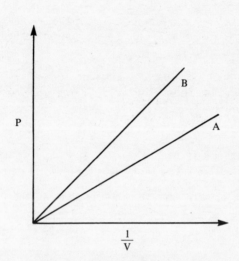

**PRESSURE — RECIPROCAL VOLUME**

However, if the amount of substance were increased, then the plots would be shown in B for each case.

Now from the p against 1/V graphs it is clear that the gradient is proportioned to the number of moles of substance. But this gradient is equal to the constant in Boyle's law.

Hence

$$pV \; \alpha \; n$$

where n = number of moles of substance

Boyle's law holds true for air at room temperature and for other gases such as oxygen, nitrogen, hydrogen and helium. However, at lower temperatures or higher pressures, it is no longer true. We define an ideal gas as one for which Boyle's law is obeyed for all temperatures and pressures.

Now, by definition, the pressure of an ideal gas, p, is proportioned to the Kelvin temperature of the gas, T. This fact is the basis of the constant volume gas thermometer used to realise the thermodynamic scale of temperature.

We can therefore write

$$pV \quad \alpha \quad nT$$

Introducing a constant of proportionality, R, we have

$$pV = nRT$$

This equation is known as the ideal gas equation or the equation of state of an ideal gas.

R is referred to as the molar gas constant.

Its units may be found by re-arranging the equation and substituting units

$$\therefore \quad R = \frac{pV}{nT} = \frac{Pa \ m^3}{mol \ K} = \frac{Nm^{-2} \ m^3}{mol \ K} = \frac{Nm}{mol \ K} = \frac{J}{mol \ K}$$

The magnitude is 8.31

$$\therefore \quad R = 8.31 \ J \ mol^{-1} \ K^{-1} \text{ for all ideal gases}$$

The equation of state may be re-written using the relationship thus

$$n = \frac{m}{M} \qquad \text{(see 17.2.1)}$$

Hence

$$pV = \frac{m}{M} RT$$

---

**EXAMPLE**

Calculate the magnitude of the universal gas constant given that 1 mole of gas at standard temperature and pressure (273K and $1.013 \times 10^5$Pu) occupies a volume of 22.4 litre.

Thus

$$p = 1.013 \times 10^5 \ Pa$$
$$V = 22.4 \ litre = 22.4 \times 10^{-3} \ m^3$$
$$n = 1 \ mole$$
$$T = 273K$$

Substituting in
$$pV = nRT$$

$$R = \frac{pV}{nT} = \frac{1.013 \times 10^5 \times 22.4 \times 10^{-3}}{1 \times 273}$$

$$= 8.31$$

$\therefore$ Magnitude of gas constant $= 8.31$

The ideal gas equation may be used to investigate the variation in pressure with temperature of an ideal gas. For such a gas the volume, mass and molar mass are all constant.

For pressure $p_1$ at temperature $T_1$
$$p_1V = \frac{m}{M} RT_1$$

For pressure $p_2$ at temperature $T_2$
$$P_2V = \frac{m}{M} RT_2$$

Hence by division
$$\frac{p_1}{p_2} = \frac{T_1}{T_2}$$

This relation is used in the constant volume gas thermometer where

$$\frac{P_T}{P_{TR}} = \frac{T}{273.15} \qquad \left( \begin{array}{l} \text{See Chapter 9} \\ \text{Question 2} \end{array} \right)$$

i.e. $\qquad T = 273.15 \frac{P_T}{P_{TR}}$

with
$$P_{TR} = \text{pressure at triple point}$$
$$273.15K = \text{temperature of triple point}$$

## 17.3 REAL GASES

Air, oxygen, nitrogen and hydrogen obey Boyle's law to within less than one part in a thousand at ordinary temperature and pressure.

At higher pressures and lower temperatures the deviations are more pronounced. Experiments show that pV depends upon the pressure.

For each gas there is a certain temperature called the Boyle temperature at which pV is independent of p and Boyle's law is obeyed exactly.

The variation of pV with p for various gases is shown in Fig. 17.3

**FIG. 17.3**

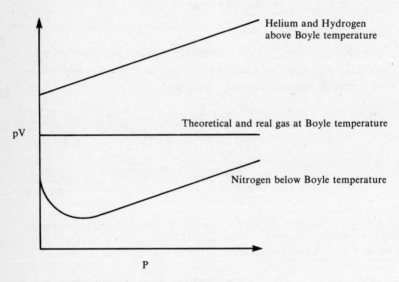

PRESSURE VOLUME — PRESSURE

The variation of pV with p at any temperature may be written as

$$pV = A \left( 1 + \frac{B}{V} + \frac{C}{V^2} + \frac{D}{V^3} \text{-----} \right)$$

when A, B, C, D etc. are constants.

At the Boyle temperature, B, C and D = 0
Above this temperature they are positive
Below this temperature they are negative

In order that the ideal gas equation should describe a real gas at higher pressures and lower temperatures, it needs modification.

The reason why the ideal gas equation breaks down under these conditions is that the gas molecules, at high pressure and low temperature, will fill an appreciable volume of their container and come closer together, thereby experiencing intermolecular forces.

The effect of these two factors are to cause the effective gas volume to be reduced and the external pressure to be increased.

The equation of state is then written as

$$\left( p + \frac{a}{V^2} \right) \left( V - b \right) = nRT$$

where a and b are constants.
This equation is known as Van der Waal's Equation.

## 17.4  KINETIC THEORY OF AN IDEAL GAS

17.4.1  The kinetic theory of an ideal gas makes several important assumptions. These are:
1)  the gas atoms/molecules are perfectly elastic spheres.
2)  there is no intermolecular attraction.
3)  between collisions the atoms/molecules travel in straight lines.
4)  the time for a collision is negligible compared with the time between collisions.
5)  the volume of the molecule is negligible compared with the total volume of gas.

17.4.2  The pressure exerted by a gas may be calculated as follows. Consider a unit cube as in Fig. 17.4. It contains n molecule, each of mass m and all travelling with constant velocity V.

**FIG. 17.4**

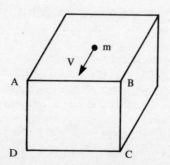

At any point there will be $n/3$ molecules moving between each pair of faces since there are n molecules and three pairs of faces.

Consider one molecule about to strike the faces ABCD. Its momentum before impact = mV. Since the molecule is perfectly elastic, the rebound velocity is numerically equal to the incident velocity but its direction is reversed. Hence, its momentum after impact = –mV.

$$\text{The change of momentum} = mV - (-mV)$$
$$= 2mV \text{ per impact}$$

Since this is a unit cube, the molecule will have to travel 2m before it hits this face ABCD again.

By definition of velocity, the time taken between impact is

$$\frac{2}{V} = T, \text{ the period}$$

Now frequency, $f = \dfrac{1}{T}$

$\therefore$ frequency of impacts $= \dfrac{V}{2}$

Thus the total change in momentum, per sec, on ABCD due to 1 molecule is

$$2mV \times \frac{V}{2}$$
$$= mV^2$$

But there are $n/3$ molecules involved

Total change in momentum, per sec, on ABCD is

$$\frac{n\, mV^2}{3}$$

Rate of change of momentum = Force

thus

$$\text{Force on ABCD} = \frac{n\, mV^2}{3}$$

and Pressure $= \dfrac{\text{Force}}{\text{Area}}$

Here Area of ABCD $= 1 \text{ m}^2$

hence Pressure = Force

So    Pressure on ABCD    =    $\dfrac{n \; mV^2}{3}$

Two modifications need to be made to this analysis.

1)  In fact, molecules are not all moving in three directions at right angles. However, each will have a component of velocity in each of the three directions x, y and z. Let the values of these components be X, Y and Z respectively in the three directions.
    Applying Pythagoras' theorem to three dimensions
    $$X^2 + Y^2 + Z^2 = U^2$$

    where U = velocity of molecule in its direction of travel. This is shown in Fig. 17.5.

**FIG. 17.5**

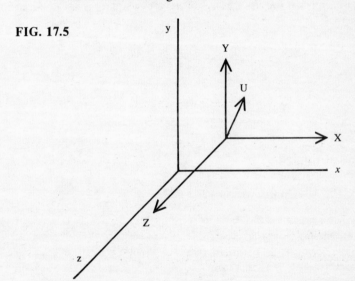

2)  All the molecules, in fact, have a different velocity and, more correctly, we should use the average value of $U^2$ for all the molecules. It can be shown by a full statistical analysis that the average value is the mean square velocity denoted by $\overline{C^2}$. For n molecules $\overline{C^2}$ is given by

    $$\overline{C^2} \;\; = \;\; \dfrac{U_1{}^2 + U_2{}^2 + U_3{}^2 + \text{------} U_n{}^2}{n}$$

The square root of the mean square velocity, $\sqrt{\overline{C^2}}$ is known as the root mean square, or R.M.S. velocity.

Note $\sqrt{\overline{C^2}}$ is not $\overline{C}$

This may be seen by considering a simple numerical example.
Consider the numbers 1 and 2.
Their mean is 1.5.
The sum of their squares is $1 + 4 = 5$
$n = 2$
So their mean square value $= \dfrac{5}{2} = 2.5$

The square root of this, the R.M.S. value is $\sqrt{2.5} = 1.58$.
It can be seen that the square root of the mean square is not equal to the mean.

As a result of the above two modifications we have

$$p = \frac{nm\ \overline{C^2}}{3}$$

Now

$nm$ = total mass of gas contained in the unit volume
= density of gas, $\rho$

thus $\quad p = \dfrac{1}{3} \rho\ \overline{C^2}$

Note: $\overline{C^2}$ is sometimes written $\langle C^2 \rangle$

Now when heat enters a system, its internal energy rises. In the case of this model, no potential energy is involved and the increase in internal energy leads to an increase in kinetic energy. Hence $\overline{C^2}$ increases, leading to an increase in pressure. Thus $p \propto T$ as was seen in the ideal gas equation. The effect of temperature on molecular speeds will be considered shortly.

17.4.3 Now $\qquad p = \dfrac{n\,m\ \overline{C^2}}{3}$

Consider 1 mole of a gas occupying a volume V. It will, by definition, contain $N_A$ molecules.

$$n = \frac{N_A}{V}$$

$$\therefore \quad p = \frac{N_A \, m \, \overline{C^2}}{3V}$$

$$pV = \frac{N_A \, m \, \overline{C^2}}{3}$$

But for 1 mole

$$pV = RT$$

Hence

$$\frac{N_A}{3} \, m \, \overline{C^2} = RT$$

$$\frac{m \, \overline{C^2}}{3} = \frac{R}{N_A} \, T$$

multiplying throughout by 3/2 gives

$$\frac{1}{2} \, m \, \overline{C^2} = \frac{3}{2} \, \frac{R}{N_A} \, T$$

Now $\quad \dfrac{R}{N_A} = \dfrac{\text{Gas constant per mole}}{\text{Number of molecules per mole}} = \text{Gas constant per mole}$

The gas constant per mole is known as Boltzmann's constant denoted by the symbol k.

So

$$\frac{1}{2} \, m \, \overline{C^2} = kT$$

Mean molecular K.E. = Boltzmann's Constant x Temperature

This equation shows that when the internal energy of a gas increases, causing a rise in temperature, the mean molecular kinetic energy increases.

---

**EXAMPLE**

Calculate the mean square velocity of hydrogen molecules at one atmosphere pressure ($1.013 \times 10^5$ Pa), given that its density is $0.099 \, Kg m^{-3}$.

Use

$$p = \frac{1}{3} \, \rho \, \overline{C^2}$$

$$\therefore \quad \overline{C^2} = \frac{3P}{\rho}$$

Here $\quad$ $P$ $\quad=\quad$ $1.013 \times 10^5$ Pu
$\rho$ $\quad=\quad$ $0.099$ Kgm$^{-3}$

$\therefore\quad \overline{C^2}\quad=\quad \dfrac{3 \times 1.013 \times 10^5}{0.099}$

$\quad\quad\quad=\quad 1.75 \times 10^3$ ms$^{-1}$

Mean Square Velocity $= 1.75 \times 10^3$ ms$^{-1}$

## 17.5 THE DISTRIBUTION OF MOLECULAR SPEEDS

It has already been stated that molecules do not all move with the same speed and so it is useful to talk of a mean square speed. Also, this mean square speed is proportional to temperature.

The variation of molecular speed in a gas when represented graphically gives what is known as a Maxwellian distribution. Its characteristic is that a small number of molecules have a low speed and a small number have a high speed. Most of the molecules move at the mean speed or thereabouts. As the temperature is increased, then the mean speed itself increases. Also, all speeds increase with fewer molecules moving at lower speeds and more moving at higher speeds.

Such Maxwellian distribution are shown in Fig. 17.6.

**FIG. 17.6**

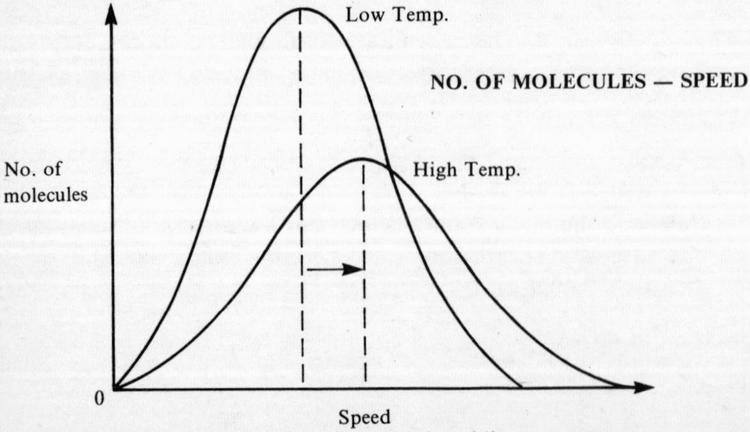

Mean speeds shown by dotted lines

It was stated earlier that

Mean speed is not $\sqrt{\text{mean square speed}}$

In fact, it follows from the mathematics of a Maxwellian distribution that

$$\sqrt{\overline{C^2}} = 1.09\,\overline{C}$$

and it can, therefore, be seen that the R.M.S. speed also moves to the right, i.e. increases, with temperature.


## QUESTIONS

1) Explain why smoke particles in the air appear to move randomly when illuminated by a projector beam in a cinema.

2) A certain fixed mass of gas at 0°C and 1 x $10^5$ Pa occupies a volume of 0.1m³. Calculate its volume at 50°C and 2 x $10^5$ Pa. (Hint: Use pV = nRT in both situations, keeping n and R constant).

3) Calculate the volume occupied by 1 mole of a gas under a pressure of 1.3 x $10^5$ Pa at a temperature of 400K.

# Chapter 18
# LIQUIDS AND SOLIDS

## 18.1 THE DIFFERENCE BETWEEN SOLID, LIQUIDS AND GASES

18.1.1   In a solid, forces exist between the atoms. At large distances, these forces are attractive and cause the atoms to approach each other. However, at small distances between atoms, the forces are repulsive. If these short range repulsive forces did not exist the atoms would continue to approach each other and solid matter would collapse in upon itself. A point is reached when the forces are zero and atoms are separated from each other by their equilibrium distance.

However, the atoms are not stationary at their equilibrium distance. They vibrate about a mean position. When the atoms are at their closest distance they repel each other and their separation increases. Once it exceeds the equilibrium position, they begin to attract each other and accordingly they begin to move towards each other. Eventually, repulsion sets in, brings them to rest and causes them to move away from each other. As a result, they vibrate about their equilibrium position, alternately attracting and repelling each other. The motion, although oscillating, is not S.H.M. since if it were, the phenomenon of linear expansivity would disappear! We refer to it as anharmonic motion. The internal energy of a solid is due to the sum of the potential and kinetic energies of the atoms as they vibrate and of course, it is equal to the potential energy alone when the atoms stop at the end of their vibrational amplitude.

If we were to plot the variation in potential energy against separation, we would find that it was at a minimum at the equilibrium distance, increasing as the displacement increased and decreased. In fact, the variation is not symmetrical and it increases much more rapidly as atoms near each other rather than when they move. So, when thermal energy enters the solid, increasing its internal energy, it increases the kinetic energy of vibration and it does this by causing an increase in the amplitude of vibration. Now since the potential is unsymmetric, this causes the atoms to move apart and increase their average separation. Expansion results from this.

The fact that the atoms repel each other or attract each other when they are less or more than the equilibrium separation, explains why energy is needed to either compress or stretch a solid.

A solid is a rigid structure because of the situation, thus its atoms are fixed, albeit vibrating. Because of this rigid structure, it is able to withstand the application of a force.

18.1.2   As the temperature of a solid is increased, the kinetic energy of its atoms increases and eventually they are partly able to overcome the interatomic forces of their near neighbours. There is less order in the atomic arrangement and the solid changes into a liquid. The energy needed to increase the disorder is indeed the latent heat of fusion. The atoms and molecules of a liquid are not much further apart than in a solid but they are moving with increased speeds at their higher temperatures and they move randomly in the liquid whilst continuing to vibrate. However, since they are slightly further apart, small attractive forces exist between them. Expansion occurs as in the case of solids.

Increasing the temperature still further and supplying latent heat of vaporisation causes the liquid to turn into a gas. The atoms now have a greatly increased kinetic energy, i.e. speed. They now move randomly through all the space available. Their vibrational energy is negligible in comparison with their translational energy. On average, at 273K and 1 atmosphere pressure they are about 10 times their diameter apart. Attraction forces exist between them with repulsive forces occurring during collisions. The increase in volume resulting from a temperature rise may be calculated from the ideal gas equation.

Since fluids (i.e. liquid and gases) are dis-ordered, they are now able to withstand the application of a force. Instead they may be subjected to pressure which transmits force through them at an atomic level. The net force which a fluid exerts upon a body may be then calculated using the relationship

$$\text{Force} \quad = \quad \text{Pressure x Area}$$

## 18.2 DENSITY AND PRESSURE

18.2.1 The volume of solids, liquids and gases increases as their temperature rises. We should always, therefore, quote the temperature of a substance whenever we state the density (i.e. the ratio of its mass to volume). In practice, whenever we quote density alone we assume that the temperature is 293K.

The molecules in a gas are much more widely spaced than in a solid or liquid, causing there to be less mass in a given volume and hence a lower density. The density of gases at any particular temperature is of the order of $10^{-3}$ times that of liquids and solids.

In the case of fluids, densities may be determined relatively easily because fluids can flow and, therefore, can be arranged to fill any given container of known volume. Their mass may be determined by subtracting the mass of the empty container from that of the container and fluid.

Solids, of course, are rigid and do not flow. It is straightforward to determine their mass. Calculation of volume is easy for a regularly shaped solid because formulae exist for this purpose. In the case of irregularly shaped solids, a displacement method must be used as shown in Fig. 18.1

**FIG. 18.1**

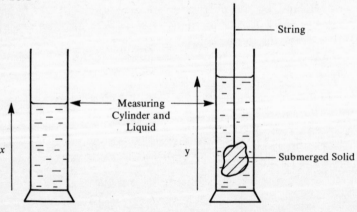

Volume of solid = y–x

A known volume of liquid is poured into a measuring cylinder. The object is then lowered in on the end of a thin string until it is completely submerged, when the solid will have displaced its own volume of liquid. The level of liquid in the cylinder will, therefore, rise and by subtracting the initial level from the final level, the volume of the solid is found.

18.2.2    At any point in a fluid the molecules exert a pressure and those near the walls of the containing vessel will exert a pressure on the container walls. Obviously the effect will be more pronounced in the case of a gas because of the greater molecular velocities at consequently greater momentum changes on impact as discussed in the previous chapter.

Additionally, at any point in a column of fluid there is a pressure generated to the weight of the column of fluid above. This is known as hydrostatic pressure. This effect is more pronounced in the case of liquids because of their greater density.

**FIG. 18.2**

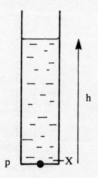

Consider Fig. 18.2. We wish to find the pressure, p, at a depth, h, below the free surface of a column of liquid. Suppose that the density of the liquid is $\rho$ and the acceleration due to gravity is g.

$$\text{Weight of liquid} \quad = \quad mg$$
$$= \quad \rho Vg$$
$$= \quad \rho Ahg$$

where A is the C.S.A. of the liquid

Thus, force on base of container $= \rho Ahg$

Now

$$\text{Pressure} \quad = \quad \frac{\text{Force}}{\text{Area}} \quad = \quad \frac{\rho A h g}{A} \quad = \quad \rho h g$$

$$\therefore \quad p = \rho g h$$

(Or $\Delta P = \rho g \Delta h$ when $\Delta P$ = change in pressure between two points $\Delta h$ apart)

This pressure acts on the base of the container. Obviously, a reaction force acts back on the liquid. Moreover, this pressure acts in all directions because of the non-rigidity of a liquid. This may be verified because if a small hole is drilled in the bottom of the container wall, at X, the liquid will escape in a jet. The pressure acting on the container wall (or rather, where the wall was) is now no longer prevented from causing motion by this wall and the liquid escapes.

18.2.3 The principle of pressure causing fluid flow is utilised in a device known as a manometer, shown in Fig. 18.3.

**FIG. 18.3**

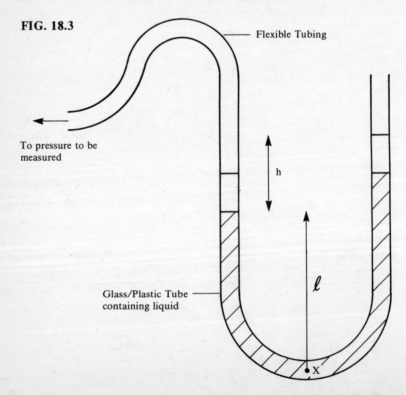

Flexible Tubing

To pressure to be
measured

h

ℓ

Glass/Plastic Tube
containing liquid

X

This consists of a glass or plastic U tube containing liquid referred to as manometric liquid. Flexible rubber tubing is fitted to one arm of the U tube and this enables the manometer to be connected to the pressure to be measured. In the absence of such a connection, the liquid levels in both sides are the same, $\ell$, since atmospheric pressure acts down on each liquid surface and each column of liquid generates its own, but equal, hydrostatic pressure. The total pressure acting at the bottom of the device, at X, is

$$\text{Atmospheric} + \rho g \ell$$

The pressure to the right generated by the left hand side is equal to that to the left generated by the right.

Suppose the rubber tube is connected to the pressure to be found (above atmospheric). This greater pressure will now cause the liquid in the left arm to be depressed, forcing the right column to be raised. The liquid will move until the hydrostatic pressure generated by the difference in liquid levels exactly balances the excess pressure. If this difference in levels is h, then

$$\text{Pressure in left arm} - \text{Pressure in right arm} = \rho g h$$

i.e.
$$\text{Pressure (being measured)} - \text{Atmospheric} = \rho g h$$
$$\text{or} \qquad \text{Excess Pressure} = \rho g h$$

The excess pressure above atmospheric is given quite straightforwardly. We may obtain the total pressure by simply adding atmospheric pressure. When measuring large pressure excesses, large values of h would be given and this is inconvenient. In such cases a liquid with high density is chosen as the manometric liquid — usually mercury. For precise results when measuring low pressures, a liquid of low density — usually a light oil is used.

In the case of sub-atmospheric pressures, the liquid moves in the opposite direction, i.e. from right to left in the diagram.

---

**EXAMPLE**

A manometer is used to measure the excess pressure of a gas supply. If the difference in levels of the oil used as a manometric is 20cm, calculate the excess pressure. Assume $g = 9.81 \mathrm{ms}^{-2}$, density of oil $= 800 \mathrm{Kgm}^{-3}$.

Use         Excess pressure = $\rho gh$
            $\rho$ = 800Kgm$^{-3}$
            g = 9.8ms$^{-2}$
            h = 20cm = 0.20m

∴    Excess pressure   =    800 x 9.8 x 0.20
                        =    1.6KPa
     Excess Pressure   =    1.6KPa

## TYPES OF SOLIDS

18.3.1   Most solids, including all metals and most minerals are said to be crystalline. Their atoms are arranged in a regular manner on a crystal lattice. This lattice is not a physical entity but a mathematical description of the repetitive pattern in which the atoms are arranged. A typical lattice structure is shown in Fig. 18.4. Various types of crystal exist, each having its own particular way of arranging its atoms on the lattice. The study of lattice arrangements is a branch of physics known as crystallography. The common feature amongst all lattice structures is their order.

**FIG. 18.4**

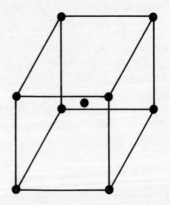

In substances such as salt and sugar, the crystal form is evident because of their regular appearance. This is less noticeable in the case of metals. A metal consists of a mass of tiny crystals called grains, at various angles to each other. It is known as a polycrystalline material. In each grain the atoms are arranged identically but from one grain to another the orientation of the lattices changes. A typical grain is about 0.25mm across and the usual sort of grain arrangement is shown in Fig. 18.5

**FIG. 18.5**

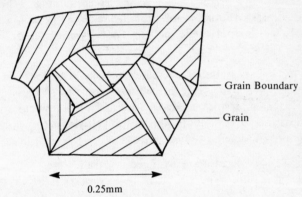

Grain Boundary

Grain

0.25mm

A characteristic of all crystals, including polycrystals, is their sharp melting points when the lattice structures break down due to the supply of energy in the form of latent heat.

18.3.2   Glasses are solids in which there is short range order. They are very viscous when they are liquid and become even more so as they cool. Thus, the lack of orderliness which they have as liquid continues when they solidify, because atoms are unable to move through the viscous liquid to settle into ordered lattice positions. As solids they have the disorder characteristic of liquids and when liquid glass solidifies it simply sets into whatever shape is determined by the forces acting on it during the solidification process.

Accordingly, glasses solidify (and melt) not at a sharp temperature but over a range of temperature and so they do not experience a sudden change of density nor require latent heat to melt them.

Glasses are very anomalous solids and much research is currently being undertaken upon them. Their specific heat capacities vary strangely at low temperatures when compared with other substances and glasses such as pyrex and spectrosil have negative expansivities which may be made positive by the introduction of extra atoms into their usual atomic structure.

18.3.3   Polymers are materials with giant molecules consisting of very long chains of atoms — from 1,000 to 100,000 atoms in each chain.

They are usually organic, i.e. substances containing carbon and include cellulose, rubber, wool, proteins, resins and silk. Man-made polymers include polythene, perspex, polystyrene, nylon, terylene and epoxy resins.

The atoms in each polymer molecule are grouped in blocks known as monomers. Every molecule of cellulose consists of monomers of glucose sugar molecules, $C_6H_{12}O_6$ varying from a few hundred to a few thousand. Every molecule of polyethylene (or polythene) consists of monomers of ethylene, $C_2H_4$.

If these giant molecules are arranged in parallel lines, the structure displays a certain type of order and is said to be crystalline. Alternatively, if they are tangled, the structure is said to be amorphous. Many polymers can exist as both crystalline and amorphous, with the crystalline material being much stiffer.

**FIG. 18.6**

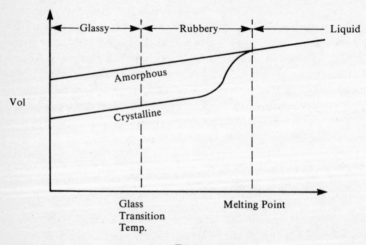

**VOLUME - TEMPERATURE**

Thermoplastics exist in a glassy state at low temperature, soften to become rubbery and flexible after passing the glass transition temperature and at higher temperatures soften and melt. In the glassy state the polymeric chains are trapped randomly in fixed positions. As the temperature rises, some parts of these chains become able to rotate and at even higher temperatures softening and melting occur as the molecules gain enough energy to be able to move independently of each other. There is no sharp melting point but a gentle softening until it becomes a liquid. However, if the polymer is crystalline there will be a noticeable increase in volume at a temperature designated as the melting point. See Fig. 18.6.

Rubbers (or elastomers) are thermoplastic polymers whose chains are very weakly bound together. Because these materials are rubbery it means they are above their glass transition temperature of –75°C. Perspex has a transition temperature of 100°C and, thus, we would consider it to be rubbery above this temperature.

Thermosetting plastics are hard and rigid and when they are heated they do not soften but eventually decompose. Strong co-valent bonds are formed between chains — known as cross-links — by the addition of chemicals. In vulcanizing raw rubber, it is heated with sulphur. A certain amount of sulphur atoms form cross-links between the chains and cause hardening. If the addition is continued, the rubber becomes ebonite. This chemical action is irreversible and the material cannot be softened by re-heating.

18.3.4   In amorphous solids, the atoms are arranged in a more disordered way and only show order over short distances with no long range order. Many types of glass are amorphous solids, as already noted.

## 18.4   THE BEHAVIOUR OF POLYCRYSTALLINE AND POLYMERIC MATERIALS UNDER FORCE

18.4.1   For most materials, it has been verified experimentally that over a considerable range the extension produced by an applied force is proportional to it. If the force is increased to a point where this relationship is no longer valid, then the elastic limit of the material is said to have been exceeded.

The linear relationship between extension and force was discovered by Hooke and is known as Hooke's Law: Provided the elastic limit is not exceeded the extension caused by a force is directly proportional to that force.

18.4.2   Suppose a sample of wire, Fig. 18.7, is stretched by applying a force along its length. This is known as a tensile force and the resultant extension is known as a tensile extension. The graph of extension against force has the general form as shown in Fig. 18.8.

**FIG. 18.7**

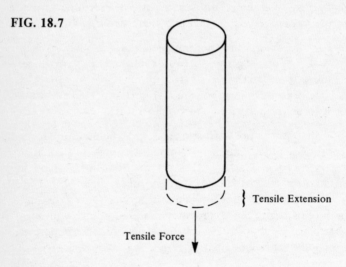

Tensile Extension

Tensile Force

**FIG. 18.8**

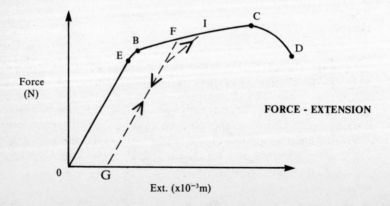

Force (N)

FORCE - EXTENSION

Ext. (x10⁻³m)

Along OE the graph is a straight line through the origin showing that extension is directly proportional to force, thus Hooke's Law is being obeyed. E is known as the limit of proportionality. As the force is increased, the graph becomes non-linear. Until point B, the deformation is known as elastic because if the force is removed, the material returns to its original length. B is called the elastic limit. Beyond it, plastic deformation begins and the sample will no longer return to its original dimensions upon removal of the force. In the plastic region a given force will produce a greater extension than previously. At C the extension will increase, despite a reduction in force applied. C is known as the yield point. Stretching will continue until D when the wire breaks. The change in direction of the curve at C is due to the formation of a constriction or "neck" occurring at one point in the wire. At this particular narrow part the wire will break at D at a value of force known as the breaking force or ultimate tensile force.

If the force is removed in the plastic region at F, the material will follow the dotted line to G. OG is called the permanent set. If another force be applied, the extension will follow GI.

For a typical wire 100cm long, an extension of up to $\frac{1}{2}$cm, which is elastic, will be obtained but a plastic extension of up to 50cm may be obtained.

It should be noted that in the case of a force being re-applied after having acquired a permanent set, the path followed is indeed along GI. The limit of proportionality and elastic limit have both been increased. This phenomenon is called work hardening and is of great value in metallurgy.

18.4.3   The case just discussed is typical of copper and steel wires, i.e. polycrystalline materials.

The behaviour of polymeric materials is shown in Fig. 18.9 (a) and (b). Rubber can undergo very large forces and still behave elastically although the loading curve differs from the unloading curve, as shown. This is known as hysterisis. However, the rubber does return to its original length when the force is removed. In the case of a polythene strip, it can be seen that at first it behaves elastically. Then there is a sudden increase in extension for a very small increase in force as plastic deformation takes place. Large permanent sets result if the force is removed.

**FIG. 18.9**

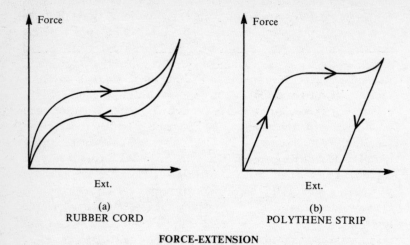

(a)
RUBBER CORD

(b)
POLYTHENE STRIP

**FORCE-EXTENSION**

## 18.5   STRESS, STRAIN AND YOUNG'S MODULUS OF ELASTICITY

18.5.1   In the above situation of a tensile force producing a tensile extension, we define

$$\text{Tensile Stress} = \frac{\text{Tensile force}}{\text{area}}$$

Thus, if the force is F and the area of the wire, in cross-section is A, then

$$\text{Tensile stress} = \frac{F}{A}$$

The units are Pascals, symbol Pa.

It will be noted that the definition is identical to that of pressure — we use the word pressure when we talk about fluids but stress when considering solids.

In 18.4.2 the mention was made of breaking force. The crucial point in the breaking of a wire is not really that of breaking force but that of breaking tensile stress or ultimate tensile stress.

Some values of ultimate tensile stress are given below in Table 18.1.

| Material | Ultimate tensile stress (x $10^6$ Pa) |
|----------|---------------------------------------|
| Copper | 200-400, depending upon method of production |
| Polythene (95% crystallisation) | 31 |
| (65% crystallisation) | 13 |

**TABLE 18.1**

18.5.2   We further define

$$\text{Tensile Strain} \quad = \quad \frac{\text{Tensile Extension}}{\text{Original length}}$$

If the extension is e and the original length is $\ell$, then

$$\text{Tensile Strain} \quad = \quad \frac{e}{\ell}$$

Since it is the ratio of two lengths, it has no units.

If we were to plot graphs of tensile stress against tensile strain, the shape of these graphs would have the same form as the force versus extension graphs considered earlier because in changing from force and extension to stress and strain, we are simply dividing by constants, namely area and length.

18.5.3   For a material which is not stretched beyond its elastic limit, or more correctly, its limit of proportionality, we define its tensile stiffness by the equation

$$E \quad = \quad \frac{\text{Tensile stress}}{\text{Tensile strain}}$$

E is called the Young's Modulus of the material. Its units are those of stress, Pascal. (Sometimes called Young's Modulus of Elasticity). Thus in terms of the earlier quantities

$$E \quad = \quad \frac{F/A}{e/\ell}$$

$$E \quad = \quad \frac{F\ell}{Ae}$$

Some approximate values of Young's Modulus appear in Table 18.2.

| Material | Young's Modulus (x $10^8$ Pa) |
|---|---|
| Steel | 2100 |
| Copper | 1300 |
| Glasses | 700 |
| Polythene | 50 approx |
| Rubber | 0.5 approx |

**TABLE 18.2**

Graphically, Young's Modulus is equal to the gradient of the linear portion of a stress versus strain graph, i.e. that portion of the graph to which Hooke's law applies.

Because of this, Hooke's law is sometimes stated in an alternative way: Provided the elastic limit is not exceeded, the tensile stress is directly proportional to the tensile strain.

**EXAMPLE**

A weight of 20N is hung on the end of a copper wire of length 1m. If the diameter of the wire is 0.50mm and the Young's Modulus of copper is $1.3 \times 10^{11}$ Pa, calculate the extension produced.

Use

$$E = \frac{F\ell}{Ae}$$

F force
$\ell$ = length

hence

A = c.s.a. of wire

$$e = \frac{F\ell}{AE}$$

e = extension

Here

$$F = 20N$$
$$\ell = 1m$$
$$E = 1.3 \times 10^{11} \text{ Pa}$$
$$A = \pi r^2 = \pi (0.25 \times 10^{-3})^2 \text{ m}^2$$

thus

$$= \frac{20 \times 1}{\pi (0.25 \times 10^{-3})^2 \times 1.3 \times 10^{11}}$$

Extension $= 7.8 \times 10^{-4}$m (or 0.78mm)

## 18.6 DETERMINATION OF YOUNG'S MODULUS FOR A WIRE

The apparatus used, known as Searle's Apparatus, is shown in Fig. 18.10. It consists of two identical long wires, typically 2m long, attached to a rigid framework, consisting of two vertical sections and two horizontal distance pieces. The top piece may be adjusted by a micrometer drum and the spirit level is used to read when the top piece is horizontal.

**FIG. 18.10**

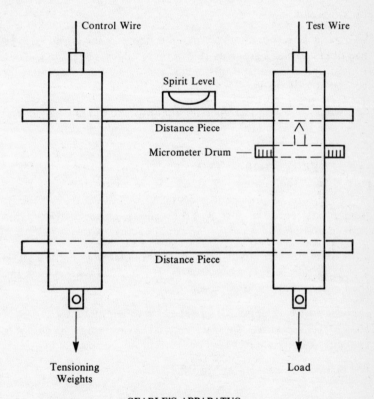

**SEARLE'S APPARATUS**

Initially, identical loads are placed on both wires, the top piece levelled and the micrometer drum reading noted. A series of loads are now attached to the test wire and the initial procedure repeated.

Before the experiment is begun, the length of the test wire is measured together with its cross-sectional area. In order to ascertain this, the diameter is measured, at four or five points, the mean diameter and area obtained.

Care should be taken not to exceed the proportional limit and this is checked by ensuring that the final length of the test wire at the conclusion of the experiment is as it was at the start. (In practice there is very little difference in physical separation between limit of proportionality and elastic limit and they may be virtually superimposed.)

A series of corresponding values of tensile stress and tensile strain is then obtained and a graph plotted of these values. The result will be a straight line, the gradient of which is equal to Young's modulus for the material of the wire.

Two wires are used to compensate for any increases in length due to expansion or movement of the support (i.e. the ceiling).

## 18.7  ENERGY STORED IN A STRETCHED WIRE
Energy must be supplied to a wire in order to stretch it. If the stretching force is provided by changing weights, there is a loss in gravitational potential energy of the weights. This is converted into deformation potential energy, or strain energy, of the wire.

If a wire is stretched to its breaking point, a large amount of strain energy is released as kinetic energy in a potentially dangerous phenomenon known as whiplash.

Suppose a wire of length $l$ is stretched by an amount e by a force F. The c.s.a. of the wire is A and its material has a Young's module of E. The wire is not stretched beyond its limit of proportionality.

The behaviour is shown in Fig. 18.11.

**FIG. 18.11**

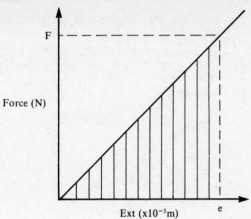

FORCE-EXTENSION

Now Work = Force x Distance moved in Direction of Force
and since the force varies constantly with extension

Work = Average force x Extension

or $$W = \frac{F}{2} \times e$$

This is stored as energy, S

thus $$S = \frac{1}{2} \times \text{Force} \times \text{Extension}$$

It is usual to calculate the strain energy per unit volume

Volume of wire = $A\ell$

∴ Strain energy per unit volume $$= \frac{Fe}{2A\ell}$$

$$= \tfrac{1}{2} \times \text{stress} \times \text{strain}$$

Strain energy is represented graphically by the area underneath a force-extension graph — i.e. the shaded area.

Strain energy per unit volume would be represented by the equivalent area underneath a stress-strain graph.

**EXAMPLE**

A vertical steel wire 3.50m long, 0.100cm in diameter, has a force of 85.0N applied at its lower end. If Young's modulus for steel is $2.00 \times 10^{11}$ Pa, calculate the resultant extension and the strain energy per unit volume of the wire.

To calculate the extension use

$$e = \frac{F\ell}{AE}$$

Here
$$F = 85.0N$$
$$\ell = 3.50m$$
$$E = 2.00 \times 10^{11}$$
$$A = \frac{\pi d^2}{4} = \frac{\pi}{4}(0.100 \times 10^{-2})^2$$

$$\therefore e = \frac{85.0 \times 3.50}{\frac{\pi}{4}(0.100 \times 10^{-2})^2 \times 2.00 \times 10^{11}}$$

$$= 1.89 \times 10^{-3}m$$

$$\therefore \text{Extension} = 1.89 \times 10^{-3}m$$

Now strain energy per unit volume is given by

$$\tfrac{1}{2} \times \text{Stress} \times \text{Strain}$$

$$\text{Stress} = \frac{\text{force}}{\text{area}}$$

$$= \frac{85.0}{\frac{\pi}{4}(0.100 \times 10^{-2})^2} = 1.08 \times 10^8 \text{ Pa}$$

$$\text{Strain} = \frac{\text{extension}}{\text{length}}$$

$$= \frac{1.89 \times 10^{-3}}{3.50} = 5.40 \times 10^{-4}$$

$$\therefore \text{Strain energy per unit volume} =$$
$$\frac{1}{2} \times 1.08 \times 10^8 \times 5.40 \times 10^{-4}$$

$$= 2.92 \times 10^4 \text{ J}$$

Strain Energy per unit volume = $2.92 \times 10^4$ J

## QUESTIONS

1) A small U tube manometer containing mercury is used to determine the pressure in a partially evacuated container. The height of the mercury on the arm connected to the container is 5.0cm higher than that in the arm open to the atmosphere. Assuming that atmospheric pressure = 101KPa, density of mercury = 13,600Kgm⁻³ and g = 9.81ms⁻², determine the pressure in the container.

2) Discuss the various types of solid in terms of their molecular arrangement.

3) Define the terms — limit of proportionality, elastic limit, tensile stress, tensile strain and Young's modulus.

4) Calculate the extension produced when a load of 5.0N is hung from the end of a wire 1.5m long, of radius 0.15mm. Assume Young's modulus for the material of the wire is $1.0 \times 10^{11}$ Pa.

# AREA 5 : FIELD PHENOMENA

## Chapter 19
## ELECTROSTATICS

### 19.1   CHARGING BY FRICTION

Suppose two insulators are rubbed together. In Fig. 19.1, polythene is rubbed with a woollen duster. It is found that the woollen duster acquires a positive charge whilst the polythene acquires a negative charge. The phenomenon is due to transfer of electrons from the surface atoms of the wool to the surface of the polythene. Effectively, electrons are being rubbed off atoms and so we refer to the effect as electrification, or charging, by friction.

**FIG. 19.1**

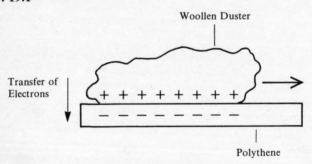

If the polythene were replaced by perspex and the procedure repeated we would find that the perspex acquired a positive charge and the duster a negative charge. This time electrons would be rubbed off the surface atoms of the perspex and travel onto the duster.

When two charged polythene strips are arranged as in Fig. 19.2, we find that repulsion occurs. This demonstrates that positive charges repel each other. A similar thing happens with two charged perspex strips. Thus negative charges repel each other.

**FIG. 19.2**

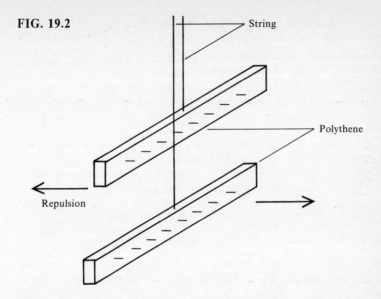

If we use one perspex strip and one polythene strip we find, Fig. 19.3, thus attraction occurs. Hence positive and negative charges attract The facts are often written as: Like charges repel, unlike charges attract.

**FIG. 19.3**

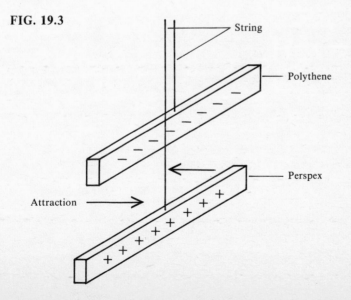

## 19.2 CONDUCTORS AND INSULATORS

In a conductor, such as a metal, some of the outermost electrons, or valence electrons, in each atom are very weakly bound and are free to wander from one atom to another right throughout the crystal lattice. We have already met the idea of such random motion and the superimposition of a drift velocity by the application of an electric field.

In the case of a semiconductor, thermally generated electron-hole pairs act as intrinsic carriers. In doped semiconductors in addition to electron-hole pairs we also have impurity electrons or holes which may migrate from one lattice site to another.

In an insulator, unlike a conductor, there are no electrons which are free to move. Any electrons which an insulator receives cannot wander throughout it replacing any "gaps" left by migrating valence electrons. Similarly, when an insulator loses electrons from its surface, there are no free electrons which can move in to replace them. Thus, in each case we are left with an insulator which has an overall negative or positive charge residing upon its surface. Thus, when the polythene rod is charged, the negative charges or electrons remain on its surface. Equally, when the perspex rod is charged, the positive charges remain on its surface.

## 19.3 CURRENT AS A RATE OF FLOW OF CHARGE

19.3.1 In Fig. 19.4, suppose now the charged polythene rod is connected to earth by a conducting wire. (The earth symbol is shown in this fig.)

**FIG. 19.4**

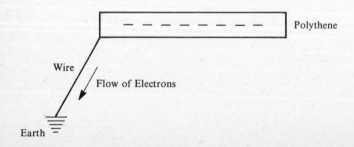

Electrons will flow from the rod until it is no longer charged. The polythene rod is said to be at a positive potential whereas the earth is at zero potential. There is, therefore, a difference of potential between the rod and the earth and it is this difference which causes the electrons to flow from a low to a higher potential. When the rod has lost all its charge, it is at zero potential just like the earth. There is no difference of potential (or electrical potential difference) between the rod and the earth and the flow of electrons ceases.

19.3.2 If the procedure is repeated with a positively charged perspex rod, electrons flow from the earth.

In this case, the rod is at a positive potential with the earth still being at zero potential. A potential difference exists and this causes electrons to flow. Since electrons flow from a low to a higher potential, here the electrons will flow from the earth to the rod.

The electron flow will continue until the rod is no longer charged and is at zero potential. The concept of potential difference will be discussed further in Chapter 20.

19.3.3 Thus, charge is flowing because of a potential difference. Now since an electric current is rate of flow of charge, this means that an electric current flows to or from the earth depending upon whether the charged body is positively or negatively charged.

The charge on a charged body may be measured by a device known as an electrometer.

The classical device is the leaf electrometer shown in Fig. 19.5. It consists of a small rectangle of fine aluminium leaf attached at the top end to the side of a brass rod. This is secured by means of an insulator into a conducting case fitted with glass windows. A small metal disc or cap is fixed to the top of the brass rod. Now if the cap is charged, then it, the rod and the leaf will acquire a charge also. The diagram shows a positive charge. Thus it will acquire a positive potential. The case is at zero potential — earthed. The resulting potential difference causes the leaf to move out. Usually the leaf moves over a scale calibrated in volts.

**FIG. 19.5**

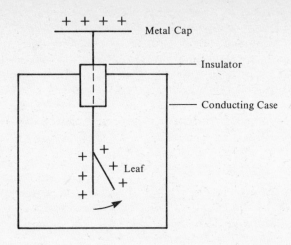

If the voltage is V volts, then the charge, Q, on the device is given by

$$Q = CV$$

where C is a constant for the meter known as its capacitance. (See Chapter 22).

The modern form of an electrometer consists of a device known as an operational amplifier connected in series with a voltmeter, as shown in Fig. 19.6, to form an electronic voltmeter.

**FIG. 19.6**

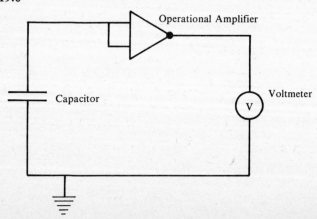

The operational amplifier will be discussed more fully in Chapter 26. Here all we need to know is that it has two inputs, one output and a very high input resistance — typically $10^{10}$ $\Omega$ . The two input terminals are connected together and then connected to one terminal of a capacitor. The output is connected via a voltmeter to the other capacitor terminal.

The voltmeter measures the voltage on the capacitor. If this voltage is V and the capacitance of the capacitor is C, then the charge Q is given by

$$Q = CV$$

The purpose of the operational amplifier is to introduce an extremely high resistance into the circuit and, therefore, slow down the discharge of the capacitor, so that the charge on the capacitor does not vary whilst the reading is being taken.

In both methods, charge to be measured may be transferred to each of the devices using a proof plane.

## 19.4  COULOMB'S LAW

Coulomb's Law states that the force between two point charges is directly proportional to the product of the charges and inversely proportional to the square of their separation.

Hence, for two charges $Q_1$ and $Q_2$ separated by a distance r then the force F may be written as

$$F \quad \alpha \quad \frac{Q_1 Q_2}{r^2}$$

This is converted to an equation by the introduction of a constant $4 \pi \epsilon_0$.

$$F \quad = \quad \frac{Q_1 Q_2}{4 \pi \epsilon_0 r^2}$$

($4\pi$   is introduced to ensure uniformity between units used in electricity and electromagnetism). We always assume that the charges are point charges. However, in the case of a spherical charge, we may regard it as being concentrated at the centre.
$\epsilon_0 = 8.85 \times 10^{-12}$   Farads Metre$^{-1}$, abbreviation Fm$^{-1}$.

$\epsilon_0$ is known as the permittivity of free space (or vacuum) and is defined by

$$\epsilon_0 \quad = \quad \frac{1}{\mu_0 \, c^2}$$

when $\qquad \mu_0 \quad = \quad$ permeability of free space

$\qquad\qquad c \quad = \quad$ speed of light in free space

---

**EXAMPLE**

Calculate the force between two charges of +1C separated by 4m in air.

Use $\qquad\qquad F \quad = \quad \dfrac{Q_1 \, Q_2}{4 \, \pi \, \epsilon_0 \, d_2}$

$\qquad\qquad Q_1 \quad = \quad 1C$

$\qquad\qquad Q_2 \quad = \quad 1C$

$\qquad\qquad d \quad = \quad 4m$

hence

$\qquad F \quad = \quad \dfrac{1 \times 1}{4\pi \times 8.85 \times 10^{-12} \times 4^2}$

$\qquad\qquad = \quad \dfrac{1}{64\pi \times 8.85 \times 10^{-12}}$

$\qquad \therefore \quad$ Force $= (+) \, 5.6 \times 10^8$ N

(The + sign indicates repulsion).

---

The force between two charges also depends upon what separates them.

If the medium is other than air, then we introduce another constant $\epsilon r$ where $\epsilon r$ is the relative permittivity of the medium which is also known as the dielectric constant of the material.

$\qquad$ Thus

$$F \quad = \quad \frac{Q_1 \, Q_2}{4 \, \pi \, \epsilon_0 \epsilon_r \, r^2}$$

Sometimes we write

$$\epsilon = \epsilon_0 \epsilon_r = \text{permittivity}$$

i.e. PERMITTIVITY = PERMITTIVITY OF FREE SPACE x RELATIVE PERMITTIVITY

## QUESTIONS

1) Explain what happens when a charged polythene rod is placed in contact with a charged perspex rod.

2) Calculate the nature and size of the force between two charges $+10^{-9}$C at $-10^{-10}$C, 20cm apart in air.

# Chapter 20
# ELECTRIC FIELDS

## 20.1  THE CONCEPT OF ELECTRIC FIELD

20.1.1  An electric field is a region where an electric charge experiences a force.

The direction of the field is the direction of the force on a positive charge placed in the field. Direction is indicated by an arrow.

We may represent an electric field by electric field lines. These lines are drawn in such a manner that
(i)   the field line at a point (or the tangent to it if it is curved) gives the direction of the field at that point.
(ii)  the number of field lines per unit cross-sectional area is proportional to the strength of the field.

20.1.2  Fig. 20.1 shows the field lines associated with a charge of +2C. They are radial lines. A positive charge located in the field would experience a force away from the charge of +2C and so the field direction is away from the +2C charge.

**FIG. 20.1**

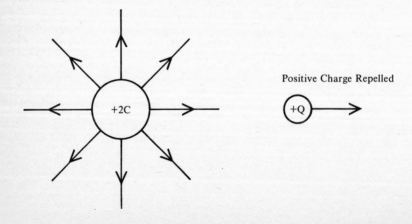

Positive Charge Repelled

If this +2C charge is replaced by a larger one, say +4C, it generates a stronger electric field and this is shown by having more field lines as in Fig. 20.2.

**FIG. 20.2**

If the original +2C charge is replaced by a negative charge of −2C and a positive charge were placed in the field, it would be attracted. The field direction is, therefore, reversed and the arrows on the field line now point radially inwards, as shown in Fig. 20.3.

**FIG. 20.3**

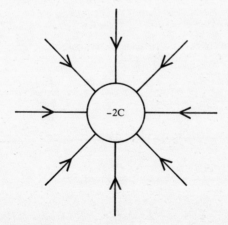

## 20.2 ELECTRIC FIELD STRENGTH AND ITS CALCULATION

20.2.1 If a very small positive charge Q is placed at any point in an electric field, it suffers a force F. We define the field strength, E as

$$E \quad = \quad \frac{F}{Q}$$

Units are Newton Coulomb$^{-1}$ or NC$^{-1}$.

We make the stipulation that the positive charge should be small (electrically) in order that it does not disturb the field which it experiences.

When the concept of an electric field was first formulated, it was regarded as a mathematical abstraction and an alternative explanation of the forces arising by action at a distance. However, it was subsequently demonstrated by Maxwell that an electric field is a real entity which can indeed propagate through space at the speed of light.

20.2.2 Suppose a small positive point charge $Q_0$ is placed a distance r away from a positive point charge Q.

The force between them is given by

$$F \quad = \quad \frac{Q \, Q_0}{4 \pi \, \epsilon_0 r^2}$$

But the field strength due to Q is given by

$$E \quad = \quad \frac{F}{Q_0}$$

Thus

$$E \quad = \quad \frac{Q \, Q_0}{4 \pi \, \epsilon_0 r^2 Q_0}$$

$$\therefore \quad E \quad = \quad \frac{Q}{4 \pi \, \epsilon_0 r^2}$$

This is called an inverse square law field.

**EXAMPLE**

Calculate the electric field strength at a point X midway on the line joining two charges, 20cm apart in air, if the charges are $+10^{-9}$C and $-10^{-10}$C.

(Take $\dfrac{1}{4\pi\,\epsilon_0}$ as 9 x $10^9$ Fm$^{-1}$)

The situation is shown in Fig. 20.4.

**FIG. 20.4**

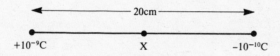

Field strength at X due to positive charge

$$= \frac{10^{-9} \times 9 \times 10^9}{(10^{-1})^2}$$

$$= \quad 900 \text{ NC}^{-1}$$

Field strength at X due to negative charge

$$= \frac{-10^{-10} \times 9 \times 10^9}{10^{-2}}$$

$$= \quad -90 \text{ NC}^{-1}$$

Now at X is our positive test charge. The positive charge would repel it and the negative charge would attract it. The resultant field is, therefore, the sum of the individual fields in the direction of the negative charge.

∴    Net field strength    =    900 + 90

                         =    990 NC$^{-1}$

              towards negative charge

(N.B. — If the $-10^{-10}$C were replaced by $+ 10^{-10}$C, the net field would be 900 – 90 = 810NC$^{-1}$ towards it.)

We may always see immediately if we are dealing with an inverse square low field since the field lines spread out with distance.

A uniform field does not change with distance and it is represented by a series of equidistant parallel lines. It occurs between the plates of a parallel plate capacitor, as shown in Fig. 20.5.

**FIG. 20.5**

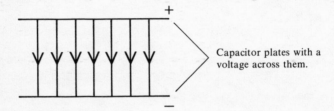

Capacitor plates with a voltage across them.

20.2.3 The charge per unit area on the surface of the conductor is called the charge density,

Thus $\quad \sigma = \dfrac{Q}{A} \qquad\qquad$ Q = total charge

$\qquad\qquad\qquad\qquad\qquad\qquad\qquad$ A = surface area

Now for a sphere $\quad A = 4\pi r^2 \qquad$ where r = radius

$\therefore \quad \sigma = \dfrac{Q}{4\pi r^2}$

But $\qquad\qquad E = \dfrac{Q}{4\pi E_0 r^2}$

Hence $\qquad\qquad E = \dfrac{\sigma}{E_0}$

This expression is true for any shaped conductor.

Incidentally, if a charge is given to a spherical conductor, or indeed, any shaped conductor, it follows that the charge resides on the surface so as to minimise the coulombic forces involved, i.e. the force between any number of charges is reduced if the charges are as far away from each other as possible.

## 20.3 POTENTIAL DIFFERENCE AND ITS RELATIONSHIP TO ELECTRIC FIELD STRENGTH

20.3.1. Suppose, as in Fig. 20.6, a positive charge, Q, is placed in a uniform electric field directed from left to right. The field will cause the charge to move away from it. Let us consider it being moved from A to B, a distance $x$ .

**FIG. 20.6**

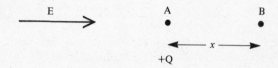

The field is doing work on the charge. Because the charge is in an electric field, it has electrical potential energy and the work done on the charge is done at the expense of this energy. There is, therefore, a difference in electrical potential energy between the points A and B.

This difference in electrical potential energy per unit charge is said to be the electrical potential difference between the two points
Thus, if
Work done by field = loss of electrical potential energy = W
and Charge = Q
then Potential difference, V $= \dfrac{W}{Q}$

The units are Joule Coulomb$^{-1}$ (JC$^{-1}$) which is a volt (V).

In order for a charge to move between two such points, an electrical potential difference must exist between the two points.

It will be seen from the above that V is
$$\frac{\text{electrical potential energy converted}}{\text{charge}}$$
and this is identical to the definition of potential difference met in electrical circuits. Indeed, in such a circuit it is the task of the battery to provide an electric field along the circuit in order to move the charges which are, of course, electrons.

Now in the above diagram, the charge is losing electrical potential as it moves from A to B, its normal direction of travel. In view of this we say that positive charges move from points of higher to points of lower potential. Negative charges, including electrons, move in reverse from a lower to a higher potential.

20.3.2   Suppose the potential difference between two points A and B is V with A being at a higher potential than B.

Thus

$$V = \text{Potential at A} - \text{Potential at B}$$

It is this **difference** of potential in which we are interested. However, if the potential at B is zero then V is the absolute potential at the point A. The earth is taken as a point of zero potential, mainly because the gain or loss of electrons by the earth does not disturb its electrical state. Also, points situated infinitely away from a charge are also at zero potential and this is discussed further below.

The field shown in Fig. 20.6 could be provided by a positive charge situated on the left. Thus, the nearer we approach a positive charge, the greater is the potential. Similarly, the nearer we approach a negative charge the less is the potential.

20.3.4   Now we have considered a field doing work in moving a charge. The electrical potential of the charge falls. But what happens to this energy? It cannot simply be lost! It is converted into kinetic energy. This idea was used in Chapter 16 in the discussion of electron acceleration.

Thus,          loss of potential energy $= QV$

Increase in kinetic energy $= \frac{1}{2}mv^2$     where $m = $ mass of charge

$v = $ increase in velocity

$$\therefore \quad QV = \frac{1}{2}mv^2$$

$$\therefore \quad v = \sqrt{\frac{2QV}{m}}$$

The rate at which the charge accelerates may be found quite easily.

By definition of electric field strength we have

$$F \quad = \quad EQ$$

E = Field Strength
Q = Charge

Now, by Newton's Second Law we have

$$F \quad = \quad ma$$

m = mass of charge
a = acceleration

$$\therefore \quad a \quad = \quad \frac{EQ}{m}$$

---

**EXAMPLE**

Calculate the acceleration of an electron when it is situated in an electric field of $25NC^{-1}$. (Take $^e/m$ for electrons as $1.8 \times 10^{11} \, CKg^{-1}$.)

$$Now \qquad a \quad = \quad \frac{EQ}{m}$$

For an electron we write

$$a \quad = \quad \frac{Ee}{m}$$

Thus

$$a \quad = \quad 25 \times 1.8 \times 10^{11}$$
$$= \quad 4.5 \times 10^{12} \, ms^{-2}$$

Acceleration of electrons $= 4.5 \times 10^{12} \, ms^{-2}$

---

20.3.5  Suppose a charge, + Q, is situated in an electric field which is not necessarily constant — Fig. 20.7.

**FIG. 20.7**

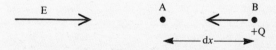

The field strength is E and the charge is moved against the field direction from B to A, a distance d $x$ .

The work done by the field, dW, is given by

$$dW = F \cdot dx$$

But

$$F = QE$$

$$\therefore \quad dW = QEdx$$

The potential difference between A and B is dV where

$$dV = \frac{dW}{Q}$$

$$\therefore \quad dW = Q\,dV$$

Hence

$$QE\,dx = Q\,dV$$

$$\therefore \quad E = \frac{dV}{dx}$$

Now the direction of increasing potential is against the direction of the electric field. To incorporate this idea we write

$$E = -\frac{dV}{dx}$$

i.e. ELECTRIC FIELD STRENGTH = – POTENTIAL GRADIENT

In the case of a uniform field we do not need to use calculus and can write

$$E = -\frac{V}{x}$$

Note: It is only usual to write the minus sign when calculations are to be performed using integration as shown in the next section, 20.3.6.

Also, from this approach, the units of E may be written as

$$\frac{\text{Volts}}{\text{Metres}} \quad \text{or} \quad Vm^{-1}$$

Hence, electric field strength may be given as $NC^{-1}$ or $Vm^{-1}$

20.3.6 We may calculate the potential difference between two points, A and B, a distance $x$ from each other, in the electric field due to a small positive charge as in Fig. 20.8.

**FIG. 20.8**

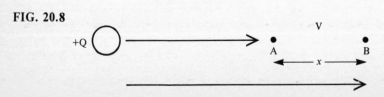

Now the field due to $+Q$ is given by at $r$ away

$$E = \frac{Q}{4\pi\,\epsilon_0 r^2}$$

But $\qquad E = -\dfrac{dV}{dr}$ $\qquad$ ($r$ = distance variable here)

Calculus must be used because the field varies with $r$.

Thus $\qquad V = -\displaystyle\int_B^A E\,dr$ $\qquad$ (B and A represent starting and finishing positions)

$$V = -\int_B^A \frac{Q}{4\pi\,\epsilon_0 r^2}\,dr$$

$$= -\frac{Q}{4\pi\,\epsilon_0}\int_B^A \frac{dr}{r^2}$$

$$= -\frac{Q}{4\pi\,\epsilon_0}\left[-\frac{1}{r}\right]_B^A$$

$$= -\frac{Q}{4\pi\,\epsilon_0}\left(-\frac{1}{A} - -\frac{1}{B}\right)$$

$$= -\frac{Q}{4\pi\,\epsilon_0}\left(-\frac{1}{A} + \frac{1}{B}\right)$$

$$V = \frac{Q}{4\pi\,\epsilon_0}\left(\frac{1}{A} - \frac{1}{B}\right)$$

In the equation

$$V = \frac{Q}{4\pi\,\epsilon_0}\left(\frac{1}{A} - \frac{1}{B}\right)$$

when $B = \infty$ , the field is zero and the positive charge has no potential

$$V = \frac{Q}{4\pi\,\epsilon_0 A}$$

V is now called the absolute potential. Thus the potential at a distance A from a charge is the change in electrical potential energy of unit charge as it is brought from infinity to the point concerned. We specify a positive unit charge. Hence a positive charge has a positive potential and a negative charge has a negative potential, given by $\dfrac{-Q}{4\pi\,\epsilon_0 A}$

**EXAMPLE**

1)  Calculate the potential at a distance of 0.5m away from a positive charge of 2C (Assume $\frac{1}{4\pi \epsilon_0}$ = 9 x $10^9$ Fm$^{-1}$).

Use $\qquad V = \dfrac{Q}{4\pi \epsilon_0 r}$

Here $\qquad Q = 2C$
$\qquad\qquad r = 0.5m$

$\qquad\qquad \therefore V = \dfrac{2 \text{ x } 9 \text{ x } 10^9}{0.5}$

$\qquad\qquad\qquad = 3.6 \text{ x } 10^{10}$ V

Potential at 0.5m $= 3.6 \text{ x } 10^{10}$ V

**FIG. 20.9**

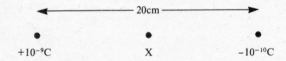

2)  In Fig. 20.9, calculate the potential at X, halfway between two charges $+10^{-9}$C and $-10^{-10}$C, situated 20cm apart in air. $\frac{1}{4\pi \epsilon_0}$ = 9 x $10^9$ Fm$^{-1}$

Use $\qquad V = \dfrac{Q}{4\pi \epsilon_0 r}$

Due to the positive charge
$\qquad V = \dfrac{10^{-9} \text{ x } 9 \text{ x } 10^9}{10^{-1}} = 90V$

Due to the negative charge
$\qquad V = \dfrac{-10^{-10} \text{ x } 9 \text{ x } 10^9}{10^{-1}} = -9V$

$\therefore$ Net potential = 90 – 9 = 81V. (Scalar quantity).

## 20.4  THE FIELD AND POTENTIAL ASSOCIATED WITH A HOLLOW CHARGED SPHERE

Fig. 20.10 shows the variation in the field and potential due to a charge Q on a hollow conducting sphere.

**FIG. 20.10**

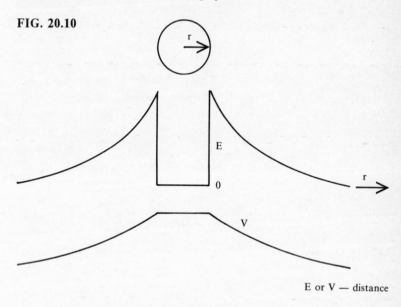

E or V — distance

Outside the sphere, the field is just the same as if the charge Q carried on its surface was concentrated at its centre.

The full strength E at a distance r from the centre of the sphere is given by

$$E = \frac{Q}{4\pi\epsilon_0 r^2}$$     where here r = sphere radius and greater values.

and thus it falls off as the inverse square of the distance.

The potential V is given by

$$V = \frac{Q}{4\pi\epsilon_0 r}$$

Now on such a sphere all the charge resides on the outside surface since the charges move to the outside to minimize the forces between them. If there is no charge on the inside there can be no field on the inside.

The field inside is, therefore, zero. Thus, the potential gradient is zero and the potential inside is constant, having the value of the potential at the surface.

## QUESTIONS

1) Calculate the force between two positive charges of 3C separated by 0.5m in glycerine. ($\frac{1}{4\pi \epsilon_0}$ 9 x $10^9$ Fm$^{-1}$, $\epsilon_r$ = 43).

2) A, B, C, D are the four corners of a square of side 1m. Point charges of $10^{-9}$C, $-2$ x $10^{-9}$C and 3 x $10^{-9}$C are placed at the corners A, B, C respectively. Find the potential at D, given that $\epsilon_0 = \dfrac{10^{-9}}{36\pi}$ Fm$^{-1}$

3) Two charges of $10^{-8}$C and $-4$ x $10^{-9}$C are placed 30cm from each other. Find the point of zero potential.

# Chapter 21
# GRAVITATIONAL FIELDS

## 21.1 NEWTONS UNIVERSAL LAW OF GRAVITATION

21.1.1   Gravitation is a universal effect operating according to the same law between every two particles in the universe.

Newton's Universal Law of Gravitation states: Every particle of matter attracts every other particle of matter with a force which is directly proportional to the product of their masses and inversely proportional to the square of the distance between them.

**FIG. 21.1**

21.1.2   In Fig. 21.1, consider two particles of mass $M_1$ and $M_2$, situated a distance r apart. The force F between them may be written

$$F \quad \alpha \quad \frac{M_1 M_2}{r^2}$$

or

$$F \quad = \quad \frac{G M_1 M_2}{r^2}$$

where G is called the Universal Constant of Gravitation
The value of G is $6.67 \times 10^{-11} \, Nm^2 \, Kg^{-2}$.

Newton showed that if the particles were replaced by spheres of uniform density, the formula still holds with r now being the distance between their centres.

Because G is so small, gravitational forces are very small and, accordingly, the gravitational force is known as a weak force. The forces are only really large in stars.

21.1.3   The principle used to calculate G is quite straightforward and involves a measurement of all variables in

$$F \quad = \quad \frac{G M_1 M_2}{r^2}$$

The first laboratory determination was performed by Cavendish at Cambridge.

**FIG. 21.2**

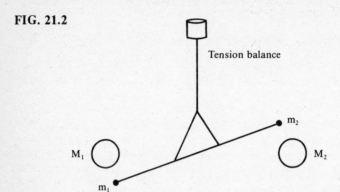

The apparatus is shown in Fig. 21.2. He measured the very small gravitational forces exerted on two very small lead balls ($m_1$ and $m_2$) by two larger ones ($M_1$ and $M_2$) using a tension balance, in which the force twists a calibrated wire.

---

**EXAMPLE**

Calculate the force of attraction between two masses of 5Kg and 13.4Kg whose centres are 0.1m apart.
Assume $G = 6.7 \times 10^{11} \ Nm^2 \ Kg^{-2}$.

$$\text{Use} \qquad F = \frac{GM_1M_2}{r^2}$$

Here
$$G = 6.7 \times 10^{11} \ Nm^2 \ Kg^{-2}$$
$$M_1 = 5 \ Kg$$
$$M_2 = 13.4 \ Kg$$
$$r = 0.1m$$

$$\therefore \quad F = \frac{6.7 \times 10^{11} \times 5 \times 13.4}{0.1^2}$$
$$= 4.5 \times 10^{-7} \ N$$

Force $= 4.5 \times 10^{-7} \ N$

---

## 21.2   THE EARTH'S GRAVITATIONAL FIELD

21.2.1   A gravitational field is a region where a mass experiences a gravitational force.

The gravitational field strength at a point is defined as the gravitational force exerted on unit mass situated at the point.

Considering again the two masses $M_1$ and $M_2$, a distance r apart

$$F = \frac{GM_1M_2}{r^2}$$

The field strength at r, due to the mass $M_1$ is the force exerted on unit mass at r.

Thus        Gravitational field strength $= \dfrac{GM_1}{r^2} = E$

$$= \frac{F}{M_2}$$

This is called an inverse square law field.

Hence, when a mass M is situated in a gravitational field of strength E, the force F is given by

$$F = EM$$

The units of gravitational field strength are Newton's Kilogram$^{-1}$, $NKg^{-1}$.

21.2.2   From the above, the gravitational field strength associated with a particular object depends upon its mass.

The largest mass we usually experience is the earth itself and its gravitational field is of great importance.

By definition of gravitational field strength, we may write that the force F, exerted on a body of mass M by the earth is

$$F = EM$$

where        $E =$ earth's gravitational field strength

But the force exerted on a body by the earth is the weight of the body W and

$$W = Mg$$

Hence

$$EM = Mg$$
$$E = g$$

In other words, the intensity of the earth's gravitational field is the same as the acceleration due to gravity. In view of this "alternative" definition of g, we sometimes see the units of it quoted as $N\,Kg^{-1}$.

21.2.3 It will be remembered that electric fields were represented pictorally by lines.

In a similar way, a gravitational field may be represented by field lines.

Gravitationally, the earth behaves as though all its mass were situated at its centre. The earth's gravitational field lines, therefore, are radial, meeting at the centre of the earth, as shown in Fig. 21.3. The direction of the field is towards the centre of the earth because the force is attractive. The field strength is inversely proportional to the square of the distance from the centre of the earth, and it would be expected that the field lines become further apart with distance from the earth's centre.

**FIG. 21.3**

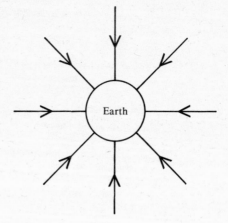

EARTH'S FIELD LINES ON A LARGE SCALE

If we imagine a small area on the earth's surface, such as England, then the curvature of the earth is negligible and the earth is effectively flat. Now, since the field lines are perpendicular to the earth's surface, as can be seen in Fig. 21.3, this means that the field lines are now parallel and vertical, as shown in Fig. 21.4. On the earth's surface, or very close to it, the field is uniform and may be represented by a set of equidistance vertical field lines.

**FIG. 21.4**

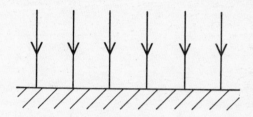

EARTH'S FIELD LINES ON A SMALL SCALE

## 21.3 THE RELATIONSHIP BETWEEN G AND g AT THE EARTH'S SURFACE

It has been shown that the intensity of the earth's gravitional field is equal to the acceleration due to gravity.

$$E = g$$

Now E at the earth's surface is given by

$$E = \frac{GMe}{r_e{}^2}$$

where $Me$ = mass of earth

$r_e$ = radius of earth

hence $g = \dfrac{GMe}{r_e{}^2}$

---

**EXAMPLE**

If the radius of the earth is 6400Km and g on the surface of the earth has a value of 9.8 ms$^{-2}$, calculate the earth's mass. G = 6.7 x 10$^{-11}$ Nm$^{-2}$ Kg$^{-2}$.

Now $g = \dfrac{GMe}{r_e{}^2}$

$\therefore$ $Me = \dfrac{gr_e{}^2}{G}$

Substituting the values

$$Me = \frac{9.8 \times (6.4 \times 10^6)^2}{6.7 \times 10^{-11}}$$

$$= 6 \times 10^{24} \text{ Kg}$$

$$\therefore \quad \text{Mass of earth} = 6 \times 10^{24} \text{ Kg}$$

The variation in g above the earth's surface is an inverse square relationship. However, g also varies below the earth's surface since only the mass of the earth inside a given radius may be considered to be at the earth's centre.

The total variation in field strength with distance from the centre of the earth is shown in Fig. 21.5.

**FIG. 21.5**

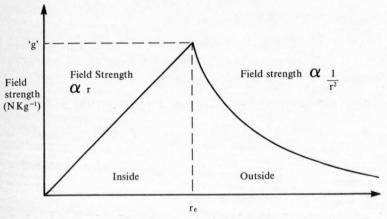

FIELD STRENGTH-DISTANCE

From this figure it may be seen that the field strength at a given distance below the earth's surface is greater than that at the same distance above the surface of the earth.

The above analysis, however, fails to take into account another factor — that of the rotation of the earth. This has two effects:—

1) All points on the surface of the earth, except those at the poles, are rotating about an axis through the centre of the earth, as shown in Fig. 21.6.

**FIG. 21.6**

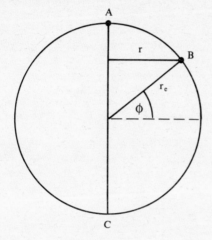

Points at A and C are at rest. Point B moves about the axis of rotation at a distance r with an angular velocity $\omega$, the angular velocity of the earth.

Accordingly, a mass m at rest at B will experience a centripetal force F given by

$$F = mr\omega^2$$

now 

$$r = r_e COS \phi$$

thus, centripetal force $= mr_e\omega^2 COS \phi$ along r

**FIG. 21.7**

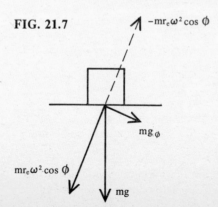

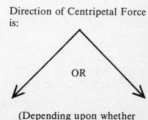

Direction of Centripetal Force is:

OR

(Depending upon whether in N. or S. hemisphere)

The attraction of the earth produces two effects:
1) It supplies the centripetal force needed to maintain the body at a constant distance from the centre of the earth.
2) It produces the acceleration due to gravity which is measured.

The net gravitational force acting at B is the vector difference between mg (the gravitational force which would be measured at B if the earth were stationary) and $mr_e\omega^2 \cos \phi$. If $g_\phi$ is the measured value of the acceleration due to gravity at B then

$$(mg_\phi)^2 = (mg)^2 + (mr_e\omega^2 \cos \phi)^2 - 2mg.\ mr_e\omega^2 \cos^2\phi$$

2) Because of its rotation, the earth is not a perfect sphere. In fact, it bulges at the equator and its equatorial radius is about 21Km greater than the polar radius — a phenomenon known as the equatorial bulge. The increase in radius causes g to decrease.

## 21.4 GRAVITATIONAL POTENTIAL DIFFERENCE

Whenever a mass moves through a gravitational field, energy is transferred.

**FIG. 21.8**

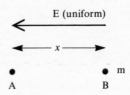

Suppose, as in Fig. 21.8, a mass m moves a distance $x$ from B to A, in the direction of a uniform field, E

$$\text{Force acting on mass} = Em$$

Now, work done by gravitational field on
this mass $= \text{force x distance}$
$= Emx$

As this work is done, energy is transferred from gravitational potential energy to kinetic energy.

Energy transferred = Field Strength x Mass x Distance moved

Thus, whenever a mass moves between two points in a gravitational field, it undergoes a difference in gravitational potential energy.

The difference in gravitational potential energy, per unit mass, between two points in a gravitational field is known as the gravitational potential difference between the two points. Symbol: V.

Consider now a body, a mass m, being moved towards a mass M as shown in Fig. 21.9, from B to A, a distance x.

**FIG. 21.9**

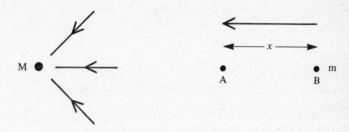

In order that the field should remain constant we need to consider only a small movement dx.

$$\text{Work done by gravity, } dW \quad = \quad E m \, dx$$
$$= \quad \frac{GM}{x^2} m \, dx$$

The total work done in moving from B to A

$$= \quad \int_B^A \frac{GMm}{x^2} \, dx$$

$$= \quad GMm \int_B^A \frac{dx}{x^2}$$

$$= \quad GMm \left[ -\frac{1}{x} \right]_B^A$$

$$= \quad GMm \left( \frac{1}{B} - \frac{1}{A} \right)$$

For a unit mass

Work done $\quad = \quad GM \left( \dfrac{1}{B} - \dfrac{1}{A} \right) \quad =$ Potential Difference, V

Now, when $B = \infty$ , the field is zero and the mass has no potential

$$\therefore \quad V \quad = \quad - \dfrac{GM}{A}$$

V is now called the absolute gravitational potential.

The potential is zero at infinity and becomes less as the unit mass approaches the given mass M. This is perfectly reasonable since the two masses attract each other.

### 21.5  WEIGHTLESSNESS

21.5.1   When a lift accelerates upwards, its passengers appear to weigh more. In Fig. 21.10, a lift accelerates upwards at a rate a. A passenger of mass m experiences a reaction R from the floor.

**FIG. 21.10**

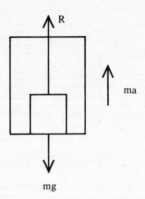

Now
$$ma \quad = \quad R - mg$$
$$\therefore \quad R \quad = \quad m(a + g)$$
Accordingly, the passengers feel "heavier".

Suppose the lift now accelerates downwards, as in Fig. 21.11.

**FIG. 21.11**

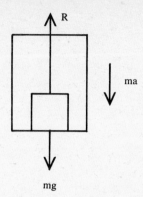

Here

$$ma = mg - R$$
$$\therefore \quad R = m(g - a)$$

If $a = g$

$$R = 0$$

The passenger would now appear to feel weightless.

For such an event, the lift would have to be in free fall and, of course, this would have fatal results when it reached the bottom of its shaft.

21.5.2 Weightlessness can also arise in space travel, both during the journey from the earth to the moon and also whilst in orbit around the earth and the moon.

Consider an astronaut travelling from the earth to the moon, as shown in Fig. 21.12.

**FIG. 21.12**

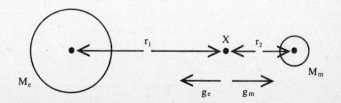

The mass of the earth is Me and that of the moon Mm. The astronaut will appear weightless at X, a distance $r_1$ from the centre of the earth and $r_2$ from the centre of the moon.

In this position

$$g_e = g_m$$

But

$$g_e = \frac{GMe}{r_1^2}$$

$$g_m = \frac{GMm}{r_2^2}$$

hence

$$\frac{r_2}{r_1} = \sqrt{\frac{m_m}{m_e}}$$

Beyond this point, the moon's gravitational acceleration will become more influential.

Now, when the astronaut is in orbit around a planet, we can apply the person-in-the-lift analysis.

Suppose the mass of the astronaut is m, his speed of orbit at a radius r. As in Fig. 21.13.

**FIG. 21.13**

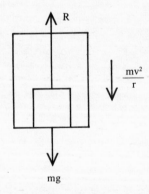

$$\frac{mv^2}{r} = mg - R$$

$$\therefore \quad R = m\left(g - \frac{v^2}{r}\right)$$

Now R = 0 when

$$g = \frac{v^2}{r}$$

or $$v = \sqrt{gr}$$

Again, the astronaut will feel weightless.

## 21.6 COMPARISON BETWEEN GRAVITATIONAL AND ELECTRIC FORCES

21.6.1 There are similarities between these forces:

Both obey inverse square laws $\quad F \propto \dfrac{1}{r^2}$

Both potentials obey inverse laws $\quad F \propto \dfrac{1}{r}$

It is also possible to define a field strength for both force fields.

21.6.2 There are also important differences.

Gravitational forces are always attractive, electric may be attractive or repulsive. This is shown in Fig. 21.14.

## FIG. 21.14

FORCE-DISTANCE

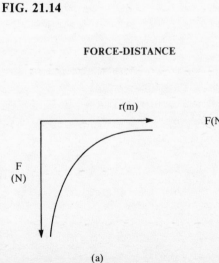

(a)
Variation of gravitational force
with distance

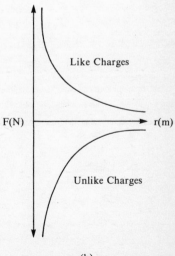

(b)
Variation of electrostatic force
with distance

Gravitational potential is negative, whereas electric potential may be negative or positive, depending upon whether the source of the field is a negative or positive charge. This is shown in Fig. 21.15.

**FIG. 21.15**

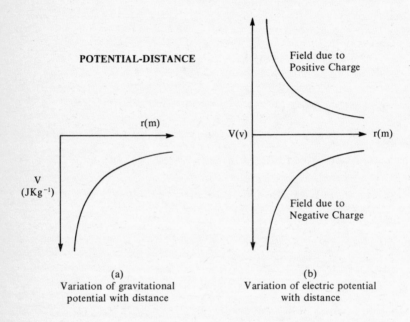

**POTENTIAL-DISTANCE**

(a)
Variation of gravitational
potential with distance

(b)
Variation of electric potential
with distance

Gravitational forces are not affected by matter but electric forces are and this is taken account of in electric forces by the introduction of the constant known as relative permittivity. We say that electric forces are screened.

---

**EXAMPLES**

1) Calculate the gravitational potential on the surface of the earth assuming that $G = 6.67 \times 10^{-11}$ Nm$^{-2}$ Kg$^{-2}$, mass of the earth $= 5.97 \times 10^{24}$Kg, radius of the earth $= 6.37 \times 10^{6}$m.

The potential, V, at a distance A from a mass M is

$$V = -\frac{GM}{A}$$

The potential on the surface of a sphere is the same as if its mass were concentrated at its centre.

Thus, if

$$Me = \text{mass of earth}$$
$$r_e = \text{radius of earth}$$

$$V = \frac{-GMe}{r_e}$$

Substituting

$$G = 6.67 \times 10^{-11} \, Nm^{-2} \, Kg^{-2}$$
$$Me = 5.97 \times 10^{24} \, Kg$$
$$r = 6.37 \times 10^6 \, m.$$

$$\therefore V = \frac{- 6.67 \times 10^{-11} \times 5.97 \times 10^{24}}{6.37 \times 10^6}$$

$$= - 6.25 \times 10^7 \, J \, Kg^{-1}$$

Potential $= - 6.25 \times 10^7 \, J \, Kg^{-1}$

2) An astronaut is in orbit around the earth at a distance of 42,200 Km above the centre of the earth. Calculate his speed if he is to be weightless.
   ($G = 6.7 \times 10^{-11} \, Nm^{-2} \, Kg^{-2}$, mass of earth $= 6 \times 10^{24} Kg$, radius of earth $= 6,400 \, Km$).

Now

$$V = \sqrt{gr}$$

and

$$g = \frac{GMe}{r^2}$$

hence

$$V = \sqrt{\frac{GMer}{r^2}} = \sqrt{\frac{GMe}{r}}$$

Substituting the values

$$V = \sqrt{\frac{6.7 \times 10^{-11} \times 6 \times 10^{24}}{4.22 \times 10^7}}$$

Speed $= 309 \, Kms^{-1}$

## QUESTIONS

1) State Newton's Universal Law of Gravitation and show that the units of G are $Nm^2 \, Kg^{-2}$.

2) Calculate the distance between the centres of two spherical masses of 2.6 Kg and 8.9 Kg if the gravitational force between them is $1.382 \times 10^{-8} N$. ($G = 6.7 \times 10^{11} \, Nm^2 \, Kg^{-2}$).

3) Assuming the sun to be a sphere of radius $6.98 \times 10^8 m$ and mass $1.99 \times 10^{30}$ Kg, calculate a value of g on its surface ($G = 6.67 \times 10^{-11} \, Nm^2 \, Kg^{-2}$).

4) Calculate the potential on the surface of Mars assuming it to be a sphere of radius $3.40 \times 10^6 m$ and mass $6.42 \times 10^{23}$ Kg ($G = 6.67 \times 10^{-11} \, Nm^2 \, Kg^{-2}$).

# Chapter 22
# CAPACITORS

## 22.1 THE MEANING AND MEASUREMENT OF CAPACITANCE

22.1.1 A capacitor is a device which stores electric charge and basically it consists of two conductors, such as a couple of parallel metal plates, separated by an insulator known as the capacitor dielectric.

In the air capacitor, used to tune radios and televisions, the plates are semi-circular metal ones separated by an air dielectric.

In electrolytic capacitors, used in low frequency A.C. circuits, the plates consist of a sheet of aluminium and a sheet of aluminium oxide separated by a dielectric of paper soaked in aluminium borate solution. This sandwich is then rolled in a cylinder rather like a "swiss roll".

The mica capacitor is made from sheets of mica, the dielectric interleaved between metal foils. Waxed paper dielectric between metal foil, wound into a "swiss roll" constitutes a paper capacitor.

22.1.2 The action of a capacitor in a circuit may be understood by considering the circuit shown in Fig. 22.1. This shows a capacitor (symbol ǁ ) connected via a current limiting resistor, a milliammeter and a switch to a battery.

**FIG. 22.1**

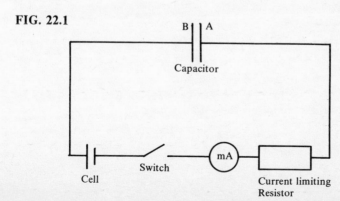

When the switch is closed, electrons begin to flow from the negative terminal of the battery onto plate A of the capacitor and this is demonstrated by a deflection on the milliammeter. As these electrons arrive at plate A they repel electrons from plate B which pass to the positive terminal of the battery. As a result, plate A acquires a negative charge and plate B a positive charge, as a current flows in the circuit.

This current is not steady, however, and it decreases as time goes by. As charge builds up on the capacitor plate, it opposes any further electron flow. The electron flow stops when the potential difference across the capacitor plates equals the external p.d., i.e. the e.m.f. of the battery. When the current flow ceases we say that the capacitor is fully charged. If the charge now on the positive plate is +Q, that on the negative plate is −Q.

Suppose now that the switch is opened. Initially, a large meter deflection in the opposite direction will be observed. This decays to zero quite rapidly. The supply voltage has been disconnected and electrons now flow back from A to B until no charge remains on either plate and the p.d. across the plate is zero.

It will be realised from the above that a capacitor will not allow the passage of current in a steady D.C. circuit. Current only flows onto and off a capacitor when it is being charged or discharged.

22.1.3 In the above case of the fully charged capacitor, the plates carry equal but opposite charges, +Q and −Q. We normally refer to this as Q and realise that equal but opposite charges are involved. Suppose that the p.d. across the capacitor is V.

The capacitance of a capacitor, C, is defined as the ratio of the charge stored to the p.d. across the plates

$$C = \frac{Q}{V}$$

The unit of capacitance is the Farad, symbol F.

The capacitance of a capacitor is 1F if a charge of 1C is stored when the p.d. across its plates is 1V.

**EXAMPLE**

A $2\,\mu$F capacitor is connected across the terminals of a 6V battery. Calculate the charge on its plates.

$$\text{Using} \qquad C \;=\; \frac{Q}{V}$$

$$\text{Hence} \qquad Q \;=\; CV$$

$$\text{Now} \qquad C \;=\; 2\,\mu\text{F} = 2 \times 10^{-6}\text{F}$$
$$V \;=\; 6\text{V}$$
$$\therefore \quad Q \;=\; 6 \times 2 \times 10^{-6}$$
$$=\; 12 \times 10^{-6}$$
$$=\; 12\,\mu\text{C}$$

$$\underline{\text{Charge} \;=\; 12\,\mu\text{C}}$$

## 22.2 FACTORS AFFECTING THE CAPACITANCE OF A PARALLEL PLATE CAPACITOR

The factors affecting the capacitance of a parallel plate capacitor may be investigated using the circuit shown in Fig. 22.2.

**FIG. 22.2**

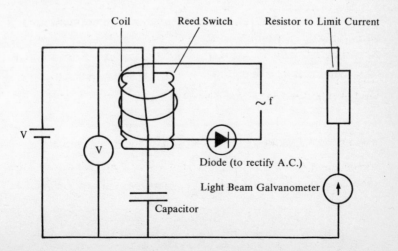

A parallel plate capacitor is alternately charged from a d.c. supply and discharged through a sensitive light beam galvanometer, f times every second by a Reed switch.

A Reed switch is shown in Fig. 22.3 and when rectified a.c. passes through the coil which is surrounding it, the reed and magnetic contact become oppositely magnetised and attract on the half cycle during which the conduction occurs. On the non-conducting half cycle the reed and magnetic contact are no longer magnetised and the reed springs back to the non-magnetic contact. The number of charge-discharge cycles every second is equal to that of the a.c. supply across the coil.

**FIG. 22.3**

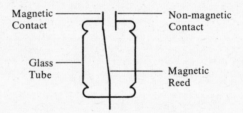

If this frequency is large enough, current pulses follow one another so rapidly that the galvanometer deflection is steady and represents the average current through it, I.

Thus, if Q is the charge stored on the capacitor and the frequency of the a.c. supply is f

$$I = Qf$$

The charging p.d. V is read off from the voltmeter.

The capacitance of the capacitor is given by

$$C = \frac{Q}{V} = \frac{I}{fV}$$

Since f is known and I and V are measured by the galvanometer and voltmeter, C is easily obtained.

If all variables except the area of the plates, A, are kept constant we find that

$$C \; \alpha \; A$$

A is altered by changing the area of overlap between the plates

If all variables except the separation of the plates, d, are kept constant, we find that

$$C \; \alpha \; \frac{1}{d}$$

If, now, all variables are kept constant but insulating materials of relative permittivity $\epsilon_r$ are introduced between the plates, we find that

$$C \; \alpha \; \epsilon_r$$

Hence

$$C \; \alpha \; \frac{\epsilon_r A}{d}$$

In order to write this relationship in the form of an equation we introduce a constant. It is $\epsilon_0$, the permittivity of free space

$$C \; = \; \frac{\epsilon_0 \epsilon_r A}{d}$$

Since $\epsilon_r$ is a ratio, it may be seen that the units of $\epsilon_0$ are the units of $\dfrac{Cd}{A}$     i.e.     $\dfrac{Farads \; Metres}{Metres^2} \; = \; \dfrac{Farads \; Metre^{-1}}{or \; Fm^{-1}}$

The insulating materials are known as dielectrics and hence $\epsilon_r$ is also known as a dielectric constant.

The reason why the capacitance is affected by plate area and separation may be understood as follows.

**FIG. 22.4**

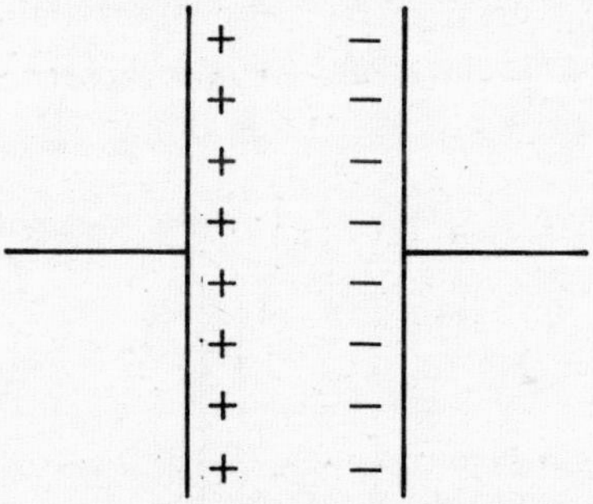

Positive and negative charges (i.e. a deficit and surplus of electrons) cover each plate as shown in Fig. 22.4. The presence of the positive charges tends to "cancel out" the charge due to the negatives, or more precisely, the positive charges reduce the negative potential due to the negative charges. Similarly, the presence of negative charges decreases the potential of the positive plate. Thus, the presence of each decreases the potential of the other and hence the potential difference across them.

The greater the area of the plates, the more charges may appear at the nearest surfaces of the plates and the lower the p.d. across the plates. Since $C = \dfrac{Q}{V}$ this means that the capacitance increases

The closer together the plates, the more influence a charge has on its opposite charge and, thus, the lower the p.d. across the plates, hence the larger the capacitance.

The reason why a dielectric medium affects the capacitance of a capacitor may be explained as follows.

Analysis shows that the charge due to electrons orbiting a nucleus may be considered to behave as if it were at the nucleus. Thus, as far as an observer is concerned the total atomic charge resides at the nucleus. If now an electric field is applied to an atom, it displaces the point at which the electron charge may be considered to be — it will move in the direction opposite to the electric field. The positive and negative charges may no longer be considered to act at the same point but are separated to form a dipole. Thus, when a dielectric medium is placed between the plates of a capacitor, the field generates dipoles in the dielectric and the result of this polarisation as it is known, is that the surfaces of the dielectric in the field direction are charged as shown in Fig. 22.5.

**FIG. 22.5**

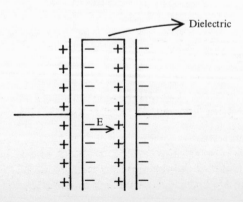

The result of this is a lowering of the p.d. across the plates and, hence, an increase in capacitance.

---

**EXAMPLE**

A parallel plate capacitor consists of two plates each of area 625cm² separated by 0.30cm. The space between the plates is filled with paper of relative permeability 2.5. Calculate the charge on the plate if a p.d. of 200V is applied. ($\epsilon_0 = 8.9 \times 10^{-12} Fm^{-1}$).

$$C = \frac{\epsilon_0 \, \epsilon_r \, A}{d}$$

$$\epsilon_0 = 8.9 \times 10^{-12} \; Fm^{-1}$$
$$\epsilon_r = 2.5$$
$$A = 625cm^2 = 6.25 \times 10^{-2} \, m^2$$
$$d = 0.30cm = 3 \times 10^{-3} \, m$$

$$\therefore \quad C = \frac{8.9 \times 10^{-12} \times 2.5 \times 6.25 \times 10^{-2}}{3 \times 10^{-3}}$$

$$C = 4.64 \times 10^{-10} \; F$$

Now 
$$C = \frac{Q}{V}$$

$$Q = CV$$
$$= 4.64 \times 10^{-10} \times 200$$
$$= 9.28 \times 10^{-8} C$$

$$\text{Charge} = 9.28 \times 10^{-8} C$$

---

## 22.3 CAPACITOR NETWORKS

22.3.1 Capacitors may be connected in series or parallel networks and will then have a resultant capacitance in a similar way to which resistors when connected in series or parallel have a resultant resistance.

Capacitors connected in series are shown in Fig. 22.6. A p.d. V is applied across the combination. Electrons travel to plate A of $C_1$. These repel electrons from plate B to plate C of $C_2$. Accordingly, plate B acquires a charge +Q whilst plate C acquires –Q. The negative charges on the plate repel electrons from plate D which thus acquires a charge +Q.

**FIG. 22.6**

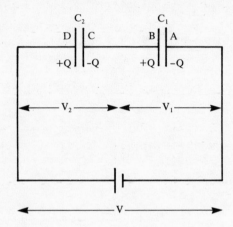

Capacitors in series, therefore, all have the same charge. The p.d.s across them are given by

$$V_1 = \frac{Q}{C_1} \quad \text{and} \quad V_2 = \frac{Q}{C_2}$$

But

$$V = V_1 + V_2$$

$$= \frac{Q}{C_1} + \frac{Q}{C_2}$$

$$= Q \left( \frac{1}{C_1} + \frac{1}{C_2} \right)$$

If the capacitors are the equivalent of a single capacitor C, it would have a charge Q upon it when the p.d. across it was V

Hence

$$\frac{Q}{C} = Q \left( \frac{1}{C_1} + \frac{1}{C_2} \right)$$

$$\therefore \quad \frac{1}{C} = \frac{1}{C_1} + \frac{1}{C_2}$$

This expression applies to any number of capacitances connected in series. It will be noted that this expression is similar to the way in which we combine resistances in parallel.

22.3.2   Capacitors connected in parallel are shown in Fig. 22.7.

**FIG. 22.7**

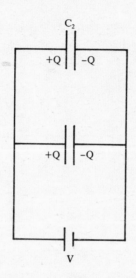

A p.d. V is maintained across the combination. The p.d. across each capacitor is the same — V. If it were not then, since all the positive and all the negative plates are connected together, electrons would flow until it were. Now, however, the charges are different and are $Q_1$ and $Q_2$.

$$Q_1 = VC_1 \qquad\qquad Q_2 = VC_2$$

The total charge on the capacitors is Q and

$$Q = Q_1 + Q_2$$
$$= V(C_1 + C_2)$$

If the capacitors are the equivalent of a single capacitor C, it would have a charge Q when the p.d. across it were V

$$\therefore \quad VC = V(C_1 + C_2)$$

$$\therefore \quad C = C_1 + C_2$$

This expression applies to any number of capacitances connected in parallel.

It will be noted that this expression is similar to the way in which we combine resistances in series.

---

**EXAMPLE**

A potential difference of 100V is maintained across the combination of a capacitor of capacitance 5.0 $\mu$F in series with one of 2.0 $\mu$F. Calculate the potential difference across each and the charge on each.

**FIG. 22.8**

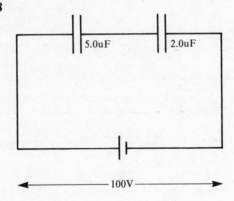

Each capacitor will have the same charge given by Q where

$$Q = VC$$

C = Effective Capacitance

Now
$$\frac{1}{C} = \frac{1}{C_1} + \frac{1}{C_2}$$

$$C_1 = 5.0 \times 10^{-6} \, F$$
$$C_2 = 2.0 \times 10^{-6} \, F$$

$$\therefore \quad \frac{1}{C} = \frac{1}{2 \times 10^{-6}} + \frac{1}{5 \times 10^{-6}}$$

$$= 5 \times 10^5 + 2 \times 10^5$$

$$= 7 \times 10^5$$

$$\therefore \quad C = 1.43 \times 10^{-6}$$

Hence $\qquad Q = 100 \times 1.43 \times 10^{-6}$
$$= 1.43 \times 10^{-4}C$$
$\therefore$ Charge on each $= 143\,\mu C$

But also

$\qquad V_1 = \dfrac{Q}{C_1} \qquad\qquad V_2 = \dfrac{Q}{C_2}$

$\therefore \quad V_1 = \dfrac{143 \times 10^{-6}}{5 \times 10^{-6}} = 28.6\ V$

$\qquad V_2 = \dfrac{143 \times 10^{-6}}{2 \times 10^{-6}} = 71.5\ V$

Voltage on each: 28.6V, 71.5V

(It will be noted that $V_1 + V_2 = V = 100V$ — the slight discrepancy between 28.6 + 71.5 and 100 being caused by mathematics in rounding the numbers).

## 22.4  DERIVATION OF THE CAPACITANCE OF A PARALLEL PLATE CAPACITOR

It was shown in Section 22.2 that for an air filled capacitor, the experiments show that
$$C = \frac{\epsilon_0 A}{d}$$

This may be derived quite easily as follows.
In Section 20.2.3 it was shown that
$$E = \frac{\sigma}{\epsilon_0}$$

$\qquad E = $ electric field strength
$\qquad \sigma = $ charge density

Now for a parallel plate capacitor the field is uniform and the numerical value is
$$E = \frac{V}{d}$$

$V = $ p.d. between 2 points, a distance d apart

(N.B. We do not need to use the minus sign — we would only include that if we were to perform a mathematical process such as integration.)

So $\qquad \dfrac{V}{d} = \dfrac{\sigma}{\epsilon_0}$

$\qquad V = \dfrac{\sigma d}{\epsilon_0}$

But $\qquad C = \dfrac{Q}{V}$

$\therefore \qquad C = \dfrac{Q}{\dfrac{\sigma d}{\epsilon_0}} = \dfrac{\epsilon_0 Q}{\sigma d}$

But $\qquad Q = \sigma A$
hence
$\qquad C = \dfrac{\epsilon_0 \sigma A}{\sigma d} = \dfrac{\epsilon_0 A}{d}$

$\therefore \qquad \underline{C = \dfrac{\epsilon_0 A}{d}}$

## 22.5  GROWTH AND DECAY OF CHARGE ON A CAPACITOR

22.5.1  The growth and decay of charge on a capacitor may be investigated using the circuit in Fig. 22.9 comprising a battery of e.m.f. V, a capacitor of capacitance C, a resistor of resistance R and a two way switch which may be used to include or exclude the battery from the circuit.

**FIG. 22.9**

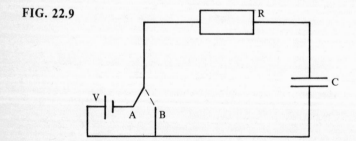

The switch is closed at A and the capacitor begins to charge
Then

$$V = IR + \dfrac{Q}{C}$$

where Q and I are the charge and current respectively

i.e.  E.M.F. = P.D. across resistor + P.D. across capacitor

Now
$$I = \frac{dQ}{dt}$$

Hence
$$V = \frac{RdQ}{dt} + \frac{Q}{C}$$

Re-arranging
$$\frac{dt}{RC} = \frac{dQ}{VC - Q}$$

Integrating, when at time t = 0, Q = 0 and where t = t, Q = $Q_t$

$$\int_0^t \frac{dt}{RC} = \int_0^{Q_t} \frac{dQ}{VC - Q}$$

$$\frac{t}{RC} = -[(\log_e (VC - Q_t) - \log_e VC]$$

$$= -\log_e \left( \frac{VC - Q_t}{VC} \right)$$

$$-\frac{t}{RC} = \log_e \left( \frac{VC - Q_t}{VC} \right)$$

Taking anti-logs
$$e^{-t/_{RC}} = \frac{VC - Q_t}{VC}$$

Re-arranging gives
$$Q_t = VC (1 - e^{-t/_{RC}})$$

Now     VC = final steady charge on capacitor = Q, say

$$\therefore \quad \underline{Q_t = Q (1 - e^{-t/_{RC}})}$$

Thus $Q_t$ the charge stored on the capacitor approaches its final steady value exponentially.


If now the fully charged capacitor is discharged by closing the switch at B, the discharge will follow the equation that was used for the charging process with V put equal to zero.

$$IR + \frac{Q}{C} = 0$$

$$\frac{dQ}{dt} R + \frac{Q}{C} = 0$$

$$Q = -CR\frac{dQ}{dt}$$

$$\frac{dt}{RC} = \frac{-dQ}{Q}$$

Integrating and using $Q = Q$ when $t = 0$, $Q = Q_t$ when $t = t$

$$\int_0^t \frac{dt}{RC} = - \int_Q^{Q_t} \frac{dQ}{Q}$$

$$\frac{t}{RC} = \log_e \frac{Q}{Q_t}$$

Taking anti-logs

$$e^{t/RC} = \frac{Q}{Q_t}$$

hence $$\underline{Q_t = Qe^{-t/RC}}$$

This is the equation of an exponential decay curve.

The form of the growth and decay graphs are shown in Fig. 22.10 and it will be seen that the charge reaches its final value asymptotically.

**FIG. 22.10**

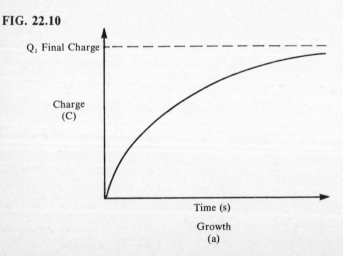

Growth
(a)

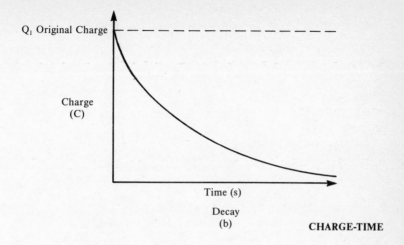

Q₁ Original Charge

Charge
(C)

Time (s)

Decay
(b)

**CHARGE-TIME**

22.5.2   Differentiation of the charging and discharging equations yield:

For charging

$$I = \frac{V}{R} e^{-t/RC}$$

But     $\frac{V}{R}$ =   Io, the initial current equal to that which would flow indefinitely if the capacitor were short circuited.

$$I = Io\, e^{-t/RC}$$

For discharging

$$I = -\frac{V}{R} e^{-t/RC}$$

$$I = -Io\, e^{-t/RC}$$

It may be seen that the rate of charging and discharging depends upon the product of the capacitance and resistance in the circuit.

## 22.6   THE TIME CONSTANT AND A COMPARISON WITH RADIOACTIVE DECAY

22.6.1   The time constant of a capacitor-resistance circuit is defined as the time taken for the charge to decay to $\frac{1}{e}$ of its original value. It is denoted by T, its unit being seconds.

Thus $$\frac{Q_t}{Q} = \frac{1}{e}$$

But the time taken for this is T

Hence $$\frac{Q_t}{Q} = e^{-T/_{RC}} = \frac{1}{e^{T/_{RC}}}$$

Therefore $$\frac{1}{e} = \frac{1}{e^{T/_{RC}}}$$

$$\frac{T}{RC} = 1$$

$$T = RC$$

The time constant is therefore equal to the product of the resistance and capacitance.

Since $e = 2.718$, the time constant really represents the time taken for the charge to fall to about 37% of its initial value.

22.6.2   Examination of the decay curve shown in Fig. 22.11 shows that it falls by the same fraction in successive equal time intervals. Hence, if it falls from Q to Q/2 in time $t_{\frac{1}{2}}$, it will then fall from Q/2 to Q/4 in the next time interval $t_{\frac{1}{2}}$ etc.

**FIG. 22.11**

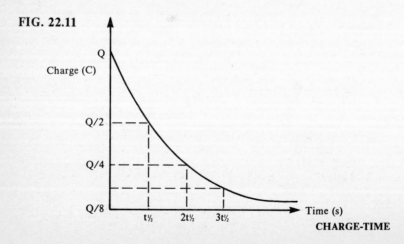

CHARGE-TIME

$t_{1/2}$ is therefore the time taken for the charge to fall by half and it is known as the half life of the decay process.

(This situation is a direct analogue of the half life of a radioactive decay process.)

Now, using the decay equation

$$Q_t = Q e^{-t/RC}$$

$$\frac{Q_t}{Q} = e^{-t/RC}$$

Now when $t = t_{1/2}$

$$\frac{Q_t}{Q} = \frac{1}{2}$$

$$\therefore \quad \frac{1}{2} = e^{-t_{1/2}/RC}$$

$$2 = e^{t_{1/2}/RC}$$

Taking logarithms

$$\log_e 2 = \frac{t_{1/2}}{RC}$$

$$t_{1/2} = \log_e 2 \; RC$$
$$= 0.693 \; RC$$

Hence $\quad t_{1/2} = 0.693 \; RC$

or $\quad t_{1/2} = 0.693 \; T$

---

**EXAMPLE**

A fully charged $500 \, \mu F$ capacitor is discharged through a $100k\,\Omega$ resistor. Calculate the time taken for the charge on the capacitor to fall to one quarter of its initial value.

The charge falls to one quarter in two half lives.

Now $\quad\quad\quad t_{1/2} = 0.693 \; RC$

Here $\quad\quad\quad R = 100k\,\Omega = 10^5\,\Omega$
$\quad\quad\quad\quad\quad C = 500 \, \mu F = 5 \times 10^{-4} \, F$

$\therefore \quad t_{1/2} = 0.693 \times 10^5 \times 5 \times 10^{-4}$
$\quad\quad\quad\quad = 50 \times 0.693$

thus $\quad 2t_{1/2} \quad = \quad 2 \times 50 \times 0.693$

$= \quad 69.3\text{s}.$

Time taken $= 69.3\text{s}.$

## 22.7 THE ENERGY OF A CHARGED CAPACITOR

Suppose a capacitor has a capacitance C and the charge on it is Q when the p.d. across its plates is V.

When the capacitor starts to discharge, charge flows from the negative to the positive plate. In doing so it reduces the p.d., causing the original motion. We therefore consider a charge dQ.

When such a charge flows, then the energy loss is

$$dE \quad = \quad VdQ$$

Now $\qquad C \quad = \quad \dfrac{Q}{V}$

$\therefore \quad V \quad = \quad \dfrac{Q}{C}$

$\therefore \quad dE \quad = \quad \dfrac{Q\,dQ}{C}$

Thus $\qquad \displaystyle\int_0^E dE \quad = \quad \dfrac{1}{C}\int_0^Q QdQ$

i.e. the energy falls from E to 0 whilst the charge falls from Q to 0.

$$E \quad = \quad \dfrac{1}{2}\dfrac{Q^2}{C}$$

and $\qquad Q^2 \quad = \quad C^2V^2$

$\therefore \quad E \quad = \quad \dfrac{1}{2}CV^2$

This, of course, is the energy stored in the capacitor.

$$\therefore \quad \text{Total Energy} = \tfrac{1}{2}CV^2$$

The energy is stored as electrical field energy in the field in the medium between the plates.

**EXAMPLE**

A 10 $\mu$F capacitor is charged from a 30V supply. Calculate the energy stored in the capacitor.

$$\text{Now} \qquad E \;=\; \tfrac{1}{2}\, CV^2$$

$$\text{Here} \qquad C \;=\; 10\,\mu F = 10^{-5}F$$
$$V \;=\; 30V$$

$$\therefore \quad E \;=\; \tfrac{1}{2} \times 10^{-5} \times 30^2$$
$$=\; 450 \times 10^{-5}$$
$$=\; 4.5\text{mJ}$$

$$\text{Stored energy} = 4.5\text{mJ}$$

## 22.8   USES OF CAPACITORS

Originally capacitors were used as charge storers, i.e. containers in which large amounts of charge could be stored at a given potential. While a body is charged, the maximum charge it can hold depends upon the dielectric, usually air, surrounding it. When the potential of the body becomes large, charge leaks away due to breakdown of the insulation offered by the dielectric — as in the case of lightening. More charge may be stored before the breakdown potential is reached if a capacitor is used. The original form of capacitor used for this purpose was known as a Leyden Jar.

In modern uses of capacitors we are concerned with their following two properties:

Firstly, their ability to discharge slowly which makes them ideal for use in smoothing circuits used in the rectification of a.c. supplies.

Secondly, it will be remembered that a capacitor does not allow the passage of a d.c. supply. It merely charges up until the p.d. across it equals the supply p.d. However, it will allow the passage of an a.c. supply as charges are alternately attracted then repelled from one plate to the other. Accordingly, capacitors are used to block out d.c. components of mixed a.c. and d.c. supplies. They are also used in a.c. timing circuits, used to tune television and radio receivers to particular signals.

## QUESTIONS

1) Calculate the charge on a $5 \mu F$ capacitor when the potential difference across its plates is 200V.

2) A parallel plate capacitor has a capacitance of $5 \mu F$ when air is between its plates and $30 \mu F$ when this space is filled with a porcelain sheet. Calculate the relative permittivity of porcelain.

3) Calculate the equivalent capacitance of two capacitors of $1 \mu F$ and $2 \mu F$ when they are connected in series and parallel.

4) A $10 \mu F$ capacitor has a stored energy of 1J. Calculate the p.d. across its plates.

5) A parallel plate capacitor consists of two fine layers of silver deposited on each side of a sheet of mica as dielectric. Each sheet, silver and mica, has an area of $2.4 \text{cm}^2$ and the capacitance of this capacitor is $1.2 \times 10^{-4} \mu F$. Calculate the thickness of the mica sheet ($\epsilon_0 = 8.9 \times 10^{-12} \text{Fm}^{-1}$, $\epsilon_r$ of mica $= 6$).

# Chapter 23
# MAGNETIC FIELDS

## 23.1 THE ORIGIN OF MAGNETIC FIELDS

Whenever electric charges move, they generate a magnetic field in the region surrounding them.

Hence, whenever an electric current flows in a wire, a magnetic field is generated. Because the field is generated by an electric current, it is known as an electromagnetic field.

However, electric charges — electrons — are also moving in their orbitals around nuclei in all materials and we can consider these electrons as internal currents. As a result certain substances, in which all these internal currents combine, have a magnetic field associated with them and are known as magnetic. Historically, magnetic substances were observed well before the discovery of electric currents and this branch of magnetism was known as magnetostatics. Electromagnetism, when it was discovered, was thought to be a completely separate phenomenon.

It is now recognised that all magnetic effects have their origins in the movement of charges and essentially, a magnetic field is merely a relativistic effect of an electric field, i.e. an electric field in motion.

A magnetic field is thus a region where a magnetic material or a current carrying conductor experiences a magnetic force.

## 23.2 MAGNETIC FLUX DENSITY AND THE FORCE ON A CURRENT CARRYING CONDUCTOR IN A MAGNETIC FIELD

The strength of a magnetic field is given in terms of its magnetic flux density, symbol B.

Suppose a current carrying conductor, in the form of a wire, is situated in a magnetic field. The field, due to the current in the conductor, will interact with the external field, resulting in a force which will act upon the wire.

Magnetic flux density is defined in terms of such a situation. If a wire of length $\ell$ carries a current I and is situated at right angles to a magnetic flux density B, then the force acting on it is given by F where

$$F = BI\ell$$

This force is perpendicular to the current and flux density directions.

In fact, F, B and I form a left-handed system as shown in Fig. 23.1 and their orientation is given by the thumb and first two fingers of the left hand, all arranged so as to be perpendicular.

**FIG. 23.1**

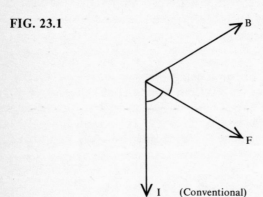

I    (Conventional)

The unit of flux density is the Tesla, symbol T.

The flux density of a field is 1T if a wire 1m long, carrying a current of 1A experiences a force of 1N when at right angles to the field. Since $F = BI\ell$, it may be seen that $1T = 1NA^{-1}m^{-1}$.

If the angle between B and I is $\Theta$ as shown in Fig. 23.2, then

$$F = BI\ell\sin\Theta$$

with F, B and $\ell\sin\Theta$ still being at right angles to each other.

**FIG. 23.2**

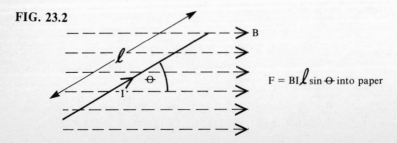

$F = BI\ell\sin\Theta$ into paper

A magnetic field may be represented by magnetic lines of force. The direction of such a line of force is the direction in which the north pole of a bar magnet would point when placed there. The stronger the field, the greater the number of lines of flux per unit area.

---

**EXAMPLE**

A wire of length 5cm, carrying a current of 15mA, lies at an angle of 30° to a uniform field of flux density 2.0T. Calculate the force acting on the wire.

$$\text{Use} \qquad F = BI\ell \sin \theta$$

$$B = 2.0\text{T}$$
$$I = 15\text{mA} = 1.5 \times 10^{-2}\text{A}$$
$$\ell = 5\text{cm} = 5 \times 10^{-2}\text{m}$$
$$\theta = 30°$$

$$F = 2.0 \times 1.5 \times 10^{-2} \times 5 \times 10^{-2} \times \sin 30$$
$$= 0.75 \times 10^{-3}\text{N}$$

$$\text{Force} = 0.75 \times 10^{-3}\text{N}$$

---

## 23.3 FORCE ON A CHARGED PARTICLE IN A MAGNETIC FIELD

We have seen that the force F on a conductor of length $\ell$ carrying a current I and situated at right angles to a magnetic field of flux density is given by

$$F = BI\ell$$

Imagine now that we consider replacing the current carrying conductor with a charge moving with a steady speed. Let the charge be q and its speed be v .

$$\text{Now} \qquad I = \frac{q}{t}$$

$$\text{and} \qquad v = \frac{\ell}{t}$$

hence

$$F = BI\ell = \frac{Bq\,vt}{t} = Bqv$$

$$\therefore \quad F = Bqv$$

In the case of a current carrying conductor, the action of this force is to cause the conductor to move if it is free to move or rotate. If it is not, then it will remain in the field.

However, no such constraint applies to a freely moving charge, since it is not moving in a body such as a wire. Thus the force acts on the charge directly and is at right angles to the direction of motion.

The effect of this force at right angles to the direction of motion is to cause the charge to follow a circular path. It may be compared with a body describing a circular path on a string where the force is always towards the centre of the circle and at right angles to the direction of travel of the body.

The motion of a charged particle is shown in Fig. 23.3.

**FIG. 23.3**

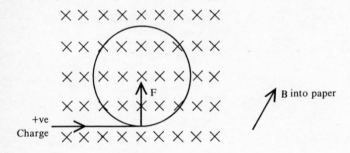

The radius of the circle may be calculated as follows:

The force acting on the charge is given by
$$F = Bqv$$

But for circular motion we have
$$F = \frac{mv^2}{r}$$

hence
$$\frac{mv^2}{r} = Bqv$$
$$r = \frac{mv}{Bq}$$

> **EXAMPLE**
> An electron is travelling in a circular path at right angles to a uniform magnetic field. Calculate its angular velocity if $B = 1.0 \times 10^{-3}$T, charge on electron $= 1.6 \times 10^{-19}$C, mass of electron $= 9.1 \times 10^{-31}$Kg.
>
> $$\text{Now} \qquad r \;=\; \frac{m\,v}{Bq}$$
>
> $$\therefore \quad v \;=\; \frac{Bqr}{m} \;=\; r\,\omega$$
>
> $$\therefore \quad \omega \;=\; \frac{Bq}{m}$$
>
> $$\text{Here} \quad B = 1.0 \times 10^{-3}\text{T}$$
>
> $$q \;=\; 1.6 \times 10^{-19}\text{C}$$
>
> $$m \;=\; 9.1 \times 10^{-31}\text{Kg}$$
>
> $$\therefore \quad \omega \;=\; \frac{1.0 \times 10^{-3} \times 1.6 \times 10^{-19}}{9.1 \times 10^{-31}}$$
>
> $$=\; 1.76 \times 10^{8} \text{ rad s}^{-1}$$
>
> $$\text{Angular velocity} \;=\; 1.76 \times 10^{8} \text{ rad s}^{-1}$$

## 23.4 MEASUREMENT OF THE SPECIFIC CHARGE OF THE ELECTRON

The specific charge of the electron is the ratio of its charge to its mass, denoted by $e/m$

One way of measuring this specific charge is to simultaneously deflect electrons by a magnetic and an electric field, using the apparatus shown in Fig. 23.4. The electrons are emitted by thermionic emission from a hot cathode and accelerated towards an anode from which they emerge in a parallel beam. They then enter the field region. An electric field is generated by applying a large voltage across two metal deflecting plates. A magnetic field is also generated in this region by two coils known as Helmholtz coils. These are two identical coils whose separation is equal to their radii. As a result a uniform magnetic field is set up. The path of the electrons is made visible by arranging that they strike a fluorescent screen between the deflection plates.

**FIG. 23.4**

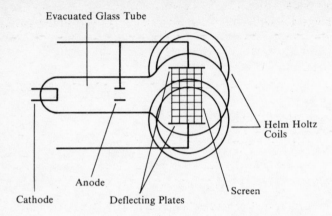

The apparatus is adjusted until the deflection caused by the electric field in one direction is exactly balanced by the deflection caused by the magnetic field in the opposite direction. When this occurs the electron beam will be undeviated.

The electric force $F_E$ caused by a field E acting on a charge e is given by

$$F_E = Ee$$

The magnetic force $F_B$ caused by a field B acting on a charge e travelling at a speed v is given by

$$F_B = Bev$$

When the beam is undeflected

$$F_E = F_B$$

i.e.
$$eE = Bev$$
$$v = \frac{E}{B}$$

Hence v may be calculated since both E and B are known because

$$E = \frac{Vp}{d}$$

$Vp =$ p.d. across deflecting plates

$d$ = plate separation — quoted by manufacturer

and
$$B = kI$$

$k$ = coil constant — quoted by manufacturer

$I$ = current through coils

Once this speed is known, e/m may be calculated from the value of the accelerating p.d., V, between cathode and anode. The kinetic energy gained by an electron accelerating through this p.d. is given by

$$\frac{1}{2} m v^2 = eV$$

$$\therefore \quad \frac{e}{m} = \frac{v^2}{2V}$$

Substituting for v we have

$$\frac{e}{m} = \frac{E^2}{2VB^2}$$

and all quantities on the right hand side of this equation are easily found.

The currently accepted value of e/m is $1.759 \times 10^{11}$ CKg$^{-1}$.

---

**EXAMPLE**

In an experiment to determine the specific charge of the electron, electrons were undeflected when the electric field strength was $8.0 \times 10^4$ Vm$^{-1}$ and the flux density was 1.9mT. If the p.d. across the anode to cathode was 5.0KV, calculate e/m

Use

$$\frac{e}{m} = \frac{E^2}{2VB^2}$$

$$E = 8.0 \times 10^4 \text{ Vm}^{-1}$$
$$B = 1.9\text{mT} = 1.9 \times 10^{-3}\text{T}$$
$$V = 5.0\text{KV} = 5.0 \times 10^{-3}\text{V}$$

$$\therefore \quad \frac{e}{m} = \frac{(8.0 \times 10^4)^2}{2 \times 5.0 \times 10^3 \times (1.9 \times 10^{-3})^2}$$

$$\frac{e}{m} = 1.77 \times 10^{11} \text{ CKg}^{-1}$$

---

## 23.5 COUPLE ON A RECTANGULAR COIL IN A MAGNETIC FIELD

Current carrying coils in magnetic fields are essential components of galvanometers.

Consider a rectangular coil of N turns pivoted that it can rotate about a vertical axis XY at right angles to a magnetic field of flux density B, as shown in Fig. 23.5(a). Let the angle between the normal to the coil plane and B be $\Theta$ as in Fig. 23.5(b).

**FIG. 23.5**

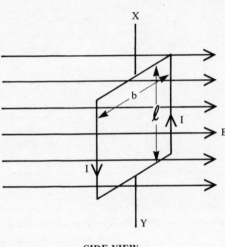

**SIDE VIEW**
(a)

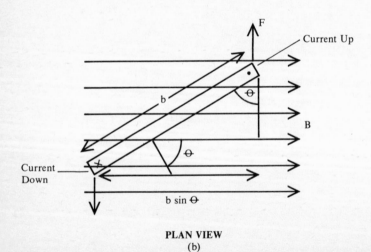

**PLAN VIEW**
(b)

When a current I flows in the coil, each side experiences a force. The forces on the top and bottom horizontal sides are parallel to XY and for the current direction here, they lengthen the coil.

The forces on the vertical limbs, each of length $\ell$ are equal and opposite and have a magnitude F given by

$$F = BI\ell N$$

The vertical sides of the coil are always at right angles to B and so F remains constant. The two forces F constitute a couple whose torque T is given by

$$
\begin{aligned}
\text{T} &= \text{one force x perpendicular distance between lines} \\
&\quad \text{of action of the forces} \\
&= \text{F x b } \sin\Theta \\
&= \text{BI}\ell\text{N x b } \sin\Theta \\
\text{But } \ell \text{ x b} &= \text{area of coil, A} \\
\therefore \quad \text{T} &= \text{BINA } \sin\Theta
\end{aligned}
$$

This torque causes the coil to experience an angular acceleration which rotates it until its plane is perpendicular to the field when sin $\Theta = 0$ at $T = 0$.

Now if the magnetic field is caused by a permanent magnet with both its north and south pole pieces being concave, then a radial field results. In such cases $\Theta = 90$ and sin $\Theta = 1$.

Hence

$$T = BINA$$

This is the principle of the moving coil galvanometer described in Section 23.6.

### 23.6   THE MOVING COIL GALVANOMETER

A moving coil galvanometer consists of a coil of fine insulated copper wire which is able to rotate in a strong magnetic field. The field is radial, being produced by two curved pole pieces. See Fig. 23.6.

The coil is pivoted on jewelled bearings and its rotation is resisted by hair springs arranged both above and below it. The current enters and leaves the coil through these springs. The fixed soft iron cylinder does not rotate — it is fixed to the magnet by an anchor, its purpose being to produce a larger radial field than would be the case if the space were merely filled by air.

**FIG. 23.6**

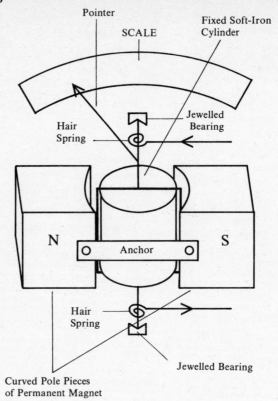

The deflecting torque is given by
$$T = BIAN \qquad \text{since the field is radial}$$
The coil rotates until the resisting torque, due to the hair springs,
$T_R$ is equal to T.

$T_R$ is given by

$$T_R = k\theta$$

k   =   torque needed to produce 1 radian twist
$\theta$   =   twist in radian

Thus, when the coil has stopped rotating
$$T = T_R$$

$$BIAN = k\Theta$$
$$\Theta = \frac{BIAN}{k}$$

B, A, N and k are constants for a particular meter and hence

$$\Theta \propto I$$

and the meter has a linear scale.

We define the current sensitivity of the meter as the deflection per unit current

$$\text{Current sensitivity} = \frac{\Theta}{I} = \frac{BAN}{k}$$

Current sensitivity may therefore be maximised by having
(i)   B as large as possible
(ii)  A as large as possible
(iii) N as large as possible
(iv)  k as small as possible

Often in any particular device, optimum values of these quantities have to be achieved. All quantities are restricted by the design limitations and the fact that an increase in one quantity affects another, e.g. if N is very large, the size of the iron cylinder will have to be decreased and this will lead to a decrease in B.

---

**EXAMPLE**

A rectangular coil 10cm x 2.0cm consisting of 100 turns is suspended vertically from the middle of a short side in a radial magnetic field of flux density $2.0 \times 10^{-2}$T. Calculate the deflecting torque on the suspension when a current of 0.25A flows through the coil.

Using $\quad T = BIAN$

$$B = 2.0 \times 10^{-2}\text{T}$$
$$I = 0.25\text{A}$$
$$A = 10^{-1} \times 2.0 \times 10^{-2} = 2.0 \times 10^{-3}\text{ m}^2$$
$$N = 100$$

$$\therefore \quad T = 2.0 \times 10^{-2} \times 0.25 \times 2.0 \times 10^{-3} \times 100$$
$$1.0 \times 10^{-3}\text{ Nm}$$

$$\therefore \quad \text{Deflecting torque} = 1.0 \times 10^{-3}\text{ Nm}$$

### 23.7 SOME MAGNETIC FIELD PATTERNS

The magnetic field patterns due to conductors of different shapes can be obtained using iron filings. The field direction due to a current may be obtained using the Right Hand Grip Rule: Clench the right hand into a fist and point the thumb "upwards". If the thumb points in the current direction, the fingers will point in the field direction. See Fig. 23.7.

**FIG. 23.7**

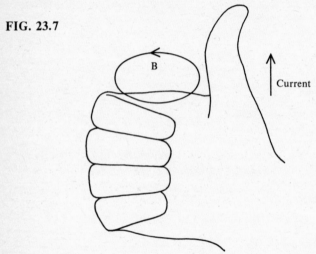

Current

The field pattern, due to a long straight wire, is shown in Fig. 23.8. It consists of a series of concentric circles centred upon the wire.

**FIG. 23.8**

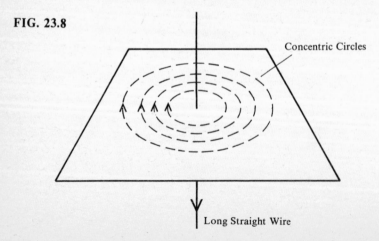

Concentric Circles

Long Straight Wire

The field pattern, due to a current in a plane circular coil, is shown in Fig. 23.9.

**FIG. 23.9**

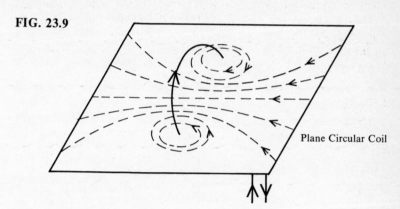

Plane Circular Coil

In Fig. 23.10 we see a long cylindrical coil known as a solenoid. The left hand end behaves like a north pole of a bar magnet with the right hand end behaving as a south pole. The diagram shows how the pole nature is related.to the current direction in the solenoid.

**FIG. 23.10**

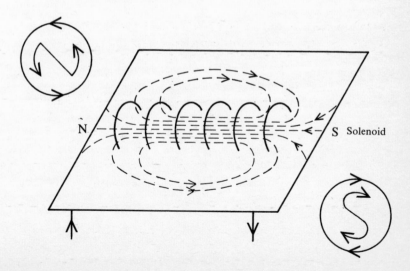

Solenoid

### 23.8 USE OF THE HALL EFFECT TO DETERMINE FLUX DENSITY

When a current carrying conductor is placed in a magnetic field, we find that a potential difference is developed between the sides of the conductor in a direction perpendicular to the field. This p.d. is known as the Hall voltage with the effect known as the Hall effect.

Suppose, in Fig. 23.11 a current I is passed through the slab of conductor between the edges A and B and a magnetic field B is applied at right angles to the faces of the slab. The Hall voltage will appear across faces C and D.

**FIG. 23.11**

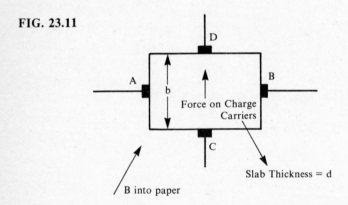

In accordance with the left hand rule, the magnetic field causes the charges in the conductor to drift sideways across the slab from C to D, creating the Hall voltage because of the charge accumulation at D. The direction of the force is always the same whether the charged particles are positive or negative (since a flow of positive charges from A to B is equivalent to a flow of negative charges from B to A). Thus the charges will build up on D and the sign of the p.d. may be used as a direct test of the sign of the charges which carry the current in any given material. If D becomes negative with respect to C, the charge carriers must be negative electrons, but if D becomes positive with respect to C then conduction is due to holes. In an intrinsic semi-conductor, since the number of electrons is equal to the number of holes, the net voltage is zero. However, in an n type semi-conductor a negative Hall voltage will be obtained whereas in a p type, a positive Hall voltage will occur.

The equation of the effect may be derived as follows

When the charge carriers accumulate on the slab they generate an electric field E where

$$E = \frac{V_H}{b}$$

$V_H$ = Hall voltage
b = slab width

The accumulation will cease when the force on the charge carriers due to this electric field exactly balances the force on them due to the magnetic field.

Now the electric force, $F_E$ is given by

$$F_E = qE$$

q = charge
E = electric field strength

The magnetic force, $F_B$ is given by

$$F_B = Bqv$$

B = flux density
v = speed of charge

Thus

$$qE = Bqv$$

∴

$$q\frac{V_H}{b} = Bqv$$

$$\frac{V_H}{b} = Bv$$

Now

$$v = \frac{I}{nAq}$$

(see Chapter 16)

where    n = no. of charge carriers per unit volume
A = cross sectional area through which current I passes

Hence

$$\frac{V_H}{b} = \frac{BI}{nAq} \qquad \left( \text{Hall Coefficient} = \frac{1}{nq} \right)$$

But A = bd

∴

$$\frac{V_H}{b} = \frac{BI}{nbdq}$$

$$V_H = \frac{BI}{nqd}$$

$V_H$ is therefore inversely proportional to the carrier concentration. This is large in a metal and thus $V_H$ is unobservable. However, n is less in an extrinsic semiconductor and the Hall voltage is detectable — although even here it is still small.

$$\text{Now} \qquad B = \frac{nqd\ V_H}{I}$$

Accordingly the Hall effect provides a simple and direct method for measuring flux density. If a constant current flows through a suitable slice of germanium, the Hall p.d. may be measured. The slice is mounted in the end of a rod through which the leads pass — an arrangement known as a Hall probe. In order to find the direction of the field, the probe is rotated until the Hall p.d. is a maximum at which point the direction of the field is then at right angles to the germanium slice.

---

**EXAMPLE**

Calculate the flux density at a point where the Hall voltage in a lightly doped slice of germanium is 0.16V. The germanium has a electron concentration of $1.0 \times 10^{20}$ m$^{-3}$, carries a current of 100mA and is 0.20mm thick. ($q = 1.6 \times 10^{-19}$C)

$$\text{Use} \qquad B = \frac{nqd\ V_H}{I}$$

Here

$$n = 1.0 \times 10^{20}\ \text{m}^{-3}$$
$$q = 1.6 \times 10^{-19}\text{C}$$
$$d = 0.20 \times 10^{-3}\text{m}$$
$$V_H = 0.16\text{V}$$
$$I = 100\text{mA} = 10^{-1}\text{A}$$

$$\therefore \quad B = \frac{1.0 \times 10^{20} \times 1.6 \times 10^{-19} \times 0.20 \times 10^{-3} \times 0.16}{10^{-1}}$$

$$= 5.12\text{mT}$$

$$\text{Flux density} = 5.12\text{mT}$$

---

## 23.9 SOME MAGNETIC FLUX DENSITIES

Magnetic flux densities may be investigated using a Hall probe.

The field B at a distance r from a long straight wire is given by

$$B = \frac{\mu_0 I}{2\pi r}$$

I = current flowing in wire

$\mu_0$ = permeability of free space = $1.26 \times 10^{-6} NA^{-2}$

The field B in a solenoid is given by

$$B = \frac{\mu_0 NI}{\ell}$$

$\mu_0$ = permeability of free space = $1.26 \times 10^{-6} NA^{-2}$

N = number of turns

I = current

$\ell$ = length of solenoid

Note: the ratio $N/\ell$ is known as the turns per metre. $\mu_0$ is sometimes given as $4\pi \times 10^{-7} NA^{-2}$ for better cancelling in calculation.

---

**EXAMPLE**

What current is flowing in a horizontal overhead cable running at 10m above ground level if it produces a magnetic flux density of $1.8 \times 10^{-5} T$ at ground level. ( $\mu_0 = 4\pi \times 10^{-7} NA^{-2}$ ).

Assuming that the cable behaves as a long wire

$$B = \frac{\mu_0 I}{2\pi r} \qquad \begin{array}{l} I = \text{current} \\ r = \text{distance from wire} \end{array}$$

$$\therefore \quad I = \frac{2\pi r B}{\mu_0}$$

Substituting

$$r = 10m$$
$$B = 1.8 \times 10^{-5} T$$

$$\therefore \quad I = \frac{2\pi \times 10 \times 1.8 \times 10^{-5}}{4\pi \times 10^{-7}}$$

$$= 900A$$

$$\therefore \quad \text{Current flowing} = 900A$$

---

### 23.10   $\mu_0$ AND THE DEFINITION OF THE AMPERE

The definition of the Ampere was considered in Chapter 1. It will now be shown how this leads to a value for $\mu_0$.

In the definition of the Ampere we consider two infinitely long wires, situated a given distance from each other and each carrying currents flowing in the same direction.

In Fig. 23.12, the magnetic field produced by the left hand conductor at the position of the right hand one is into the paper. The flux density of this field is given by

$$B = \frac{\mu_0 I_1}{2\pi r}$$

**FIG. 23.12**

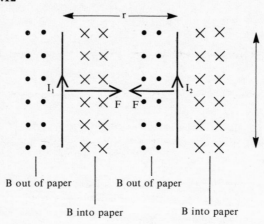

Thus the right hand conductor "sees" a field acting into the paper, generated by the left hand conductor. In accordance with the left hand rule, the force on the right hand conductor is to the left. The force on the right hand conductor is given by

$$F = BI_2\ell$$

$$\therefore \quad F = \frac{\mu_0 I_1 I_2 \ell}{2\pi r}$$

Now we may repeat this analysis to find the force on the left hand conductor. The left hand conductor sees the field due to the right conductor

$$B \quad = \quad \frac{\mu_0 I_2}{2\pi r}$$

acting out of the paper.

In accordance with the left hand rule, the force on the left hand conductor is to the right and is given by

$$F \quad = \quad BI_1 \ell$$

$$= \quad \frac{\mu_0 I_2 I_1 \ell}{2\pi r}$$

Thus the two conductors attract one another with a force

$$F \quad = \quad \frac{\mu_0 I_1 I_2 \ell}{2\pi r}$$

In the definition of the ampere we specify

$$\ell \quad = \quad 1m$$
$$r \quad = \quad 1m$$
$$I_1 \quad = \quad I_2 = 1A$$
$$F \quad = \quad 2 \times 10^{-7} N$$

Hence

$$\mu_0 \quad = \quad \frac{2\pi r F}{I_1 I_2 \ell}$$

$$= \quad \frac{2\pi \times 1 \times 2 \times 10^{-7}}{1 \times 1 \times 1}$$

$$= \quad 4\pi \times 10^{-7}$$

Units are

$$\frac{mN}{AAm} \quad = \quad NA^{-2}$$

Hence, $\mu_0 = 4\pi \times 10^{-7} NA^{-2}$

## 23.11 RELATIVE PERMEABILITY AND MAGNETIC SHIELDING

23.11.1  It has been seen that the flux density inside a solenoid is given by

$$B = \frac{\mu_0 NI}{\ell}$$

$N$ = no. of turns
$\ell$ = length
$I$ = current

B may be increased by filling the coil with magnetic material. Then

$$B = \frac{\mu_0 \mu_r NI}{\ell}$$

where $\mu_r$ is a constant known as the relative permeability of the material.

For a vacuum (or free space), $\mu_r = 1$ but in strong magnetic materials it can reach $10^5$.

Thus in an electromagnet, the coils are wound on a soft iron core. This increases the flux generated and also loses its magnetism when the current in the coils is switched off.

The phenomenon of magnetic shielding may be used to prevent a magnetic field from entering into a region.

If a soft iron ring is placed in a magnetic field, the field enters the iron but does not pass into the air space inside the ring. This occurs because the relative permeability of iron is so high that all the magnetism stays in the ring rather than pass into the air. The inside of the ring is, therefore, shielded from the field.

Magnetic shielding is put to important practical use. Delicate measuring instruments which are liable to be affected by external magnetic fields can be protected by enclosing them in thick walled soft iron boxes.

## QUESTIONS

1) Calculate the force exerted on a straight wire 2m long carrying a current of 0.5A situated at right angles to a magnetic field of $2 \times 10^{-5}$T.

2) Electrons moving with a speed of $3.287 \times 10^{7}$ ms$^{-1}$ enter a uniform magnetic flux of 0.010T at right angles to their motion. If the specific charge for the electron is $1.8 \times 10^{11}$C Kg$^{-1}$, calculate the radius of the electron orbit.

3) The coil of a galvanometer has 50 turns each of length 4cm and width 2cm. The coil hump with its length vertical and its plane inclined at 30° to a flux density of 0.5T. Calculate the couple acting on the coil when a current of 10mA flows through it.

4) Calculate the value of the Hall voltage produced by a flux density of 1T across a specimen of n type germanium 1mm thick carrying a current of 2.0A if the Hall coefficient for this germanium is $1.3 \times 10^{-5}$ C$^{-1}$.

# Chapter 24
# ELECTROMAGNETIC INDUCTION

### 24.1 THE PHENOMENON OF ELECTROMAGNETIC INDUCTION

24.1.1 Whenever a conductor cuts across the lines of force of a magnetic field, an electromotive force is induced in it.

Faraday demonstrated that this e.m.f. was proportional to
1) the strength of the magnetic field, B
2) the area of the field occupied by the conductor, A
3) the speed of the relative motion between the field and the conductor.

**FIG. 24.1**

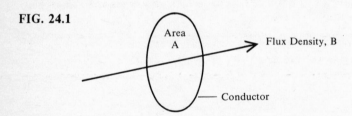

24.1.2 The first two factors are combined in the notion of magnetic flux. In Fig. 24.1, consider a conductor occupying an area A in a flux density, B. The magnetic flux, $\Phi$, through this area is defined as

$$\text{Flux} = \text{Flux density} \times \text{Area}$$
$$\Phi = BA$$

**FIG. 24.2**

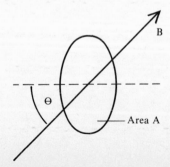

If the normal to the plane of the area, A, makes an angle $\Theta$ with the direction of the flux density, as in Fig. 24.2, then the magnetic flux through A is

$$\Phi = BA \cos\Theta$$

Now when B is in teslas and A is in m² then the unit of $\Phi$ is Weber, symbol Wb.

24.1.3  Faraday's conclusion may then be combined: the induced e.m.f. is proportional to the rate of change of magnetic flux through the circuit. Hence the e.m.f. E may be written as

$$E \; \alpha \; \frac{d\Phi}{dt}$$

The unit of flux density, the tesla was selected so that this may be written as an equation. Thus when $\Phi$ is in webers and t in seconds the e.m.f. will be in volts.

We also introduce a minus sign into the equation in order that the direction of the induced e.m.f. will be in agreement with Lenz's law: the direction of the induced e.m.f. will be such as to oppose the charge producing it.

$$\therefore \; E \; = \; -\frac{d\Phi}{dt}$$

The direction of the e.m.f. may be remembered by using the right hand rule. If the thumb and first two fingers of the right hand are held in mutually perpendicular directions, then the thumb gives the direction of motion, the first finger that of the flux and the second finger that of the induced e.m.f.

## 24.2  FLUX LINKAGE

If the conductor in the above experiment consists of a wire in the shape of a circle, we find

$$E \; = \; -\frac{d\Phi}{dt}$$

If we repeat the experiment with a circle containing N turns, i.e. we use a coil, we then find

$$E = -\frac{N\, d\Phi}{dt}$$

$$= -\frac{d\,(N\Phi)}{dt}$$

The product of $N\Phi$ is known as the flux linkage associated with coil and its units are Weber turns.

Thus, for a coil containing a number of turns

Induced E.M.F. = Rate of change of flux linkage

### 24.3 INDUCED E.M.F. AND CONSERVATION OF ENERGY

Lenz's law states that: the direction of the induced e.m.f. is such as to oppose the change producing it. This is in accordance with the principle of conservation of energy as may be seen in the following analysis.

Suppose a coil is connected to a sensitive galvanometer, as shown in Fig. 24.3. If now a magnet is plunged into the coil with its south pole facing the coil, the coil will be cut by a changing magnetic flux and consequently an e.m.f. will be induced. In a complete circuit a current will flow.

**FIG. 24.3**

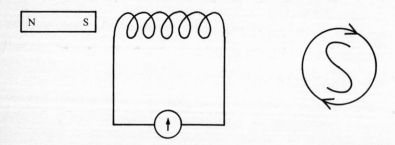

If the deflection is observed on the meter it will be found to correspond to a clockwise current flowing around the coil. Thus, the coil will have a south pole induced at its end nearest to the bar magnet. This induced south pole will oppose the motion of the magnet's south pole. Accordingly, work will have to be done in plunging the magnet into the coil. The mechanical work done is converted into electrical energy, i.e. the induced e.m.f.

When the magnet is withdrawn, the current direction changes and the end of the coil now becomes a north pole in order that it can oppose the withdrawal of the south pole of the magnet.

## 24.4 EXAMPLES OF INDUCED E.M.F.s

### 24.4.1 A WIRE MOVING PERPENDICULARLY TO A UNIFORM FLUX DENSITY

**FIG. 24.4**

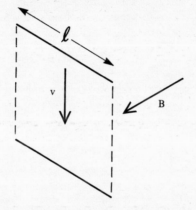

Consider Fig. 24.4 which shows a wire of length $\ell$ moving perpendicularly to a flux density, B, at a speed v.

The numerical value of the e.m.f. is given by

$$E = N \frac{d\Phi}{dt}$$

$$= NB \frac{dA}{dt}$$

Now in 1s, the wire travels a distance v. It sweeps out an area equal to v$\ell$. Thus every second an area given by v$\ell$ and consisting of 1 turn is swept out

$$N = 1 \qquad \frac{dA}{dt} = \ell$$

$$\therefore \quad E = B\ell v$$

## 24.4.2 A ROTATING COIL

Consider Fig. 24.5 which shows a coil having N turns, area A and being rotated about a horizontal axis in its own plane at right angles to a uniform flux density, B.

**FIG. 24.5**

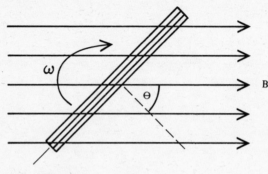

Coil, N Turns, area A

$$E \quad = \quad -N d\frac{\Phi}{dt}$$

If the coil makes an angle $\Theta$ with the field at time t then

$$\Theta = \omega t$$
$$\omega = \text{angular velocity}$$

Hence

$$\Phi = BA \cos \omega t$$

$$\therefore \quad E \quad = \quad -N\frac{d(BA \cos \omega t)}{dt}$$

$$= \quad -BAN\frac{d \cos \omega t}{dt}$$

$$E \quad = \quad BAN \, \omega \sin \omega t$$

This e.m.f. is an alternating one which varies sinusoidally with time and would cause an alternating current in a load connected across the coil.

When the plane of the coil is parallel to B, $\Theta = \omega t = 90°$, $\sin \omega t = 1$ and E has its maximum value, $E_0$, given by

$$E_0 = BAN\omega$$

Thus

$$E = E_0 \sin \omega t$$

It will be noted that the minus sign must be included in the original equation because of the subsequent calculus.

---

**EXAMPLES**

1) A straight wire of length 50cm moves sideways with a velocity of $15ms^{-1}$ at right angles to a uniform magnetic field of flux density $2.0 \times 10^{-3}T$. Calculate the size of the induced e.m.f.

   Use

   $$E = B\ell v$$
   
   $$B = 2.0 \times 10^{-3}T$$
   $$\ell = 50cm = 0.50m$$
   $$v = 15ms^{-1}$$

   $$\therefore \quad E = 2.0 \times 10^{-3} \times 0.50 \times 15$$
   $$= 15mV$$

   Induced e.m.f. $= 15mV$

2) Calculate the maximum induced e.m.f. when a coil of area $1.0 \times 10^{-2}m^2$ with 800 turns rotates at 600 revolutions per minute in a uniform flux density of $5.0 \times 10^{-2}T$.

   Use

   $$E_0 = BAN\omega$$
   $$B = 5.0 \times 10^{-2}T$$
   $$A = 1.0 \times 10^{-2}M^2$$
   $$N = 800$$

   600 revs/minute $= 10$ revs/sec
   $$\therefore \quad \omega = 20\pi \text{ rad s}^{-1}$$

   $$\therefore \quad E = 5.0 \times 10^{-2} \times 1.0 \times 10^{-2} \times 800 \times 20\pi$$
   $$= 25V$$

   Maximum induced e.m.f. $= 25V$

## 24.5 SELF INDUCTION

24.5.1   The flux due to a current in a coil links the coil itself. If the current changes, then also does the flux and this induces an e.m.f. in the coil itself. This effect is known as self-induction and the coil is said to have a self-inductance or more simply, an inductance. As usual, the direction of the e.m.f. is such as to oppose the change producing it. It is known as a back e.m.f.

The self-inductance of a coil, symbol L, is defined in terms of the back e.m.f. as follows:

$$E \quad = \quad -L\frac{dI}{dt}$$

i.e. Back e.m.f. = – Self Inductance x Rate of change of current

The unit of self-inductance is the Henry; symbol H.

A coil has a self-inductance of 1H when a back e.m.f. of 1V results from a rate of change of current of $1As^{-1}$.
Thus $1H = 1VsA^{-1}$

The self-inductance of a coil may also be related to the flux as follows

$$E \quad = \quad -L\frac{dI}{dt}$$

But
$$E \quad = \quad -\frac{d(N\Phi)}{dt}$$

$$\therefore \quad \int_0^I LdI \quad = \quad \int_0^\Phi Nd\Phi$$

Since $\Phi = 0$ when $I = 0$ and $\Phi = \Phi$ when $I = I$ the limits are as above.

$$\therefore \quad N\Phi \quad = \quad Li$$

$$\therefore \quad L \quad = \quad \frac{N\Phi}{i}$$

As $\Phi$ always depends upon the geometry of a particular coil, then so does L.

24.5.2   A coil will inevitably have both resistance and inductance. We may think of it as though it consisted of a pure inductance in series with a pure resistance as shown in Fig. 24.6. It must be remembered that these properties are physically inseparable and our approach is a mere model.

**FIG. 24.6**

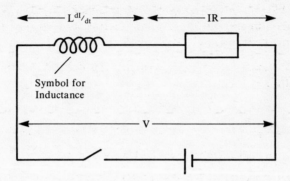

Symbol for
Inductance

If the current in such a coil is to be I and this is to grow at a rate of dI/dt, the applied p.d. must be made up of two components:

1)  A p.d. equal in size but opposing the induced e.m.f. which is needed to maintain the growth of current in the inductance.
    This equals $\quad\quad \dfrac{L\,dI}{dt}$

2)  A p.d. is also required to maintain the current in the resistance.
    This equals $\quad\quad IR$

The total p.d., V, across the inductive coil is, therefore, given by
$$V \;=\; \frac{L\,dI}{dt} \;+\; IR$$

When the current has reached its final steady value, dI/dt equals zero and the first term on the right of the equation, therefore, vanishes

$$\therefore \quad V_{FINAL} \;=\; IR$$

When the current is switched on, I = 0. The growth of current is controlled entirely by the inductance of the coil and

$$\therefore \quad V_{INITIAL} \;=\; \frac{L\,dI}{dt}$$

Thus, at the moment of switching on, the induced e.m.f. in the coil is exactly equal to the applied p.d. and this enables the current to grow.

In fact, if the equation for total p.d. is re-arranged, we obtain

$$\frac{L}{R}\frac{dI}{dt} = \frac{V - I}{R}$$

This equation indicates that the current grows exponentially in an inductor until it reaches its final value, V/R, as shown in Fig. 24.7.

**FIG. 24.7**

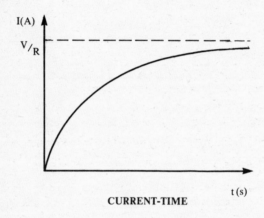

**CURRENT-TIME**

In a similar way to a capacitor, we may define a time constant of the combination defined as the time taken for the current to grow to $1/e$ of its final value. It may be shown that the time constant is given by $L/R$.

In order to circumvent self-induction phenomenon in coils, most of them are non-inductively wound. The wires used are doubled back upon themselves, resulting in a cancellation of magnetic flux, hence eliminating self-induction.

**EXAMPLE**

A coil of inductance 0.10H and resistance 4.0Ω is connected to a 12V battery of negligible resistance. Calculate the initial rate of growth of current and the final steady current in the coil.

$$\text{Now} \qquad \frac{dI}{dt} \quad = \quad \frac{V}{I}$$

$$= \quad \frac{12}{0.10} \quad = \quad \underline{120As^{-1}}$$

$$\text{The final current I} \quad = \quad \frac{V}{R}$$

$$= \quad \frac{12}{4.0} \quad = \quad \underline{3.0A}$$

Initial rate of growth $= 120As^{-1}$
Final steady current $= 3.0A$

## 24.6   MUTUAL INDUCTION

Suppose we have the circuit shown in Fig. 24.8. The "primary" circuit contains a cell and a coil together with a variable resistor and a switch. The "secondary" circuit contains a coil and a galvanometer. Normally the coils are linked together, usually by being wound on the same former. If the current in the primary is changed, then a changing magnetic flux cuts the secondary circuit and gives rise to a current in this secondary circuit as evidenced by a deflection on the galvanometer.

**FIG. 24.8**

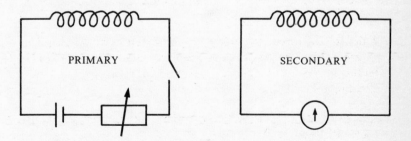

This is the principle of the transformer and arises because of the phenomenon of mutual induction.

The mutual inductance of the arrangement, symbol M, is defined in terms of the e.m.f. induced in the secondary in terms of the rate of change of current in the primary.

Hence

$$E_s = - M \frac{d I_p}{dt}$$

Subscripts s and p denote secondary and primary

But

$$E_s = - \frac{d(N\Phi_s)}{dt}$$

$$\therefore \int_0^{I_p} M \, dI_p = \int_0^{\Phi_s} N \, d\Phi_s$$

$$\therefore M I_p = N \Phi_s$$

$$\therefore M = \frac{N \Phi_s}{I_p}$$

As $\Phi_s$ depends upon the geometry of the arrangements, then so does M.

It can be shown that the mutual inductance of two coils is the same if current flows in the secondary and the flux links the primary, causing an induced e.m.f. in the primary.

i.e. $M I_s = N \Phi_p$

M has the same units as L, Henrys. Two coils are said to have a mutual inductance of 1H if an e.m.f. of 1V is induced in the secondary when the current in the primary changes at the rate of $1As^{-1}$.

## 24.7 ALTERNATIVE UNITS OF $\mu_0$

It has been seen that the units of $\mu_0$ are $Fm^{-1}$. We may now see that it is possible to use alternative units.

A mathematical analysis shows that for a solenoid

$$L = \frac{\mu_0 A N^2}{\ell}$$

A = area, $\ell$ = length, N = no. of turns

Now, substituting units into the re-arranged equation

$$\mu_0 = \frac{L \ell}{A N^2}$$

$$= \frac{H \, m}{m_2} = H \, m^{-1}$$

Thus, the alternative units are Henrys per metre, $H m^{-1}$.

## 24.8   THE TRANSFORMER

A transformer changes an alternating p.d. from one value to another, larger or smaller, using the principle of mutual induction.

Two coils called the secondary and primary are wound on a soft iron core, as in Fig. 24.9. When an alternating p.d. is applied to the primary, a large alternating flux links the secondary and induces an e.m.f. in it. A step up transformer has more turns on the secondary and increases the primary voltage. A step down has more turns on the primary and decreases the primary voltage.

**FIG. 24.9**

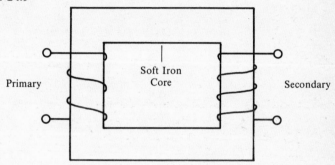

Consider an ideal transformer in which the primary has negligible resistance and all the flux in the core links both primary and secondary.

Suppose that the flux in the core is $\Phi$ at turn t.

If a p.d. $V_p$ is applied to the primary, then the back e.m.f. $E_p$ induced in the primary of $N_p$ turns, due to its self inductance, is given by

$$E_p \;=\; \frac{dN_p\Phi}{dt} \;=\; N_p\frac{d\Phi}{dt}$$

The primary coil has zero resistance and hence

$$V_p \;=\; E_p \;=\; N_p\frac{d\Phi}{dt}$$

The e.m.f. $E_s$ induced in the secondary, of $N_s$ turns, by the same flux in the core is given by

$$E_s \;=\; \frac{d\,N_s\Phi}{dt} \;=\; N_s\frac{d\Phi}{dt}$$

If the current taken from the secondary is small, then

$$V_s = E_s$$

and hence

$$V_s = N_s \frac{d\Phi}{dt}$$

Therefore

$$\frac{V_p}{V_s} = \frac{N_p}{N_s}$$

Note the assumptions made:
(i) resistance of primary coil is small
(ii) secondary current is small
(iii) no flux escapes from the core.

Additionally, if there are no energy losses in the transformer

$$\text{Power input} = \text{Power output}$$

i.e.

$$I_p V_p = I_s V_s \qquad \begin{array}{l} I_p = \text{primary current} \\ I_s = \text{secondary current} \end{array}$$

$$\therefore \quad \frac{V_p}{V_s} = \frac{I_s}{I_p}$$

Thus, if the voltage is stepped up, the current is stepped down.

In practice, some of the energy is converted into internal energy in the transformer. This happens in the coils and core.

---

**EXAMPLE**
A resistance of $3\Omega$ is connected to the secondary coil of a transformer. Calculate the current flowing through the resistance if the primary voltage is 240V and the secondary and primary turns are 60 and 1200.

Now

$$\frac{V_s}{V_p} = \frac{N_s}{N_p}$$

Here

$$V_p = 240V$$
$$N_s = 60$$
$$N_p = 1200$$

$$\therefore \quad V_s = \frac{V_p N_s}{N_p}$$

$$= 240 \times \frac{60}{1200}$$

$$= \quad 12V$$

Now $\quad V_s = I_sR$

$$I_s \quad = \quad \frac{V_s}{R}$$

$$= \quad \frac{12}{3} \quad = \quad 4A$$

Current $= 4A$

## 24.9 THE D.C. GENERATOR

A generator or dynamo produces electrical energy by electromagnetic induction. Fundamentally, it consists of a coil which is rotated between the poles of a magnet so that the flux linkage changes.

It has been shown in Section 24.4 that the induced e.m.f., E, is given by

$$E = BAN\omega \sin \omega t$$

E is zero when the plane of the coil is perpendicular to the flux direction and is a maximum when the plane of the coil is parallel to the flux.

In an a.c. generator or alternator this alternating e.m.f. is taken off the coil by means of two spring loaded graphite blocks called brushes which press against two copper slip-rings.

However, in a d.c. generator, a commutator is used instead of slip-rings, as shown in Fig. 24.10. This consists of a split ring of copper with the two halves insulated from each other and joined to the ends of the coil. The brushes are arranged so that the change-over of contact from one split ring to the other occurs when the coil is vertical. In this position the e.m.f. induced in the coil reverses and as a result one brush is always positive and one negative. Accordingly, the e.m.f. is undirectional and produces d.c. in an external circuit. The output is shown in Fig. 24.11.

**FIG. 24.10**

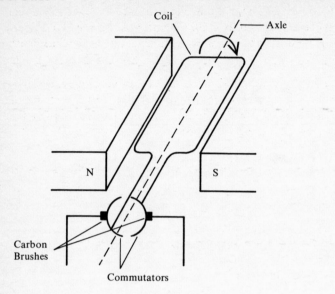

**FIG. 24.11**

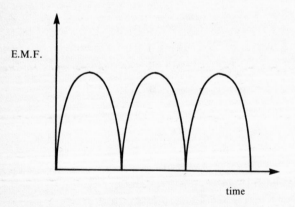

E.M.F. — Time

When a d.c. generator works in reverse and instead of supplying movement and obtained a d.c. voltage, we supply a d.c. voltage in order to obtain movement, we have a d.c. motor.

## QUESTIONS

1) Calculate the maximum e.m.f. induced in a circular coil of 100 turns of radius 0.10m rotating at an angular velocity of $100\pi$ rad s$^{-1}$ about a diameter at right angles to a flux density of 0.20T.

2) A coil having a resistance of $2\Omega$ and an inductance of 5H is connected in a circuit with a 10V battery of negligible resistance. When the circuit is completed, find the maximum current and the greatest rate of change of current.

# Chapter 25
# ALTERNATING CURRENTS

## 25.1 PEAK VALUES

In a direct current (d.c.) the drift velocity superimposed on the random motion of the charge carriers is in one direction only. However, in an alternating current (a.c.) the direction of the drift velocity repeatedly reverses.

The effects of a.c. are essentially those of d.c. but its great advantage is that it can be transformed.

An alternating current or e.m.f. varies periodically with time, both in magnitude and direction. One complete alternation is called a cycle and the number of cycles occurring in one second is termed the frequency of the supply, in $H_z$. In the U.K. this frequency is $50H_z$.

The simplest a.c. e.m.f. can be represented by
$$E = E_0 \sin \omega t$$
This is a sin wave of amplitude $E_0$. $E_0$, the maximum voltage is known as the peak voltage. $\omega = 2\pi \times$ frequency, i.e. $\omega = 2\pi f$.

The simplest a.c. current is similarly represented by
$$I = I_0 \sin \omega t$$
$I_0$ is the peak current.

## 25.2 ROOT MEAN SQUARE VALUES

The average value of an alternating current (and e.m.f.) is zero. However, it is found that an a.c. current has a heating effect just as does a d.c. current. Indeed, we find that the heating effect of an a.c. supply is identical to that of the d.c. supply if we measure the a.c. supply in terms of its root mean square (or R.M.S.) value.

Thus, the heat energy conveyed by a d.c. current I flowing in a resistor R is given by IR.

Now if the d.c. current is replaced by an a.c. supply then heat energy $= I_{RMS}R$

$I_{RMS}$ is the square root of the mean value of the squares of the current.

Now $I = I_0 \sin \omega t$

$\therefore$ $I_{RMS}$ $=$ $\sqrt{\text{mean value of } I^2}$

$=$ $\sqrt{\text{mean value of } I_0{}^2 \sin^2 \omega t}$

$=$ $I_0$ $\sqrt{\text{mean value of } \sin^2 \omega t}$

By plotting a graph of $\sin^2 \omega t$ versus t we find that the average value of $\sin^2 \omega t$ is $\frac{1}{2}$

$\therefore$ $I_{RMS}$ $=$ $I_0$ $\sqrt{\frac{1}{2}}$

$I_{RMS}$ $=$ $\dfrac{I_0}{\sqrt{2}}$ $=$ $0.707\, I_0$

Similarly

$V_{RMS}$ $=$ $\dfrac{V_0}{\sqrt{2}}$ $=$ $0.707\, V_0$

---

**EXAMPLE**

Calculate the peak value of the U.K. domestic mains of R.M.S. value 240V.

Now $V_0 = \sqrt{2}\ V_{RMS}$

$V_{RMS}$ $=$ $240V$

$\therefore$ $V_0$ $=$ $\sqrt{2} \times 240$

$=$ $339V$

$\therefore$ Peak value of voltage $= 339V$

---

## 25.3 POWER IN A.C. CIRCUITS

The general expression for the power absorbed by a device at any instant is VI where V and I are the instantaneous values of the current through it and the p.d. across it.

For an a.c. supply

$V$ $=$ $V_0 \sin \omega t$

$I$ $=$ $I_0 \sin \omega t$

Hence

Instantaneous power, $P = I_0 V_0 \sin^2 \omega t$

The mean power, $\overline{P}$, is given by the mean value of $I_0V_0 \sin^2 \omega t$. It has already been shown that the mean value of $\sin^2 \omega t$ is $\frac{1}{2}$

Hence

$$\overline{P} = \frac{I_0V_0}{2}$$

Using the relationships between peak and R.M.S. values, we may write

$$\overline{P} = I_{RMS} \times V_{RMS}$$

Now for a resistor $\qquad V_{RMS} = I_{RMS} \times R$

$$\therefore \quad \overline{P} = I_{RMS}^2 \times R = \frac{V^2_{RMS}}{R}$$

It will be seen that these are analogous to the d.c. expressions with steady d.c. values replaced by their R.M.S. equivalents.

A full mathematical analysis shows that no power is absorbed by capacitors or inductors when a.c. current flows through them.

---

**EXAMPLE**
The R.M.S. voltage across a resistor carrying an R.M.S. current of 4.7A is 19V. Calculate the mean power dissipated and calculate the value of the resistance in ohms.

$$
\begin{aligned}
\text{Now} \qquad \overline{P} &= I_{RMS} \times V_{RMS} \\
&= 4.7 \times 19 \\
&= 89W
\end{aligned}
$$

$$
\begin{aligned}
\text{Also} \qquad R &= \frac{V_{RMS}}{I_{RM}} \\
&= \frac{19}{4.7} \\
&= 4\,\Omega
\end{aligned}
$$

Mean power = 89W, Resistance = $4\,\Omega$

## 25.4  RECTIFICATION

25.4.1  In order to convert a.c. to d.c., a process known as rectification must be performed. This is achieved by means of a semiconducting device known as a junction diode.

A junction diode is a layer of p type semiconductor joined, crystallographically, to a layer of n type material.

When the layers are joined, some electrons from the n type material will diffuse across the junction. Simultaneously, some holes from the p type region will diffuse in the opposite direction, to the n type material. Recombination of electrons and holes produces a narrow layer, known as a depletion layer, in which no free carriers remain. However, the layer still contains the fixed positive ions left behind on the n side and the fixed negative ions left behind on the p side. Thus, an electric field is created leaving the n type material at a positive potential with respect to the p type. Diffusion across the junction will only continue until the field inhibits further movement. The situation is shown in Fig. 25.1.

**FIG. 25.1**

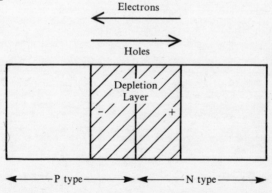

If now a small external voltage is applied so that A is positive with respect to B, charges will gain sufficient energy to flow across the junction with electrons moving towards A and holes towards B. Thus a current is created and maintained by the battery providing the voltage.

Now since the direction of hole movement is opposite to that of electron movement we obviously have a net conventional current flow in the direction of positive to negative potential.

Consider what will now happen if the polarity of the external voltage were to be reversed. Instead of electrons and holes being urged across the junction they will be prevented from doing so. There will, however, be a minute charge flow across the junction. This is due to minority carrier movement. In the n type material these are holes whereas in the p type, they are electrons and the external voltage will be in the correct direction to drive these across the junction.

Effectively the device only conducts one way when the p type material is at a positive potential with respect to the n type material. Such a situation is known as forward bias. When the polarity of the voltage is reversed, a situation known as reverse bias, negligible conduction occurs.

This fact may be remembered because current only flows effectively if an external voltage is applied

negative to n side

positive to p side

as shown in Fig. 25.2.

**FIG. 25.2**

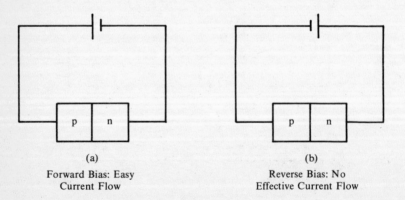

(a)

Forward Bias: Easy
Current Flow

(b)

Reverse Bias: No
Effective Current Flow

The characteristic curve of current against voltage for such a device has already been shown (see Fig. 13.6.)

The circuit symbol for a junction diode is shown in Fig. 25.3. The arrow points in the direction of easy conventional current flow. Thus, as marked in this diagram, the arrow points from + to – potential.

**FIG. 25.3**

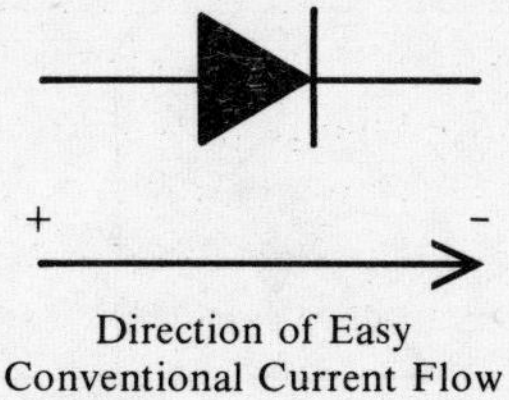

+                                    –
→

Direction of Easy
Conventional Current Flow

25.4.2  If an alternating potential difference is applied across a diode it will conduct current only during those alternate half-cycles when it is forward biased. This is known as half-wave rectification and is shown in Fig. 25.4.

**FIG. 25.4**

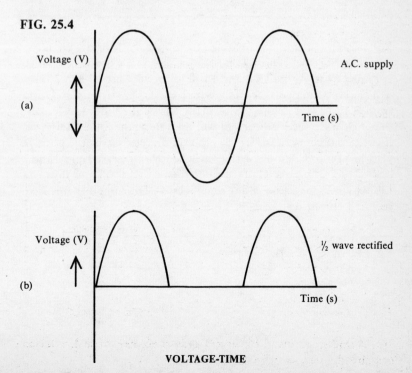

**VOLTAGE-TIME**

**FIG. 25.5**

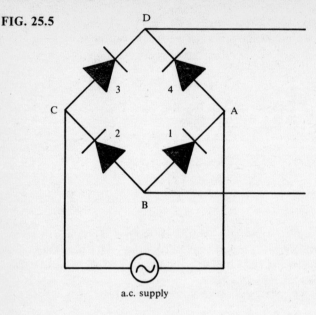

a.c. supply

Full wave rectification is obtained by using a diode bridge circuit as shown in Fig. 25.5. During that half of the cycle when C is positive with respect to A, diodes 3 and 1 will be forward biased and 2 and 4 will be reverse biased. Accordingly, current can pass from C to D and from B to A. If a connection is made across the output terminals, then half wave rectified current will flow along the route CDBA via the external connection. In the other half cycle, when A is positive with respect to C, diodes 2 and 4 will be forward biased and 3 and 1 will be reverse biased. Half wave rectified current will now flow, via the external connection, along route ADBC. The combined full wave rectified output will be as in Fig. 25.6.

**FIG. 25.6**

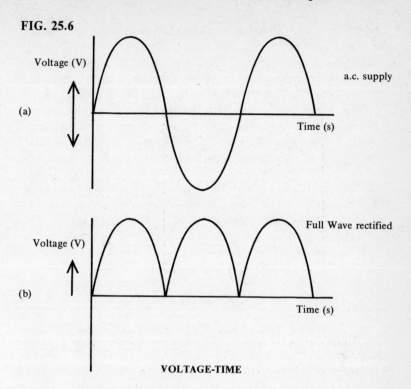

Voltage (V)

a.c. supply

(a)

Time (s)

Full Wave rectified

Voltage (V)

(b)

Time (s)

**VOLTAGE-TIME**

25.4.3   We often require a smooth full wave output rather than the one already shown in Fig. 25.6.

In order to achieve such smoothing, we connect a capacitor across the output, in parallel with the load, as in Fig. 25.7.

**FIG. 25.7**

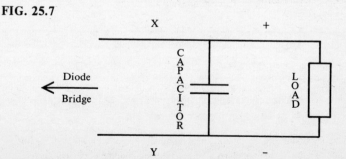

X              +

Diode

Bridge

CAPACITOR

LOAD

Y              −

The action of the capacitor may be understood as follows. During the first quarter cycle the voltage across the capacitor and load will build up to the peak voltage, $V_P$. Current will flow along X through the load and then through Y, with X being at a positive potential with respect to Y. Simultaneously the capacitor will charge up to $V_P$, the top plate being positively charged. During the next quarter cycle, the p.d. applied across the capacitor and load begins to fall. As a result, the capacitor now begins to discharge. It cannot do so by current flowing back along the bridge, entering at D, because both diodes 3 and 4 would be reverse biased by such an action. Accordingly, the current flows from one plate of the capacitor to the other via the load. Since the capacitor discharges exponentially it will cause the voltage across the load to fall exponentially. This discharge will continue until that point in the next quarter cycle when the voltage across the diode bridge exceeds the voltage across the capacitor. At this point the capacitor will stop discharging and the voltage across the capacitor and load will increase once again until they reach the peak value. The process will then be repeated. The resultant is a smoother voltage which contains a small ripple as shown in Fig. 25.8. The amount of the ripple may be simply adjusted by arranging that the time constant of the RC circuit is suitably long.

**FIG. 25.8**

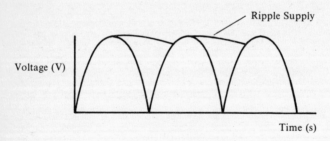

VOLTAGE-TIME

## QUESTIONS

1) The American electricity supply is 115V, 60H$_z$. Calculate the peak value of this supply and its period.

2) In the above example, calculate the mean power absorbed when the voltage is applied to the ends of a resistor of 200 $\Omega$.

# Chapter 26
# ELECTRONICS

## 26.1 THE NATURE OF ELECTRONICS

Electronics is that branch of physics which is concerned with the amplification of very small voltages.

The original devices used for such amplification were known as triodes and depended for their operation on the effect of thermionic emission. With the introduction of semi-conductors, devices known as transistors replaced triodes. A transistor is essentially a thin layer of p type semiconductor sandwiched between two much thicker layers of n type. Continuing advances in semi-conductor technology have led to the development of transistors, capacitors and resistors together in an integrated circuit. Such a device is called an operational amplifier. We treat this device as a "black box" and rather than investigate what it contains, we observe what we get out whenever we put in certain quantities.

## 26.2 THE OPERATIONAL AMPLIFIER

The operational amplifier (OP AMP) is an amplifier with a very large voltage amplification or gain, particularly at low frequencies. It has a very high input resistance, typically $> 10^{12}\ \Omega$ so that there is always negligible current through its input terminals.

The op. amp is so-called because it can perform electronically the mathematical operations of addition, multiplication (and their inverses), differentiation, integration and comparison. These operations form the basis of analogue computing and it was originally designed for this purpose.

The symbol for the op. amp is shown in Fig. 26.1(a). There are two separate inputs — the inverting input (marked –) and the non-inverting input (marked +). There is one output. Additionally, there are as shown in Fig. 26.1(b), two connections for the necessary power supply — one positive and one negative terminal. There are also two balance terminals known as offset nulls which are to allow for adjustment so that there is no output when there is no input. In general, whenever we represent an op. amp in a circuit diagram, we only indicate the two inputs and the output.

**FIG. 26.1**

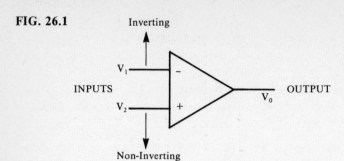

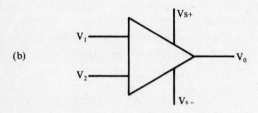

(b)

The device is a difference amplifier in that it amplifies the difference between the input terminals such that

$$V_0 = A_0 (V_2 - V_1)$$
where $A_0$ is the open loop gain

If a positive voltage $V_1$ is applied to the inverting input and the non-inverting input earthed, an amplified negative voltage $-A_0V_1$ is produced between the output terminal and 0V. If a negative voltage $-V$ the output will be $A_0V_1$. Similarly, a positive voltage $V_2$ applied to the non-inverting input and the inverting input earthed gives an amplified positive voltage $A_0V_2$ and if the applied voltage is negative $-V_2$ then the output is $-A_0V_2$.

The transfer characteristics show the relationship between the input and the output voltages. These are shown for both inverting and non-inverting inputs in Fig. 26.2. It can be seen that the device is only linear over a very small range, i.e. the output is proportional to the input for only a very small input range. Outside this range of input, the output does not change and is approximately equal to the

**FIG. 26.2**

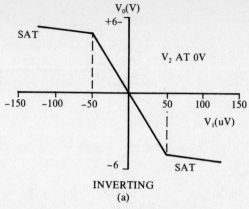

INVERTING
(a)

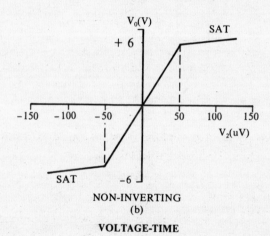

NON-INVERTING
(b)

**VOLTAGE-TIME**

positive or negative supply voltage. In this condition the op-amp is said to be saturated.

## 26.3  NEGATIVE FEEDBACK

Because the open loop gain is so great, as can be seen from the transfer characteristics, only very tiny input voltages may be used if the device is to behave linearly. In practice, this is often not possible. Instead we employ negative feedback, in which we sacrifice some of the open loop gain, $A_0$, in order to achieve greater linearity of response.

**FIG. 26.3**

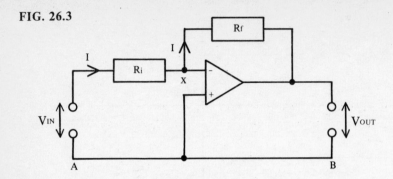

We arrange that some of the amplifier output is fed back into the inverting input. This feedback will be out of phase with the input and will partly cancel it out. Hence the term negative feedback.

The effect of negative feedback is to make the op. amp. less dependent upon its own properties and instead dependent upon the value of the resistances used in the feedback network. Because the response of a resistor is linear, the response of the whole operational amplifier becomes linear too and the gain, now denoted A, becomes precisely predictable.

Consider the circuit shown in Fig. 26.3. The output is connected to the inverting input through the feedback resistor, $R_F$. Another resistor, $R_i$ is joined in series with the input.

The potential at X only varies by a minute amount from zero because as already stated, only minute voltages are applied to the device.

Thus, with reference to the common potential, along AB,
$$V_{IN} = \text{p.d. across } R_i$$
Also the feedback resistor is joined between the output terminal and X.

Thus, with reference to the common potential
$$V_{OUT} = \text{p.d. across } R_F$$

Now only a minute amount of current enters the op. amp. through the inverting input because of its high input resistance. Thus, the same effective current, I, flows through the resistors $R_I$ and $R_F$.

Hence
$$V_{IN} = IR_i$$
$$V_{OUT} = IR_F$$

$$\therefore \text{Gain, } A = \frac{V_{OUT}}{V_{IN}} = \frac{R_F}{R_i}$$

It must be remembered that the output is in anti-phase with the input because the inverting input has been used. We, therefore, use a minus sign

Hence
$$A = -\frac{R_F}{R_i}$$

This equation is completely independent of the characteristics of the amplifier — it depends upon external resistors. If these are ohmic resistors made of identical metals then their ratio will be completely independent of temperature variations, providing of course, that both resistors undergo identical temperature changes.

Because A does not depend upon the characteristics of the device, it must not be thought that the device itself is unnecessary! The equation derived hinges upon the fact that negligible current enters the input terminal. The negligible signal that is applied at input is amplified and fed back, out of phase, to the input.

Notes:
1.   In practice, the common potential rail, AB, is earthed.
2.   If the offset nulls are not adjusted, it is necessary to include a resistor, at least 10k  , between the non-inverting input and the common potential.

Sometimes the feedback network is part of a "potential divider" arrangement as shown in Fig. 26.4. Using the analysis of the previous circuit we now have

$$V_{IN} = IR_i$$
$$V_{OUT} = I(R_i + R_F)$$
$$\therefore A = -\frac{R_i + R_F}{R_i}$$

**FIG. 26.4**

## 26.4   POSITIVE FEEDBACK

An electrical oscillator is a generator of alternating current and it basically consists of an operational amplifier which feeds back a small part of its output to its non-inverting input. This feedback is in phase with the input and when it is sufficient to compensate for resistive energy losses, undamped oscillations will occur.

**FIG. 26.5**

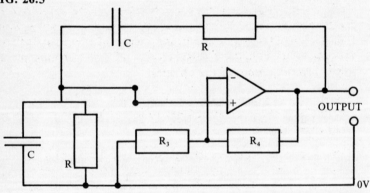

Such an oscillator circuit is shown in Fig. 26.5. Once the current has been "started", an undamped a.c. output is obtained. This type of circuit is known as a twin -T- circuit and when $R_4 = 2R_3$ the frequency of the oscillations, f, is given by

$$f \quad = \quad \frac{1}{4\pi^2\,RC}$$

## 26.5 SWITCHING

Operational amplifiers are used as switches in many important electronic circuits.

The basic principle involved may be understood from a consideration of Fig. 26.6.

**FIG. 26.6**

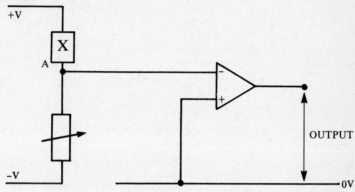

X, the control device may be, for instance, a variable resistor, a light sensitive diode or a thermistor. It is connected in series with a rheostat and a the top of this arrangement is at a potential +V, with the bottom at –V. Between this rheostat and X at A an input is taken to the inverting input of the op. amp.

When the resistance of X is equal to that of the rheostat, the potential at A is zero. The input potential to the op. amp. is also zero and hence the output is zero.

If the state of X changes such that its resistance changes, A will no longer be at zero potential and hence the potential applied to the op. amp. input will have a value. Amplification will take place such that a saturated output will be obtained.

The inputs and outputs may be summarised as follows:
if input is low (0V), the output is low (0V)
if input is high ($<\sim 50\mu$V), the output is high (V of supply).

### 26.6 LOGIC

26.6.1    Binary logic is concerned with the combination of two state or binary situations. Such two state systems are exemplified by true/false, high/low or on/off. The system is either in one state or the other.

26.6.2    Binary systems may be combined using the AND concept. Switches in series perform the AND operation as shown in Fig. 26.7.

**FIG. 26.7**

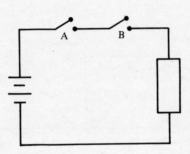

If switch A is closed and switch B is closed then current is transmitted.

We may represent a true statement by 1 and a false statement by 0. Thus A = 1 represents switch A closed, A = 0 represents switch A open and similarly for B. The output = 1 when the current flows and is equal to 0 when the current does not flow. The output represents A AND B, denoted A.B. The results may be summarised in a truth table.

| A | B | A.B |
|---|---|-----|
| 0 | 0 | 0 |
| 0 | 1 | 0 |
| 1 | 0 | 0 |
| 1 | 1 | 1 |

26.6.3    Binary systems may also be combined using the OR concept. Switches in parallel perform the OR operation as shown in Fig. 26.8.

**FIG. 26.8**

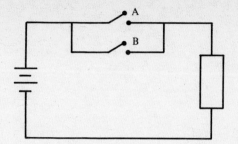

Current will now be transmitted if either switch A or switch B or both switches A and B are closed.

The output now represents A OR B, denoted A + B. The results may be summarised in a truth table.

| A | B | A+B |
|---|---|-----|
| 0 | 0 | 0 |
| 0 | 1 | 1 |
| 1 | 0 | 1 |
| 1 | 1 | 1 |

26.6.4   The NOT concept involves changing from one state of a binary state to the other. Thus, if the input is A, the output is NOT A denoted by $\overline{A}$. The results may be represented in a truth table.

| A | $\overline{A}$ |
|---|---|
| 0 | 1 |
| 1 | 0 |

26.6.5   Two further possible combinations are possible, the NAND — an abbreviation for NOT AND when an AND combination is NOTed and also the NOR — an abbreviation for NOT OR when an OR combination is NOTed. The truth tables are shown below.

NAND

| A | B | $\overline{A.B}$ |
|---|---|---|
| 0 | 0 | 1 |
| 0 | 1 | 1 |
| 1 | 0 | 1 |
| 1 | 1 | 0 |

NOR

| A | B | $\overline{A+B}$ |
|---|---|---|
| 0 | 0 | 1 |
| 0 | 1 | 0 |
| 1 | 0 | 0 |
| 1 | 1 | 0 |

## 26.7 LOGIC GATES

26.7.1 Logic gates are circuits in which op. amps are used to perform logic operations. They are used in pocket calculators and computers and their output depends upon the inputs and is either high — at the supply voltage (+5V in most computers) or low (near to 0V).

The symbols for the gates are as shown in Fig. 26.9.

**FIG. 26.9**

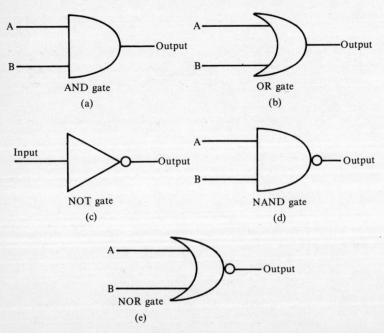

It will be noted that the NOT gate has only one input.
The gates are constructed as follows.

26.7.2   A NOT gate or inverter uses an op. amp as a simple switch and is shown in Fig. 26.10. (In practice, the switch shown in the input is not there but this merely represents the absence or presence of an applied voltage. In the absence of this voltage, the input is earthed, as illustrated in Figs. 26.10 to 26.14).

**FIG. 26.10**

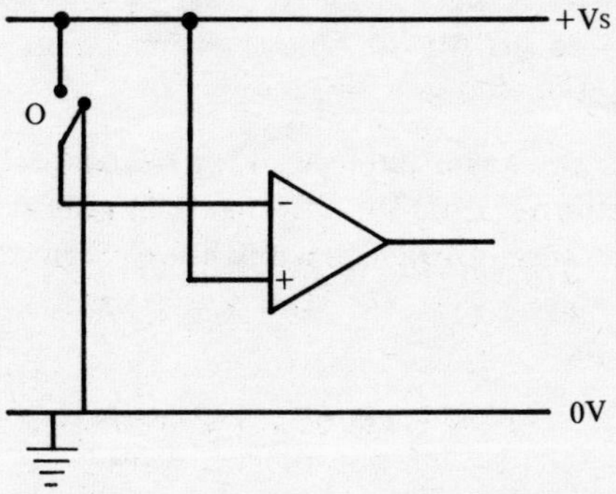

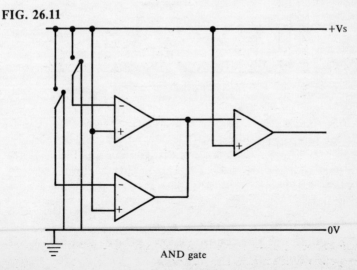

**CONSTRUCTION OF A NOT GATE OR INVERTER**

The non-inverting input is connected to the supply voltage and is in state 1. The inverting input is connected by a switch to the supply voltage. When the switch is open, there will be an input signal $V_s$. The saturated output will also be $V_s$ — or state 1. Thus, an input of 0 (switch open) has been NOTed to 1. Equally, when the switch is

**FIG. 26.11**

AND gate

closed, the input signal will be $V_s - V_s = 0$. The output will be zero, 0. Thus, an input of 1 (corresponding to the switch being closed) has been NOTed to 0.

26.7.3   An AND gate uses two op. amps in parallel with each other, this combination being connected in series with a third op. amp, as shown in Fig. 26.11. All the non-inverting inputs are connected to supply voltage.

There will only be an output (= 1) when both switches are closed. In that case, the output from the op. amps in parallel will be 0. The third op. amp behaves as an inverter and the 0 input is NOTed to a 1 output.

26.7.4   An OR gate uses two op. amps, one acting as an inverter. As shown in Fig. 26.12, all non-inverting inputs are at the supply voltage and the signals to be ORed are fed in parallel to the inverting input of the first op. amp.

**FIG. 26.12**

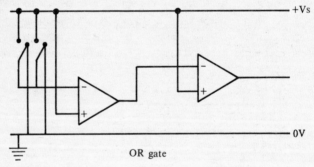

OR gate

In addition to there being an output when both switches are closed, as in the previous example, there is now an output when only one switch is closed. Suppose A is closed. The input is then 1 on the inverting input of the first op. amp. The input signal will, therefore, be $V_s - V_s = 0$. This is inverted by the next op. amp and thus the final output is 1.

26.7.5   A NAND gate consists of an AND gate joined to a NOT gate, as shown in Fig. 26.13.

**FIG. 26.13**

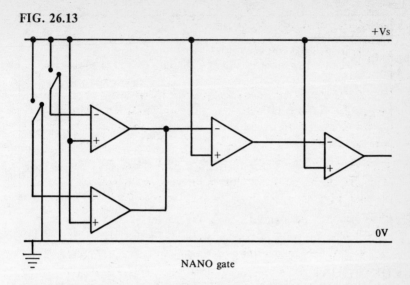

NANO gate

26.7.6   A NOR gate consists of an OR gate minus the inverter, as shown in Fig. 26.14.

**FIG. 26.14**

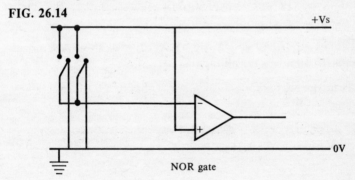

NOR gate

**EXAMPLE**

An operational amplifier gives a saturated output of +6V when the input p.d. reaches −50 V. Calculate the open loop gain.

Now $\qquad A_0 \quad = \quad \dfrac{V_{OUT}}{V_{IN}}$

Here $\qquad V_{OUT} \quad = \quad 6V$

$\qquad V_{IN} \quad = \quad -50\mu V = -5 \times 10^{-5}\,V$

$$A_0 \quad = \quad \frac{6}{-5 \times 10^{-5}} \quad = \quad -1.2 \times 10^{5}$$

Open loop gain $= -1.2 \times 10^{5}$
(used in inverting mode)

**QUESTIONS**

1) Using the AND gate as shown, verify that the AND truth table is obtained for all inputs.

2) Using the OR gate as shown, verify that the OR truth table is obtained for all inputs.

3) Using the NAND gate as shown, verify that the NAND truth table is obtained for all inputs.

4) Using the NOR gate as shown, verify that the NOR truth table is obtained for all inputs.

5) In a negative feedback circuit, the input resistor has a value of 10kΩ and the feedback resistor has a value of 100kΩ Calculate the gain obtained.

# AREA 6: WAVE PHENOMENA

## Chapter 27
## MECHANICAL WAVES

### 27.1 CLASSIFICATION OF WAVES AS MECHANICAL

27.1.1   Waves may be classified as mechanical or electromagnetic. Mechanical waves are produced by a vibrating body and need a medium for their transmission. The particles of the medium oscillate to and fro. Such waves can be seen, felt or heard and they include water waves on stretched strings and sound waves. The properties of mechanical waves may be easily demonstrated using water waves in a ripple tank.

27.1.2   Electromagnetic waves were originally thought to be mechanical and the medium of transmission was mystically known as the "ether". Einstein demonstrated that no such substance existed. These waves consist of a disturbance in the form of varying electric and magnetic fields. No medium is required for their transmission and they travel with greatest speed in vacuum. These waves will be considered in greater detail in later chapters.

### 27.2   PROGRESSIVE WAVES

27.2.1   A progressive wave (or travelling wave) consists of a disturbance which moves away from a source and in doing so transfers energy.

Suppose a large vane is steadily and repeatedly dipped into the surface of a large expanse of water. If we look at the surface of the water we will observe a wave, as shown in Fig. 27.1.

Along the wave, particles of the medium move up and down, generating a series of crests and troughs.

We define the amplitude of the wave as the maximum displacement from the rest position, i.e. the height of a crest or trough above the rest position.

## FIG. 27.1

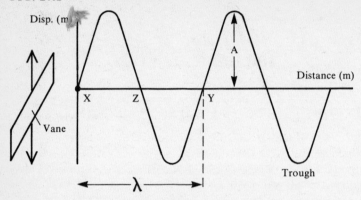

**DISPLACEMENT-DISTANCE**

Points such as X and Y are always in step, i.e. their motion is identical at all times. We say that they are in phase. X and Y are the closest together that is possible and are said to be one wavelength apart. Wavelength is denoted by the Greek letter lambda, $\lambda$. Points such as X and Z or Z and Y are at opposite points in their motion. They are said to be out of phase and are half a wavelength apart. Between all points (except those $\lambda$ or $\lambda_2$ or their multiples) there is a general phase difference.

Phase difference may also be expressed as an angle.
One wavelength corresponds to 360° or $2\pi^c$.

The motion of the particles is shown in Fig. 27.2.

## FIG. 27.2

**DISPLACEMENT-DISTANCE**

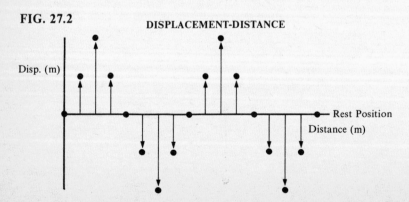

So far we have considered the points along a wave at a particular time. Let us now consider what happens as time goes by. In Fig. 27.3, a wave is shown at a given time (solid line). A short time later the appearance changes (dotted line). Some particles of the medium will have moved downwards whilst some will have moved upwards, as shown by the arrows. Accordingly, the wave profile will move to the right, as indicated, at the wave velocity. Again, in this diagram it will be observed that points which are one wavelength apart are exactly in phase. The number of wavelengths passing a given point every second is the frequency of the wave, in Hertz, $H_z$. We use the symbol f.

**FIG. 27.3**

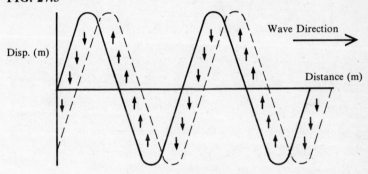

**DISPLACEMENT-TIME**

If we now confine our attention to one particle in the wave, we observe that it oscillates up and down about its rest position, as shown in Fig. 27.4. Such oscillations are simple harmonic.

**FIG. 27.4**

The motion may be plotted against time and this is displayed in Fig. 27.5.

**FIG. 27.5**

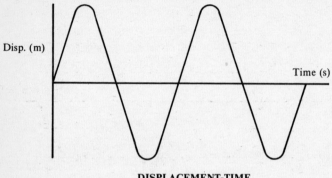

**DISPLACEMENT-TIME**

In this water wave, the direction of oscillation of the particles is perpendicular to the direction of travel, or propagation, of the wave — see Fig. 27.6. Such a wave is known as a transverse wave. Other mechanical transverse waves include waves on a spring or a string which is shaken to and fro.

**FIG. 27.6**

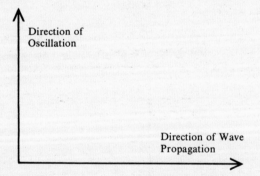

27.2.2 The other type of progressive wave is one in which the direction of oscillation of the particles is in the same direction as the direction of propagation. This is a longitudinal wave.

Such a wave is shown in Fig. 27.7. Corresponding to the troughs and crests of a transverse wave (a), we have rarefactions and compressions (b). For clarity this diagram, (b), shows only those displaced particles undergoing maximum displacements.

**FIG. 27.7**

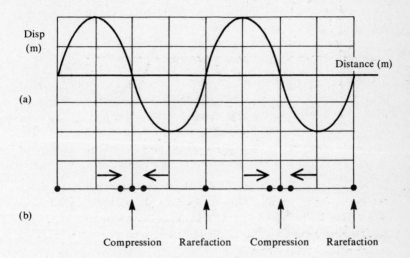

(a)

(b)

Compression   Rarefaction   Compression   Rarefaction

In Fig. 27.8 the relationship between the directions of oscillation and propagation is shown.

**FIG. 27.8**

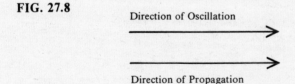

Direction of Oscillation

Direction of Propagation

The compressions are regions of high particle density because particles are moving, in both directions, towards their centre. The rarefactions are regions of low particle density because particles are moving, in both directions, away from their centre. Particles at the centre of compressions and rarefactions are instantaneously at rest.

Both compressions and rarefactions move in the direction of travel of the wave whilst the particles of the medium vibrate to and fro about their undisturbed positions.

A longitudinal wave may be graphically represented by a transverse wave as can be seen in Fig. 27.7.

All the terms used in connection with transverse waves, namely amplitude, phase, frequency, wavelength and speed, apply equally well to longitudinal waves. However, transverse waves may be polarised, unlike longitudinal waves (see Chapter 29).

Mechanical longitudinal waves include waves on a spring (formed when the coils at one end are gathered together and then released) where the compressions and rarefactions are formed by the coils being nearer and further apart than is normal and sound waves where the compressions and rarefactions are formed by the atoms of the medium being nearer and further apart than is normal in the undisturbed medium.

## 27.3   THE RELATIONSHIP BETWEEN WAVELENGTH, FREQUENCY AND SPEED

A progressive wave of frequency f will be generated by a source vibrating at the same frequency.

Each time the source makes a complete vibration, the wave moves through a distance equal to one wavelength.

Thus, if the source vibrates at a frequency, f, then simultaneously the wave will advance by $f\lambda$

$$\therefore \quad \text{Distance moved by wave} = f\lambda$$

But this distance has been travelled in one second and it is, therefore, equal to the speed of the wave, V

Hence

$$V = f\lambda$$

This relationship holds for both transverse and longitudinal waves.

**EXAMPLE**

If the speed of sound in air is 330ms$^{-1}$, calculate the wavelength of a 20.0KH$_z$ wave.

$$\text{Use} \qquad v = f\lambda$$
$$\text{hence} \qquad \lambda = \frac{v}{f}$$

Substituting the values

$$\lambda = \frac{330}{20.0 \times 10^3} = 16.5 \times 10^{-3}\text{m}$$

$$\text{Wavelength} = 16.5\text{mm}$$

## 27.4  SOME EXPRESSIONS FOR WAVE SPEEDS

Some important expressions are stated below. Their derivation involves sophisticated mathematics, beyond the scope of 'A' level.

1) Longitudinal waves in a rod

$$V = \sqrt{\frac{E}{\rho}}$$

$E$ = Young's Modulus $\Big\}$ of material of rod
$\rho$ = density

2) Longitudinal waves in a fluid

$$V = \sqrt{\frac{K}{\rho}}$$

$K$ = constant, known as Bulk Modulus of fluid
$\rho$ = density of fluid

3) Transverse waves on a string

$$V = \sqrt{\frac{T}{m}}$$

$T$ = tension in string
$m$ = specific mass (i.e. mass per unit length) of string

4) Transverse waves on the surface of deep water

$$V = \sqrt{\frac{2\pi\gamma}{\lambda\rho}}$$

$\gamma$ = constant, known as Surface Energy for water
$\lambda$ = wavelength
$\rho$ = density of water

## 27.5 MEASUREMENT OF SPEED OF SOUND IN FREE AIR

The speed of sound in air at 288K is 340ms$^{-1}$.

This may be verified experimentally using the apparatus shown in Fig. 27.9. A signal generator drives a loudspeaker with a sinusoidal p.d. This p.d. is fed simultaneously to the X plates of a cathode ray oscilloscope. A microphone detects the output from the loudspeaker and the signal which it receives is fed via an amplifier, to the Y plates of the C.R.O.

**FIG. 27.9**

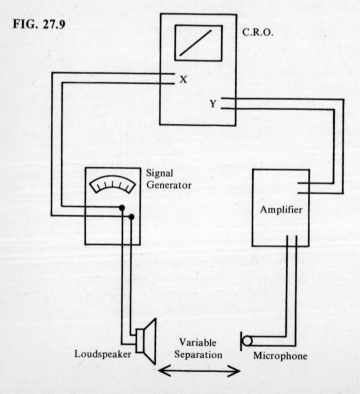

Now the C.R.O. is receiving two simple harmonic signals, the phase difference between which will depend upon the separation between the loudspeaker and the microphone. The resultant patterns produced on the C.R.O. are known as Lissajous Figures.

Thus, the distance between the loudspeaker and microphone is adjusted until a straight line, running from top right to bottom left is observed on the C.R.O. screen. This distance is increased and the pattern will change into an ellipse followed by a straight line running from top left to bottom right, an ellipse and finally the original straight line will re-appear. This new distance is measured. The traces obtained are shown in Fig. 27.10.

**FIG. 27.10**

The increased separation of the loudspeaker and microphone is obtained by subtracting their original separation from their final. This distance is equal to one wavelength. The frequency of the signal is read off directly from the frequency generator.

Hence $$V = f\lambda$$

$\lambda$ = wavelength, as measured

f = frequency, as read off signal generator

In practice, the time base on the C.R.O. is switched off and its earth is connected to the earth terminal on the signal generator. The experiment is very effective when f = 3KH$_z$.

## 27.6 WAVEFRONTS

Suppose a rod with a number of strings attached is vibrated up and down. A number of transverse waves will be generated — one along each string. The waves will all be in phase, as shown in Fig. 27.11.

**FIG. 27.11**

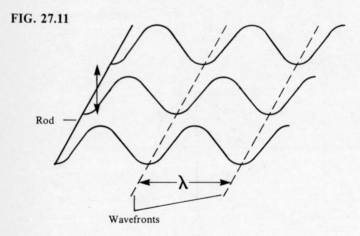

Rod —

λ

Wavefronts

It is rather inconvenient drawing a series of such waves and an alternative representation known as wavefronts is often used. A wavefront is a locus of in-phase points. Successive wavefronts are one wavelength apart as shown in this diagram and are always at right angles to the direction of travel of the waves.

A line source generates plane waves and the associated wavefronts, known as plane wavefronts, are a series of parallel lines.

A point source generates circular waves in two dimensions and the associated wavefronts are a series of concentric circles centred upon the source, as shown in Fig. 27.12.

**FIG. 27.12**

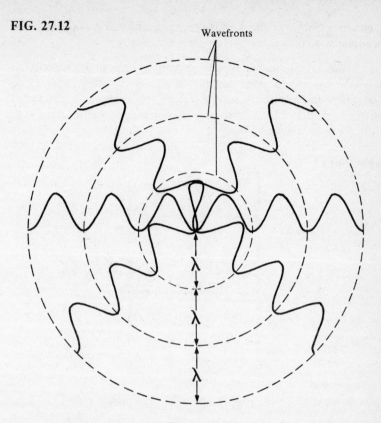

In three dimensions, a point source generates spherical waves and the associated wavefronts are a series of concentric spheres, rather like the layers of an onion.

A line at right angles to a wavefront which shows its direction of travel is called a ray.

## 27.7 THE PROPAGATION OF WAVEFRONTS

Huygen's Theory of Secondary Wavelets enables the new position of a wavefront to be found if its original position is known. It can be used to explain the reflection and refraction of waves.

The theory states that: Every element of a wavefront behaves just like a small source, radiating waves of the same wavelength in all directions but most strongly in the forward direction.

The new position of the wavefront is given by the envelope of these secondary wavelets.

As a simple example of the propagation of a plane wavefront, consider Fig. 27.13. AB is a plane wavefront travelling from left to right. The new wavefront at time t later is the common tangent OP of the spherical wavelets of radius Vt, centred upon points along AB. V is the speed of the waves.

**FIG. 27.13**

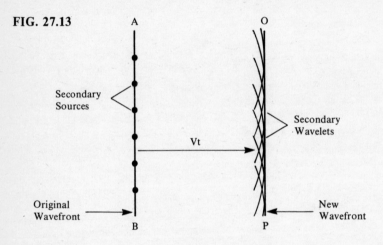

Fig. 27.14 shows the propagation of a circular wavefront.

**FIG. 27.14**

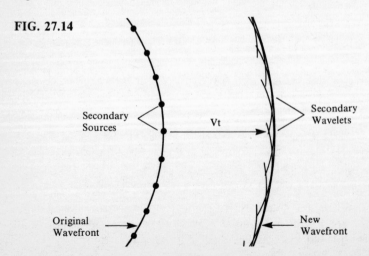

## 27.8  THE LAWS OF REFLECTION

Suppose parallel rays are incident upon a reflecting surface BC, as shown in Fig. 27.15. Imagine a plane wavefront BD normal to the rays reaching this surface.

**FIG. 27.15**

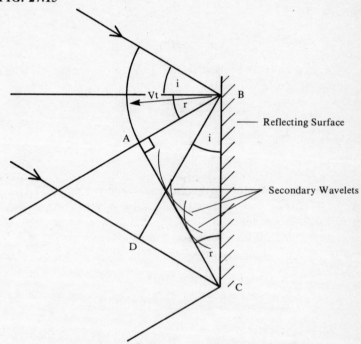

At the instant that the point B acts as a centre of disturbance, the disturbance at D is still travelling towards the surface. By the time that D reaches C when it acts as a centre of disturbance, the disturbance from B will have travelled a distance Vt where V is the wave velocity and t is the time between B acting as a centre of disturbance and D reaching C.

Points on the incident wavefront between B and D will reach the reflector at different times and accordingly, the secondary wavelets will travel different distances. Thus, at a given time we will have a series of arcs of circles (the secondary wavelets), all of different radius. The locus of these constitutes the reflected wavefront.

Now, it can be seen from the diagram that

$$\angle DBC = \text{angle of incidence, i}$$
$$\angle BCA = \text{angle of reflection, r}$$

But

$$\frac{DC}{BC} = \sin i$$

and

$$\frac{AB}{BC} = \sin r$$

now

$$AB = DC$$

since they represent the distances travelled in equal time by waves travelling at identical speeds.

$$\therefore \quad \frac{DC}{BC} = \sin r$$

Hence

$$\sin i = \sin r$$

so

$$i = r$$

Thus, the angle of incidence is equal to the angle of reflection. This may be effectively demonstrated using water waves in a ripple tank when it will also be seen that the waves are in the same plane — see Fig. 27.16. Hence, it may be shown from a wave viewpoint that the laws of reflection are valid.

**FIG. 27.16**

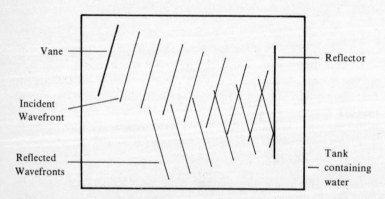

## 27.9 THE LAWS OF REFRACTION

Suppose that parallel rays are travelling in a medium towards a second medium. Imagine a plane wavefront BD normal to the rays.

The boundary between the two media is shown by the line BC. The initial speed of the waves in the first medium is $V_1$ and in the second medium the speed of the waves is $V_2$. The situation is shown in Fig. 27.17.

**FIG. 27.17**

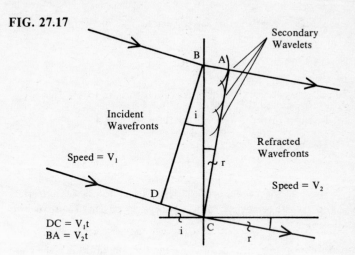

Now, in the time t that D reaches C, the wavelet from B acting as a centre of disturbance, will have travelled a distance $V_2t$.

Points on the incident wavefront between B and D will reach the boundary at different times and accordingly, the secondary wavelets will travel different distances. Thus, at a given time we will have a series of arcs of circles (the secondary wavelets) in the second medium and they will all have different radii. The locus of these constitutes the refracted wavefront.

It can be seen from the diagram that

$$\sin i = \frac{DC}{BD} = \frac{V_1t}{BD}$$

$$\sin r = \frac{AB}{BD} = \frac{V_2t}{BD}$$

Hence

$$\frac{\sin i}{\sin r} = \frac{\dfrac{V_1 t}{BD}}{\dfrac{V_2 t}{BC}} = \frac{V_1}{V_2}$$

Now $V_1$ and $V_2$ are constants for the particular medium.

Hence

$$\frac{\sin i}{\sin r} = \frac{V_1}{V_2} = \text{constant} \qquad \underline{\text{Snell's Law}}$$

The constant is called the refractive index for waves travelling from the first medium into the second medium, denoted $_1n_2$

Hence

$$_1n_2 = \frac{\sin i}{\sin r} = \frac{V_1}{V_2} = \frac{n_1}{n_2}$$

where $n_1$ and $n_2$ are the absolute refractive indices of materials 1 and 2 and are the refractive indices for waves passing from air into material 1 or 2.

The phenomenon may also be observed in a ripple tank. A large glass block is placed in one half of the tank, as shown in Fig. 27.18.

**FIG. 27.18**

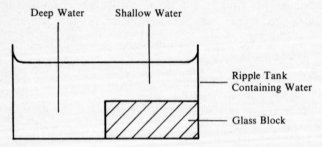

If now, plane waves are incident upon the boundary between the deep and shallow water, at a given angle of incidence, refraction will be observed. A decrease in wavelength will also be seen as in Fig. 27.19. It will also be observed that the incident and refracted waves are in the same plane.

**FIG. 27.19**

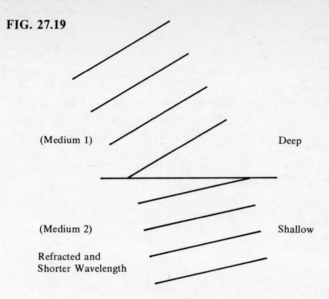

(Medium 1)                                          Deep

(Medium 2)                                          Shallow

Refracted and
Shorter Wavelength

The results may be explained as follows. The speed of surface waves in shallow water (when the depth is not large compared with the wavelength) depends, amongst other factors, on the depth of the water. Water ripples travel more slowly in shallow water than they do in deeper water.

So

$$V_1 > V_2$$
$$\therefore \quad \sin i > \sin r$$
$$i > r$$

and the waves are refracted towards the normal

Now, the frequency of the waves cannot change — such a change would be unphysical and would lead to waves piling-up at the boundary. Thus, the frequency of waves in both media is identical, f.

Since $V = f\lambda$, this means that the wavelength must change and, here, must also decrease since

$$V_1 > V_2$$
$$f\lambda_1 > f\lambda_2$$
$$\therefore \quad \lambda_1 > \lambda_2 \qquad \text{i.e. the wavelength decreases}$$

The action of a lens is merely to change the shape of an incident wavefront. For light waves the lens would obviously be made of glass or plastic but for sound waves we would use a balloon containing hydrogen or other gas.

---

**EXAMPLE**

Surface waves travel across water and strike a boundary between the water and shallower water at an angle of 30°. They are refracted at an angle of 20° and then travel at a speed of $10 \text{cms}^{-1}$. Calculate their speed before they enter the shallower water and the refractive index when they travel from the water into the shallower water.

Now $$_1n_2 \quad = \quad \frac{\sin i}{\sin r} \quad = \quad \frac{V_1}{V_2}$$

Here
$$i \quad = \quad 30°$$
$$r \quad = \quad 20°$$
$$V_2 \quad = \quad 10 \text{cms}^{-1}$$

$$\therefore \quad \frac{\sin 30}{\sin 20} \quad = \quad \frac{V_1}{10}$$

$$\therefore \quad V_1 \quad = \quad \frac{10 \sin 30}{\sin 20} \quad = \quad 10 \times 1.46 \quad = \quad 14.6 \text{cms}^{-1}$$

$$_1n_2 \quad = \quad \frac{14.6}{10} \quad = \quad 1.46$$

$$\therefore \quad \text{Original speed} \quad = \quad 14.6 \text{cms}^{-1}$$
$$\text{Refraction index} \quad = \quad 1.46$$

---

**QUESTIONS**

1) Draw a diagram to show longitudinal waves on a spring.

2) Water waves are caused to travel across the surface of a shallow tank. If the distance between two successive crests is 3.0cm and the waves travel 25.2cm in 1.2s, calculate the wavelength, frequency and velocity of the waves.

3) Calculate the speed of longitudinal waves in a copper rod. (Assume E for copper $= 1.30 \times 10^{11} \text{ N m}^{-2}$, density of copper $= 8.90 \times 10^3 \text{Kg m}^{-3}$).

## Chapter 28
# THE SUPERPOSITION OF MECHANICAL WAVES

**FIG. 28.1**

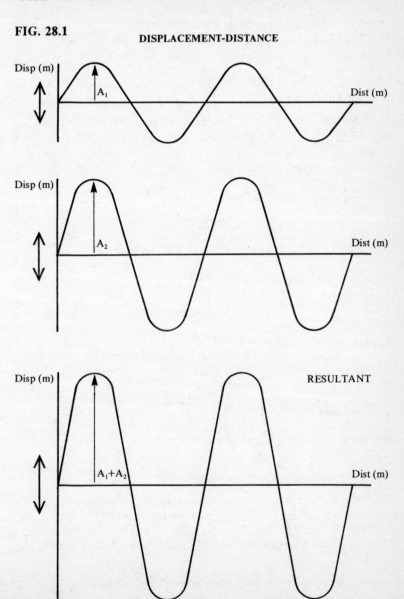

DISPLACEMENT-DISTANCE

## 28.1 THE PRINCIPLE OF SUPERPOSITION

The Principle of Superposition states: The resultant displacement of two or more waves is the algebraic sum of the individual displacements. Thus, in Fig. 28.1, the resultant wave due to two waves of amplitudes $A_1$ and $A_2$ has an amplitude $(A_1+A_2)$.

## 28.2 SUPERPOSITION OF WAVES FROM SEPARATE SOURCES

28.2.1 Suppose two small spheres, attached to the same vibrating bar are repeatedly dipped into a ripple tank. Fig. 28.2 shows the appearance of the water surface as circular waves travel outwards from each sphere.

**FIG. 28.2**

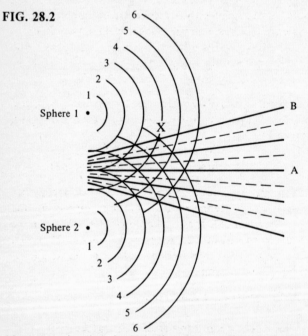

Along certain directions, indicated by solid lines, the amplitude of the wave is double that of either of the component waves from both spheres.

Along other directions indicated by dotted lines and which lie half-way between the solid lines, the amplitude of the wave is zero.

The waves interfere with each other and the result is an interference pattern. Along the solid lines, constructive interference occurs whilst along the dotted lines, destructive interference occurs. The explanation of the pattern is as follows.

The waves from both spheres start out in phase. All points on the solid line, A, are equidistant from both sphere 1 and sphere 2 — this is borne out by the fact that equal numbered wavefronts from both spheres meet there. Thus, waves meeting along this line have started out in phase and travelled equal distances. They must, therefore, still be in phase when they meet with the maximum of one wave meeting the maximum of the other. In accordance with the Principle of Superposition, the resultant amplitude is doubled.

Consider now a point such as X on line B. Waves from sphere 1 have travelled 4 wavelengths whilst those waves from sphere 2 have travelled 6 wavelengths. Thus, one wave has travelled 2 wavelengths further than the other and so both waves are in phase and constructive interference occurs again because the maximum of one wave is again meeting the maximum of the other.

The requirement for constructive interference is that the extra distance travelled by one wave compared to the other, called the path difference, is given by

$$\text{Path difference} = \text{Whole number of wavelengths}$$
$$= n\lambda \qquad \text{where n is an integer}$$

Mid way between the directions of constructive interference are those of destructive interference. Along these directions the maximum of one wave meets the minimum of the other. In the diagram, the wavefronts from one source are half-way between those from the other. In accordance with the Principle of Superposition, the resultant amplitude is zero.

The requirement for destructive interference is

$$\text{Path difference} = \text{Odd number of half wavelengths}$$
$$= (n + \tfrac{1}{2})\lambda \qquad \text{where n is an integer}$$

The lines along which constructive interference occurs are known as antinodal lines whilst those along which destructive interference occurs are known as nodal lines.

The integer n used above is sometimes referred to as the order of the antinodal line. Thus, along B, the 2nd line (A is the 0th), the path difference is 2$\lambda$.

The way in which the waves combine is shown in Fig. 28.3 and 28.4. (Note: Fig. 28.3 would also apply for two minima).

**FIG. 28.3**

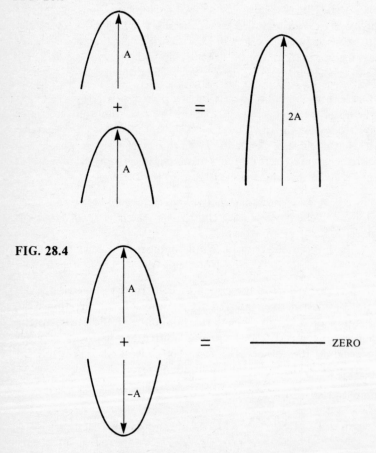

**FIG. 28.4**

It should be noted that the Principle of Conservation of Energy applies to an interference pattern. There is four times the energy from one source at a maximum and zero energy at a minimum. The average energy over the whole pattern is twice the energy from one of the sources which is to be expected.

28.2.2 There are three conditions necessary for interference:

1) The interfering waves must be monochromatic, i.e. of exactly the same frequency. If they are not monochromatic then the interference pattern which they form will be rapidly changing and will consequently be unobservable. Thus, in Fig. 28.5, if two waves of different frequencies are in phase at a certain time, $T_1$ then at a later time $T_2$ they will be out of phase. The resultant will oscillate so rapidly between constructive and destructive interference that no pattern will be seen.

**FIG. 28.5**

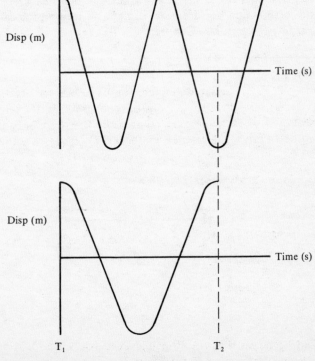

**DISPLACEMENT-TIME**

2) The waves must have approximately equal amplitudes. If the individual amplitudes are $A_1$ and $A_2$ then the resultant amplitude when they are in phase is $(A_1 + A_2)$ and when they are out of phase $(A_1 - A_2)$. If $A_1 > A_2$, the difference between $(A_1 + A_2)$ and $(A_1 - A_2)$ will be very small and the difference between constructive and destructive interference will be unobservable.

3) The interfering waves must be coherent. This means essentially that the phase difference between the wavefronts of the two sources must not change with time.

In the example considered of interfering water waves, all three conditions are met because the two sources are connected to the same vibrator. The waves they generate have the same frequency and amplitude and they are coherent with the phase difference between the sources (and hence the waves, when they start out) being zero and constant. Such conditions are more difficult to meet in the case of electromagnetic waves (see Chapter 30).

---

**EXAMPLE**

Two speakers are situated 3m apart and an observer sits 4m away from, and directly in front of, one speaker. A mono. signal is fed to each speaker. What is the first frequency at which destructive interference will occur? (Velocity of sound $= 330$ ms$^{-1}$).

The situation is shown in Fig. 28.6.

**FIG. 28.6**

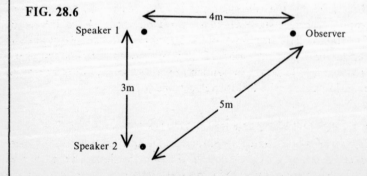

The arrangement is obviously at 3, 4, 5 triangle
Hence

$$\text{distance from observer to speaker 1} = 4\text{m}$$
$$\text{distance from observer to speaker 2} = 5\text{m}$$
$$\text{path difference} = 1\text{m}$$

Now, for destructive interference, minimum path difference is half a wavelength

$$\therefore \quad \frac{\lambda}{2} \quad = \quad 1\text{m}$$

$$\lambda \quad = \quad 2\text{m}$$

Now $\qquad V = f\lambda$

$$\therefore \qquad\qquad f \quad = \quad \frac{V}{\lambda}$$

Substituting the values

$$f \quad = \quad \frac{330}{2} \quad = \quad 165\text{Hz}$$

Lowest frequency = 165Hz

## 28.3 RESONANCE

If a diving springboard is bent and released, it oscillates with a frequency which is called its natural frequency. When a diver on the edge of the board begins to jump up and down repeatedly, the board is forced to vibrate at the frequency of the jumps. At first, when the amplitude is small, the board is said to be undergoing forced vibrations. As the diver jumps up and down, the frequency of jumping reaches a stage where it is the same as the natural frequency of the board. The amplitude of the board becomes very large and the board is said to be in resonance. This phenomenon has already been discussed in Chapter 2 in connection with S.H.M. but is worthy of repetition before the following sections.

## 28.4 STATIONARY OR STANDING WAVES

If two waves of the same amplitude and frequency travel in opposite directions along a straight line in the same medium, the two waves combine in a special way to form a stationary or standing wave. Such a wave is shown in Fig. 28.7 and it is so called because it does not seem to be travelling along in either direction.

**FIG. 28.7**

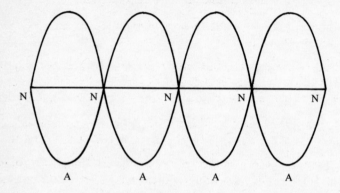

On such a wave, there are points such as N, called nodes, where the displacement is always zero. They are half a wavelength apart.

Within one loop, all particles oscillate in phase but with different amplitudes although all particles have their maximum displacement simultaneously. Points such as A with the greatest amplitude are called antinodes. They too are half a wavelength apart.

The oscillations in any loop are out of phase with those in an adjacent loop.

The wavelength of the stationary wave is thus twice the distance between successive nodes or antinodes and is, naturally, equal to the wavelength of either of the constituent progressive waves.

Unlike progressive waves there is no energy transmission. Large amounts of energy are stored locally in the stationary wave.

**28.5   THE FORMATION OF STATIONARY WAVES
      ON A STRING**

The formation of stationary waves on a string may be observed using Melde's Experiment. In this a thin string is clamped at one end and attached to a vibrator at the other end, as shown in Fig. 28.8.

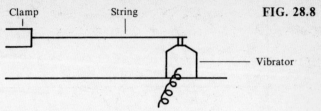

Clamp    String    **FIG. 28.8**

Vibrator

To Signal Generator

When the vibrator is switched on, a transverse wave travels along the string until it meets the clamp. Here it is reflected and the reflected wave interferes with the incident wave to form a stationary wave.

Whenever a wave is reflected at a fixed boundary such as a clamp, it undergoes a phase change of 180°, equivalent to half a wavelength.

In Fig. 28.9, the broken curves are the displacement — distance curves for the incident and reflected waves at successive time intervals. The continuous curve in each case is the resultant stationary wave.

**FIG. 28.9**

**DISPLACEMENT-DISTANCE**

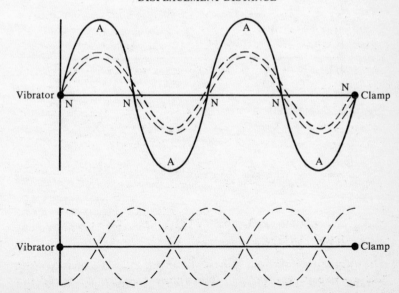

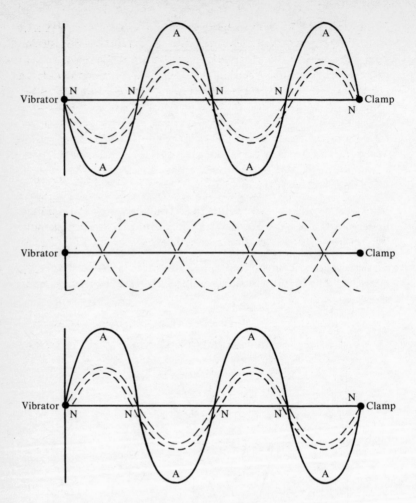

Dotted Lines = Progressive Incident and Reflected Waves
Solid Lines = Resultant Stationary Waves

The clamped end must be a node at all times since it is clamped. Along the string there will be a series of nodes and antinodes, indicated by N and A.

By comparison with the amplitude of the string's vibration, the vibrator is also a node (strictly speaking, the node is just behind the vibrator).

If the vibrator makes an integral number of vibrations in the time which it takes for the wave to travel to the clamp and be reflected back again, the wave will arrive back in phase with the vibrator. Very little energy will be absorbed and the amplitude of the wave will reach a maximum. This is a resonance phenomenon. For any other distance between the vibrator and the clamp, the reflected wave will arrive back at the vibrator out of phase with it. The wave will oppose the motion of the vibrator and a large amount of energy will be absorbed.

Similarly for a fixed distance between vibrator and clamp, the string will have a number of natural frequencies of vibration when resonance occurs. At these values the reflected wave will arrive back in phase with the vibrator enabling it to be a node. Thus, the resonant frequencies will be such that a complete number of loops can be fitted in between vibrator and clamp.

When only one loop is fitted in, the string is vibrating in its fundamental mode.

If $\ell$ = distance between vibrator and clamp = length of string then

$$\ell = \text{distance between 2 successive nodes}$$
$$\ell = \frac{\lambda}{2}$$
$$\lambda = 2\ell$$

Now
$$v = f\lambda$$
$$v = 2\ell f$$

$$\text{Resonant frequency } f = \frac{v}{2\ell}$$

Now since
$$v = \sqrt{\frac{T}{m}} \qquad \text{(See Chapter 27)}$$

hence
$$f = \frac{1}{2\ell}\sqrt{\frac{T}{m}}$$

For the next mode of vibration, two loops are fitted in and

$$\ell = \lambda$$

Whenever a stationary transverse wave is produced on a string, a progressive sound wave is produced in the surrounding air with the same frequency.

### 28.6 THE FORMATION OF STATIONARY WAVES IN AIR COLUMNS

28.6.1   Stationary waves may be produced in air columns in pipes. A disturbance is created at one end of the pipe. It is reflected at the other end which may be open or closed and it interferes with the incident wave. The wavelength of some waves will be such that the reflected wave will arrive back at the disturbance source in phase and resonance will result.

In pipes, the closed end, where the sound originates, is always a node. If the other end is closed it too is a node. If the other end is open, it is an antinode. Thus, in an open pipe, the fundamental frequency occurs when the pipe is $\lambda/4$ long whereas in a closed pipe, the fundamental frequency occurs when the pipe is $\lambda/2$ long.

Open pipes occur in organs, recorders and oboes etc. A closed pipe occurs in a drum.

28.6.2   Stationary waves in an air column may be used to find the speed of sound in air, by the resonance tube technique.

**FIG. 28.10**

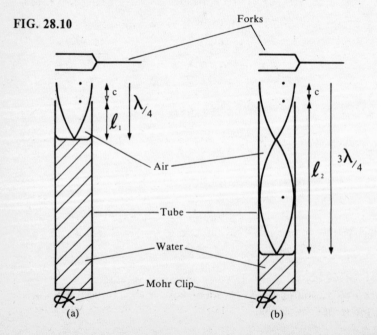

The apparatus is shown in Fig. 28.10. The tuning fork is struck and held over the top of the tube. The water level is lowered by opening the mohr clip until the intensity of the note is a maximum. at this point there is resonance and the fundamental frequency of the air column equals the frequency of the fork.

Thus

$$\frac{\lambda}{4} = \ell_1 + c$$

$\ell_1$ = distance from top of tube to water

$c$ = end correction

The water level is further lowered until a second position of resonance is found. The new length of air, $\ell_2$ plus C is now equal to $3\lambda/4$

$$\frac{3\lambda}{4} = \ell_2 + c$$

By subtraction

$$\ell_2 - \ell_1 = \frac{\lambda}{2}$$

$$\therefore \lambda = 2(\ell_2 - \ell_1)$$

and

$$V = f\lambda = 2f(\ell_2 - \ell_1) \qquad \text{where f = fork frequency}$$

Alternatively, using several forks of known frequency and finding the fundamental length for each

$$\ell + c = \frac{\lambda}{4} = \frac{V}{4f}$$

$$\therefore \ell = \frac{V}{4f} - c$$

A graph of $\ell$ against $\frac{1}{f}$ will be a straight line of slope $\frac{V}{4}$ and intercept $-c$.

The end correction, c, is a correction factor to allow for the fact that the air at the top of the tube is not completely free to move because of the effects of the top of the tube. It can be shown that c = 0.6 x tube radius.

**EXAMPLE**

When a tuning fork of frequency 384Hz is used with a resonance tube, the first position of resonance is when the water is 20.3cm from the top of the tube. A second position of resonance is obtained when the water is 63.5cm below the top of the tube. Calculate the speed of sound in the tube.

Using

$$\frac{\lambda}{2} = \ell_2 - \ell_1$$

$$\lambda = 2(\ell - \ell_1)$$
$$= 2(0.635 - 0.203)$$
$$= 0.864m$$
$$f = 384Hz$$

But

$$V = f\lambda$$

Substitute the values

$$V = 384 \times 0.864$$
$$= 332ms^{-1}$$

Speed of Sound $= 332ms^{-1}$

## 28.7 DIFFRACTION OF WATER WAVES AT A SLIT

The diffraction of water waves at a slit may be studied in a ripple tank. A bar is used to produce plane wavefronts and these strike an aperture in a barrier.

In Fig. 28.11 the aperture is wide compared to the wavelength and the incident waves emerge almost unchanged, save for a little bending at the extreme edges. A fairly sharp shadow of the aperture is obtained.

**FIG. 28.11**

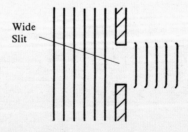

Wide
Slit

However, in Fig. 28.12 the aperture is much narrower and is approximately equal to the wavelength. The emerging waves now spread out or are diffracted. A sharp shadow is no longer obtained but the waves spread out into a cone. They disappear and then re-appear to form two very narrow cones of very weak intensity.

**FIG. 28.12**

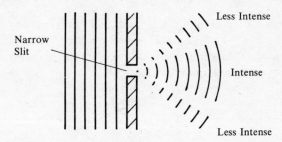

This phenomenon is known as diffraction and the associated pattern is referred to as a diffraction pattern.

The patterns can be considered to arise from the interference of the secondary wavelets on the same wavefront produced by the point sources imagined to exist at the unrestricted part of the wavefront which falls upon the aperture.

**QUESTIONS**

1) State and explain the three conditions necessary for interference.

2) Calculate the fundamental frequency of an air column in an open pipe of length 72.0cm. Ignore the end correction and assume speed of sound in air = $330ms^{-1}$.

3) A loudspeaker is sounded above a resonance tube 40cm long. The frequency of the sound generated is increased from 200 to 1200Hz. At what frequencies will resonance occur? Assume speed of sound in air is $344ms^{-1}$. Ignore end correction.

# Chapter 29
# ELECTROMAGNETIC WAVES

## 29.1  THE NATURE OF ELECTROMAGNETIC WAVES

Electromagnetic waves are transverse and are unique in that they are able to travel through a vacuum.

They consist of oscillating magnetic and electric fields and are propagated at a very high velocity — $3 \times 10^8$ ms$^{-1}$ in vacuum. The fields are always at right angles to one another and to the direction of propagation, as shown in Fig. 29.1.

**FIG. 29.1**

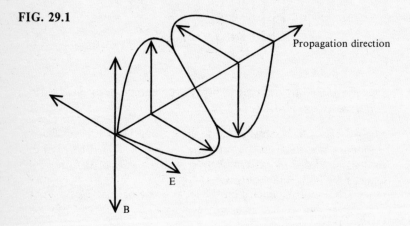

Propagation direction

E

B

The simple harmonic oscillations of the electric field are always exactly similar to those of the electric field and hence it is usually quite adequate to represent an electromagnetic wave by a single sinusoidal oscillation just as in the case of progressive waves along a stretched string. Wiener, in 1890, showed that most of the activity associated with an electromagnetic wave was due to the electric field and hence this single sinusoidal oscillation represents the electric field.

The quantity in an electromagnetic wave which is equivalent to displacement in a mechanical wave is field strength or flux density with the equivalent of amplitude being maximum field strength or flux density.

The terms wavelength, frequency, velocity and period have the same meaning as they have for any other kind of mechanical wave.

## 29.2 THE ELECTROMAGNETIC SPECTRUM AND ITS PRODUCTION

29.2.1 A whole family of electromagnetic radiations is known. The full range of the spectrum as it is known is shown in Fig. 29.2.

**FIG. 29.2**

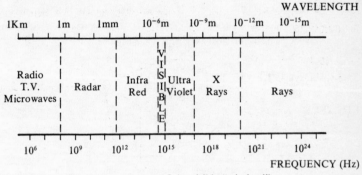

(Note the narrowness of the visible "window")

We may consider the radiation either in terms of wavelength (the longer wavelength occuring on the left hand side) or in terms of frequency (low frequencies on the left). It is more useful to refer to frequency since this is invariant when the waves travel from one medium to another.

All of these waves exhibit the properties of waves which have already been met — they can be reflected, refracted, diffracted and they interfere. Additionally X rays and $\gamma$ rays can penetrate matter and all waves excluding radio (radio, T.V. and microwaves) and radar affect a photographic plate.

The energy of electromagnetic waves increases as we move from left to right and hence $\gamma$ rays are the most energetic and hence most dangerous.

29.2.2 Electromagnetic waves are always produced whenever charges are accelerated or decelerated.

ɣ rays — produced as a result of energy changes in the nucleus when charged particles are decelerated.

X rays — produced by the rapid deceleration of electrons when they strike a metal target. The method is described fully in 29.3.

U.V., Visible and IR — produced by electrons falling from one orbital to one nearer the nucleus. In such a situation they are in an electric field (which increases as the nucleus is neared because $E \alpha \frac{1}{r^2}$) and so will accelerate.

RADIO (radio, T.V. and micro) AND RADAR — produced by a.c. — i.e. oscillating electric currents. In such a supply the electrons are repeatedly being accelerated and decelerated since their motion is simple harmonic.

## 29.3 PRINCIPLE OF THE X RAY TUBE

**FIG. 29.3**

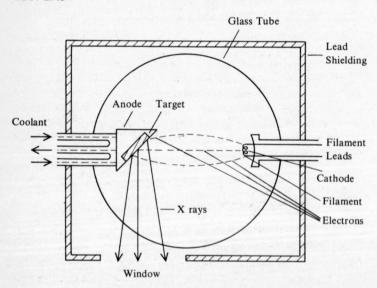

29.3.1 A modern form of X ray tube is shown in Fig. 29.3. It is a highly evacuated glass tube and contains an anode and a tungsten filament connected to a cathode. Electrons are liberated from the filament by thermionic emission and they are accelerated to the anode by a p.d. of up to 100KV. The anode is a copper block inclined to the electron stream and on it is a small target of tungsten or other high melting point metal. When the high speed electrons strike this target, they are rapidly decelerated and X rays are emitted. The tube has a lead shield with a small window to allow for the passage of the X rays.

Less than $\frac{1}{2}$% of the kinetic energy of the electrons is converted into X rays. The majority is converted into internal energy of the anode which must, therefore, be cooled, usually with oil.

The tube can only operate on alternate half cycles of the supply voltage since it acts as its own rectifier.

29.3.2   The intensity of the X rays increases when the number of electrons hitting the target increases and this is controlled by the filament current. The quality (or penetrating power) of the X rays is determined by the speed reached by the electrons and this obviously depends upon the p.d. across the tube.

Soft X rays only penetrate such objects as flesh, whereas hard X rays can penetrate much more dense material.

The higher the frequency (and lower the wavelength) of X rays, the greater their energy. In fact, the energy E is given by

$$E = hf$$

$f$ = frequency in $H_z$
$h$ = Planck's Constant = $6.6 \times 10^{-34}$ Js.

## 29.4   REFLECTION AND REFRACTION OF ELECTROMAGNETIC WAVES

29.4.1   The reflection of light is an everyday phenomenon. The reflecting surface used is a mirror (although a highly polished sheet of glass will act as partial reflector). By allowing a ray of light to strike such a mirror, as shown in Fig. 29.4, the laws of reflection will be found to apply, as in the case of water waves.

**FIG. 29.4**

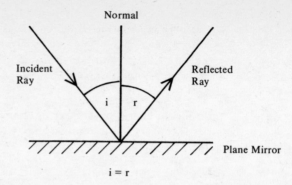

The reflection of microwaves having a wavelength of about 30mm, may be investigated using a transmitter and receiver, as shown in Fig. 29.5. The reflecting surface is a metal plate whilst a metal screen is also used to ensure only reflected signals reach the receiver. Again the laws of reflection will be obeyed.

**FIG. 29.5**

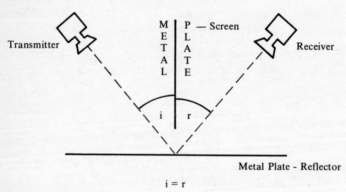

29.4.2 As in the case of light reflection, light refraction is a commonly observed phenomenon. Light is refracted when it passes through glass, as in the case of the glass prism, shown in Fig. 29.6.

**FIG. 29.6**

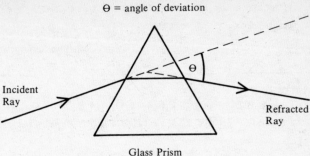

$\Theta$ = angle of deviation

Incident Ray

Refracted Ray

Glass Prism

Similarly, microwaves are refracted. In Fig. 29.7, microwaves from the transmitter are refracted by the paraffin oil and are then detected by the receiver.

**FIG. 29.7**

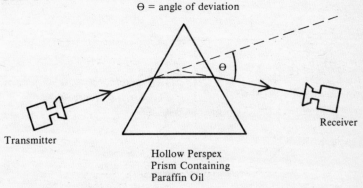

$\Theta$ = angle of deviation

Transmitter

Receiver

Hollow Perspex Prism Containing Paraffin Oil

In all cases of refraction of electromagnetic waves as they travel from medium 1 to medium 2, we may apply Snell's Law.

$$_1n_2 = \frac{c_1}{c_2}$$

We use c to denote the speed of electromagnetic waves

But $\qquad c = f\lambda$

$$\therefore \quad _1n_2 = \frac{f\lambda}{f\lambda_2} = \frac{\lambda_1}{\lambda_2}$$

When the electromagnetic waves pass from air (or vacuum) into a medium 1, we have the absolute refraction index of the medium.

$$n_1 = \frac{c}{c_1} = \frac{\lambda}{\lambda_1}$$
where c and $\lambda$ refer to the speed and wavelength in air

---

**EXAMPLE**

If the speed of light in vacuum is $3.0 \times 10^8$ ms$^{-1}$, calculate its speed in glass, the (absolute) refractive index of which is 1.5.

Use
$$n_1 = \frac{c}{c_1}$$

$$\therefore \quad c_1 = \frac{c'}{n_1}$$

Substituting values
$$c_1 = \frac{3.0 \times 10^8}{1.5}$$
$$= 2.0 \times 10^8 \text{ ms}^{-1}$$

Speed in glass $= 2.0 \times 10^8$ ms$^{-1}$

---

## 29.5 DISPERSION

If the speed of waves in a given medium depends upon the frequency (and thus wavelength) of the waves, then when refraction occurs, its extent will also depend upon the frequency.

**FIG. 29.8**

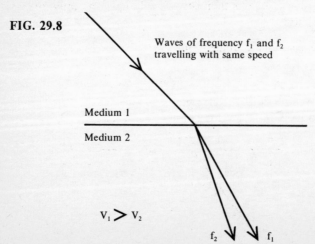

Waves of frequency $f_1$ and $f_2$ travelling with same speed

Medium 1

Medium 2

$V_1 > V_2$

$f_2 \quad f_1$

In Fig. 29.8, the waves of frequency $f_1$ and $f_2$ travel with the same speed in medium 1. But in medium 2, the wave with frequency $f_1$ travels at a speed $V_1$ and $f_2$ at $V_2$ which is less (i.e. $V_1 > V_2$). Accordingly $f_2$ suffers greater deviation than $f_1$. Dispersion is said to occur. Medium 1 is a non-dispersive medium whilst medium 2 is dispersive.

Air is a non-dispersive medium but glass is dispersive with red light travelling faster than blue light (red light has a wavelength of about $0.7\mu$m while blue light has a wavelength of around $0.4\mu$m). Hence if white light travels from air to glass, the blue light is refracted more than the red and dispersion occurs. A glass prism effectively demonstrates this.

## 29.6 TOTAL INTERNAL REFLECTION

When light travels in a medium such as glass to a boundary with another medium such as air, some of the light will be reflected from the boundary when it meets it and some will undergo refraction.

If the angle of incidence is increased beyond a certain value, then no light will be refracted; instead it will all be reflected back into the glass. The effect is known as total internal reflection.

In connection with this effect we define the critical angle as the angle of incidence in the medium such that the refracted ray skims along the surface of the boundary (i.e. the angle of refraction is 90°). For an angle of incidence greater than the critical angle, $\Theta_c$, total internal reflection occurs.

In Fig. 29.9, the critical angle is shown.

**FIG. 29.9**

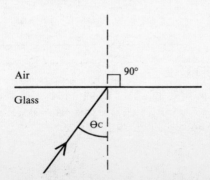

Now for light travelling from air to glass, the (absolute) refractive index of glass is given by

$$n_g = \frac{\sin i}{\sin r}$$

In this case, light travels in reverse from glass to air. Light though is reversible and so for travel from air into glass then

$$i = 90°$$
$$\therefore \quad \sin i = \sin 90° = 1$$
$$r = \Theta_c$$
$$\therefore \quad \sin r = \sin \Theta_c$$

hence

$$n_g = \frac{1}{\sin \Theta_c}$$

or

$$\sin \Theta_c = \frac{1}{n_g}$$

The phenomenon of total internal reflection is used in fibre optic cables.

---

**EXAMPLE**

Calculate the critical angle for glass of refractive index 1.5.

Now

$$\sin \Theta_c = \frac{1}{n_g}$$

Substituting the values

$$\sin \Theta_c = \frac{1}{1.5}$$
$$\therefore \quad \Theta_c = 41° \, 49^1$$

Hence Critical Angle $= 41° \, 49^1$

---

## 29.7 POLARISATION

29.7.1 Polarisation is an effect which only occurs with transverse waves. It may be demonstrated with mechanical waves using a rope on a string, as shown in Fig. 29.10.

**FIG. 29.10**

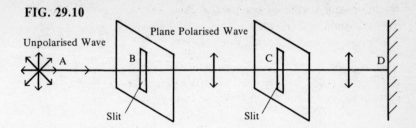

The rope ABCD is fixed at end D and passes through two vertical slits at B and C. If end A is vibrated in all directions, as shown by the arrows, vibrations of the rope occur in all planes and hence transverse waves in all planes travel towards B. At B, only waves due to vibrations in a vertical plane can emerge from the slit. The waves between A and B are said to be unpolarised whilst those between B and C are said to be plane polarised in the plane containing the slit i.e. the vertical plane. This first slit polarises the incident waves and it is known as a polariser.

If now the plane polarised wave meets a slit at C, it is found that the wave only passes through when the slit is in the same plane as the polariser. The second slit is known as the analyser and the polariser and analyser are here said to be aligned.

As the analyser is rotated, less of the wave is transmitted beyond it. In fact, only that component of the wave in the plane of the analyser will be transmitted.

When the angle between the polariser and analyser is 90°, they are said to be crossed and there is no transmission beyond C.

**29.7.2** Electromagnetic waves may also be polarised and this provides evidence for their transverse nature.

As explained in Fig. 29.11 we produce plane polarised light waves by using some effect which
1)  selects two planes XX and YY in perpendicular directions.
2)  resolves the amplitude of each wave into components at right angles along these directions as $A \cos \Theta$ and $A \sin \Theta$.
3)  effectively adds up the two sets of components as $\Sigma A \cos \Theta$ and $\Sigma \sin \Theta$.

4) removes or diverts one set and so
5) transmits only the sum of the components polarised in the other plane — either $A_X = \Sigma A \cos \Theta$ or $A_Y = \Sigma A \sin \Theta$.

**FIG. 29.11**

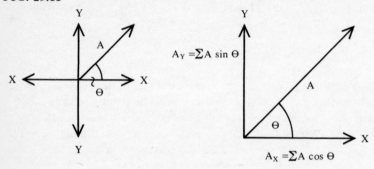

A substance which may do this is a dichroic crystal such as found in Polaroid ©. Normal light is unpolarised. It may be made plane polarised by passing it through a sheet of polaroid. The fact that polarisation has occured may be checked by using a second sheet of polaroid as analyser, as shown in Fig. 29.12. The variation in intensity, I, of the transmitted light as the analyser is rotated with respect to the polariser is shown in Fig. 29.13.

**FIG. 29.12**

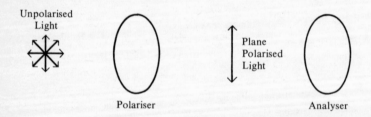

Whenever light is reflected, it is found that the reflected wave is partially plane polarised and indeed, for one particular angle (which depends upon the refractive index of the reflecting medium) the reflected wave is totally plane polarised.

If this reflected light passes through a sheet of polaroid which is not aligned with its plane of polarisation, the sheet of polaroid will act as an analyser and remove some of the reflected light intensity. This is why polaroid sunglasses are so effective.

**FIG. 29.13**

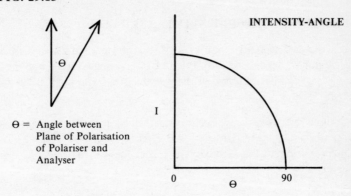

INTENSITY-ANGLE

Θ = Angle between
Plane of Polarisation
of Polariser and
Analyser

29.7.3   It will be remembered that the direction of the electric field is taken as that of an electromagnetic wave and whenever we represent the polarisation of such a wave in a diagram, we are showing the directions of the E waves.

However, Heaviside and Trouton actually demonstrated that when light is polarised by a medium, it is the magnetic field which is actually "removed".

Strictly speaking, it is irrelevant whether it is the magnetic field or electric field which is removed since each generates the other and the removal of one means that the other also vanishes.

**QUESTIONS**
1) List the similarities and differences between different electro-magnetic waves.

2) Calculate the energy of X rays of wavelength $5 \times 10^{-11}$m. Assume speed of light $= 3 \times 10^8$ ms$^{-1}$, Planck's Constant $= 6.6 \times 10^{-34}$ JS.

3) Explain why polaroid spectacles enable you to see into a swimming pool.

# Chapter 30
# SUPERPOSITION OF ELECTROMAGNETIC WAVES

## 30.1  YOUNG'S DOUBLE SLIT EXPERIMENT

30.1.1  It was seen in Chapter 28 that interference effects occur when water waves meet at a point. The interfering sources also need to be close together in terms of the wavelength of the waves they are generating.

Since light is a wave, it would be expected that similar interference effects are obtainable. Indeed such effects were first observed by Thomas Young in his Double Slit Experiment, illustrated in Fig. 30.1.

**FIG. 30.1**

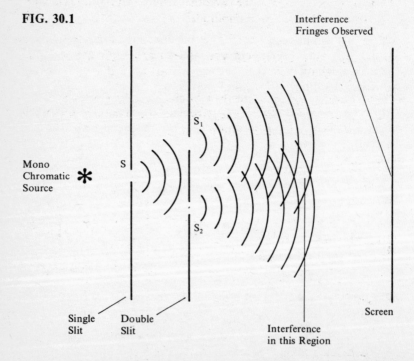

Interference Fringes Observed

Mono Chromatic Source

S

$S_1$

$S_2$

Single Slit

Double Slit

Interference in this Region

Screen

A monochromatic light source, S, is placed behind a narrow slit. The waves passing through this are diffracted into a "cone". Parts of the same wavefront fall upon slits $S_1$ and $S_2$ which now act as coherent sources because they are both derived from the same wavefront. The waves from these sources are diffracted and where they overlap, interference occurs. Alternate bright and dark bands, parallel to the slits, can be observed on a screen placed in the path of the waves. These bands are known as interference fringes.

30.1.2   It would not be possible to obtain interference patterns from two separate light sources because in any light source the phase is constantly changing as light is emitted in short bursts. In general, this is also true for light coming from different parts of the same source. Hence, we cannot use two sources. Neither can we use one large extended source. Coherence is only achieved by deriving the two sources from the same wavefront.

In doing so, we also meet the two other requirements of interference — equal wavelengths and amplitudes.

## 30.2   THE EQUATION OF YOUNG'S DOUBLE SLIT EXPERIMENT

30.2.1   In Fig. 30.2, suppose the two slits (i.e. sources) $S_1$ and $S_2$ are a distance, S, apart. The distance from the slits to the screen is D. The centre of the interference pattern is at 0.

**FIG. 30.2**

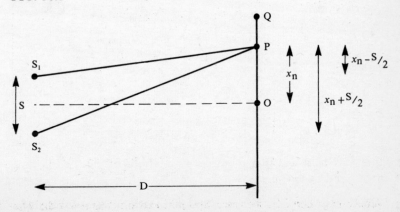

The $n^{th}$ bright fringe is at P and the distance from 0 to P is $x_n$. The next bright fringe, the $(n + 1)^{th}$ is at Q, a distance $x_{n+1}$ from 0.

The wavelength of the light is $\lambda$.

Now for the $n^{th}$ fringe at P

$$\text{Path difference} = n\lambda$$
$$\text{But path difference} = S_2P - S_1P$$
$$\therefore \quad S_2P - S_1P = n\lambda$$

From the geometry

$$S_2P^2 = D^2 + (x_n + {}^S/_2)^2$$
$$= D^2 + x_n^2 + S x_n + S^2/_4$$

Similarly
$$S_1P^2 = D^2 + (x_n - {}^S/_2)^2$$
$$= D^2 + x_n^2 - S x_n + S^2/_4$$

Hence
$$S_2P^2 - S_1P^2 = 2S x_n$$

But
$$S_2P^2 - S_1P^2 = (S_2P - S_1P)(S_2P + S_1P)$$

In practice S is small ($\approx 0.5$mm) compared with D($\approx 1$m) and, of course, P is very near to Q. Hence $S_2P$ and $S_1P$ are each just greater than D.

We may write $(S_2P + S_1P) = 2D$

$$\therefore \quad 2D(S_2P - S_1P) = 2Sx_n$$
$$S_2P - S_1P = \frac{Sx_n}{D} = n\lambda$$

The $(n + 1)^{th}$ bright fringe formed at Q is at a distance $x_{n+1}$

Hence
$$S_2Q - S_1Q = \frac{Sx_{n+1}}{D} = (n + 1)\lambda$$

By subtraction
$$\lambda = \frac{S}{D}(x_{n+1} - x_n)$$

Now $x_{n+1} - x_n$ is the fringe separation, $x$, thus

$$\lambda = \frac{xS}{D}$$

i.e. $\quad$ Wavelength $= \dfrac{\text{Fringe Separation x Slit Separation}}{\text{Slit-Screen Distance}}$

It should be noted that the fringe separation is the same for both bright and dark fringes.

30.2.2 In a typical experiment to find the wavelength of sodium, S might be about 0.7mm and D about 1m. The fringe separation would then be around 0.84mm resulting in a an approximate wavelength of 600nm.

In order to maximise the fringe separation, it will be seen that the wavelength at slit-screen distance should be large whilst the slit separation should be small.

The number of fringes observed depends upon the amount of diffraction occurring at the slits and this in turn depends upon their width. The narrower the slits the greater the diffraction and so the greater the number of fringes. However, the narrower the slits, the less light passes through resulting in a fainter pattern. A balance between the two needs to be achieved.

---

**EXAMPLE**
In a Young's Double-Slit Experiment, the fringe separation was 0.275mm when sodium light of wavelength $4.00 \times 10^{-7}$m was used. If the distance from the slits to the screen was 1.00m calculate the slit separation.

From the above formula

$$\text{Slit Separation} = \frac{\text{Wavelength x Slit/Screen Separation}}{\text{Fringe Separation}}$$

Substituting values

$$\text{Slit Separation} = \frac{5.50 \times 10^{-7} \times 1.000}{0.275 \times 10^{-3}}$$
$$= 20 \times 10^{-4} \text{m}$$
$$= 2.0 \text{mm}$$

$$\text{Slit Separation} = 2.0 \text{mm}$$

---

## 30.3  THE DIFFRACTION GRATING

The diffraction grating consists of a rectangular aperture on to which is ruled a large number of parallel lines, typically 5,000 lines per cm. These lines behave like slits if the rest of the aperture is opaque so that when a plane wavefront of monochromatic light is incident upon the grating the lines behave like a set of narrow, parallel, coherent light sources. The light from each source is diffracted and where the light from all of the sources overlaps, it interferes as in Young's Slits Experiment. In the forward direction there will be no path difference between light from adjacent sources and so constructive interference results. We normally place a lens behind the grating to focus the light from all the sources, as shown in Fig. 30.3. In the forward direction a maximum will be formed.

**FIG. 30.3**

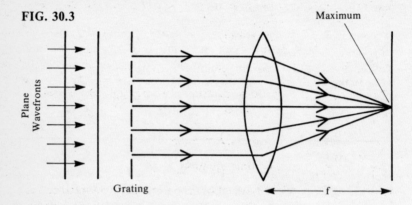

If we now move away from the forward direction we eventually reach an angle, Θ, to the forward direction for which the extra path travelled by the light from one source relative to that from an adjacent source is exactly one wavelength. All the waves will be in phase again and another maximum will be formed, known as the first order spectrum.

**FIG. 30.4**

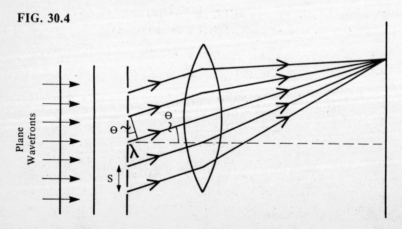

Suppose, in Fig. 30.4, the separation between the slits is S.

Then

$$\sin \Theta = \frac{\lambda}{S}$$

If we move still further from the forward direction, we eventually reach the condition that the extra path between adjacent sources is $2\lambda$. If the angle is now $\phi$

$$\sin \phi = \frac{2\lambda}{S}$$

This is the condition for the second order spectrum.

In general, for the $n^{th}$ order spectrum at some angle $\Theta$ we have

$$\sin \Theta = \frac{n\lambda}{S}$$

or

$$\underline{n\lambda = S \sin \Theta}$$

This is known as the grating equation.

In the laboratory situation the diffraction grating is mounted upon a spectrometer. This comprises a table on which the grating is actually mounted together with a collimator and telescope. The collimator consists of an adjustable slit and a lens system. The slit provides a 2D point source, i.e. a slit source and when this is situated at the focal length of the lens system, plane wavefronts are generated. These strike the grating and then pass through the telescope which serves the purpose of the lens shown in the diagram.

## 30.4   THE USE OF A LASER IN DOUBLE SLIT AND DIFFRACTION GRATING EXPERIMENTS

It has already been stated that light coming from different parts of a light source is not coherent.

The laser is an exception to this rule. The atoms in a laser are excited, i.e. an electron is caused to be in an orbital which is further from the nucleus than its "usual" orbital. This is known as an inverted population. If electromagnetic radiation is now caused to strike the excited atoms, it causes them to relax by the emission of radiation which has the same wavelength and amplitude as the initiating radiation and is also in phase with it. As a result, coherent radiation is emitted, i.e. a plane wavefront emerges.

The original laser, pioneered by Townes in 1959 was a ruby crystal laser in which the inverted population was caused by an external flash tube. More modern gas lasers use helium neon.

In addition to being coherent, laser radiation has a very high directionality (it does not diverge as it travels along) and also a very high intensity.

The diameter of the beam is around 5mm. Such a beam with the properties which it possesses is, therefore, ideal for use in interference and diffraction experiments.

If it is used in the Young's Double Slit Experiment, the single slit may be dispensed with. The double slits themselves may be placed in contact with the laser. A plane wavefront will then strike $S_1$ and $S_2$. Because of the intensity of the laser, an observable system of interference fringes will be obtained on a screen placed 1 to 2m beyond the slits.

In a diffraction grating experiment, the grating may be placed in contact with the laser and spectra observed directly on a screen placed 1 to 2m beyond the grating. The laser provides a plane wavefront which falls upon the grating. Without the lens the parallel diffracted beams will meet at infinity. In comparison with the dimensions of the wavelength of the light and the rulings on the grating, a screen 1-2m away is at "infinity". As the light is so intense, it is still observable at this distance.

---

**EXAMPLE**
A diffraction grating with 500 lines per mm is illuminated normally with yellow light of wavelength $6 \times 10^{-7}$m. Calculate the angle of the second order spectra.

$$\text{Using} \qquad n\lambda = S \sin \Theta$$
$$\sin \Theta = \frac{n\lambda}{S}$$

Here
$$n = 1$$
$$\lambda = 6 \times 10^{-7}\text{m}$$
$$S = \frac{1}{500} \text{ mm} = 2 \times 10^{-6}\text{m}$$

$$\therefore \quad \sin \Theta \quad = \quad \frac{1 \times 6 \times 10^{-7}}{2 \times 10^{-6}} \quad = \quad 0.3$$

$$\therefore \quad \Theta \quad = \quad 17°$$

Angle of first order spectra = $17°$

N.B. We use the term spectra rather than spectrum because 2 spectra are obtained, one on each side of the central maximum.

## 30.5 FRAUNHOFER DIFFRACTION AT A SINGLE SLIT AND A CIRCULAR APERTURE

30.5.1 It has been stated in Section 30.1 that when light passes through a narrow slit, it is diffracted.

The actual diffraction pattern which results may be observed using the arrangement shown in Fig. 30.5. It is called a Fraunhofer Diffraction Pattern. It consists of a central bright line, parallel to the slit, above and below which are other bright lines of rapidly diminishing intensity.

**FIG. 30.5**

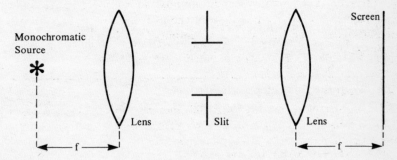

A complete derivation of how intensity varies with the angle from the forward direction is beyond the scope of 'A' level physics but the variation is illustrated in Fig. 30.6.

(No actual values are shown since $\Theta$ depends upon the slit width).

The important points are:

1) The result is symmetrical about the forward direction.

2) The intensity rapidly decays — $Io \approx 20I_1$

3) If $\Theta_1 \doteq$ angle between forward direction and first minimum
   $\lambda$ = wavelength
   a = slit width
   then $\sin \Theta_1 = \dfrac{\lambda}{a}$

**FIG. 30.6**

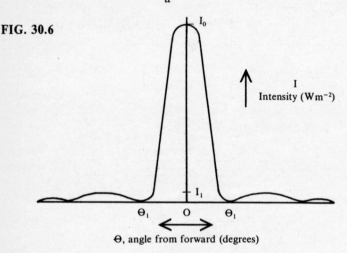

I
Intensity ($Wm^{-2}$)

$\Theta$, angle from forward (degrees)

30.5.2 If the slit is replaced by a circular aperture then

1) A similar intensity against angle variation is obtained.

2) The fall-off in intensity is much more rapid
   $$Io \approx 60I_1$$

3) With a = diameter of circular aperture
   $$\sin \Theta_1 = 1.22 \dfrac{\lambda}{a}$$

## 30.6 STATIONARY LIGHT WAVES

Wiener demonstrated stationary light waves exist just as do stationary mechanical waves.

He illuminated two inclined glass plates with monochromatic light, as shown in Fig. 30.7. Some light will be reflected from the top of the lower plate and some will be reflected from the bottom of the upper plate. The light from each will interfere, producing a series of fringes parallel to the line of contact between the plates. The condition for constructive interference is that the light from the lower plate must travel an odd number of half wavelengths extra because when the light is reflected from this bottom plate it suffers a phase change of 180°, equivalent to travelling an extra half-wavelength. The total extra paths is equivalent to a whole number of wavelengths.

**FIG. 30.7**

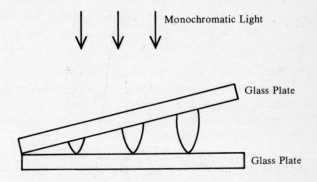

The top of the bottom plate contains light nodes whereas the bright fringes constitute anti-nodes.

Note: This chapter has concentrated upon the superposition of light waves because of its historical and experimental importance. However, similar effects take place with all electromagnetic waves including obviously, microwaves.

**QUESTIONS**

1) Sodium light of wavelength $6 \times 10^{-7}$m falls upon two narrow slits 0.2mm apart. Calculate the separation of the interference fringes formed on a screen 1m away.

2) Calculate the angle of the first order spectrum obtained when light of wavelength $6.0 \times 10^{-7}$m illuminates a diffraction grating ruled with 400 lines per mm.

3) Calculate the angle of the first minimum in the diffraction pattern due to a single slit of width $4 \times 10^{-6}$m when it is illuminated with light of wavelength $5 \times 10^{-7}$m.

# Chapter 31
# PHOTONS AND ENERGY LEVELS

## 31.1 WAVE-PARTICLE DUALITY

Newton proposed that light consisted of particles or corpuscles which were emitted by a luminous object and his so-called Corpuscular Theory of Light was adopted by many scientists of the day.

Huygens, a Dutch scientist, proposed that light was a wave motion. If his wave theory of light was correct, then light should bend round a corner just as sound does. The experimental evidence for this theory was very small and the theory was rejected until Thomas Young (he of the Double Slit Experiment) obtained evidence that light could indeed produce wave effects. Accordingly, Young revived the wave theory of light and the Newtonian Corpuscular Theory was rejected.

More recently Einstein suggested that the energy in light could be carried from place to place by packets of waves which may be considered as particles and whose energy E is given by Planck as

$$E = hf$$
$$f = \text{frequency}$$
$$h = \text{Plancks' Constant}$$

Experiments carried out at his suggestion showed that the theory was true and the particles of light energy are known as photons.

**FIG. 31.1**

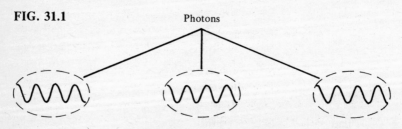

Photons

Wave properties — solid lines
Particle properties — dotted lines

It is now considered that light behaves either as a particle or a wave depending upon circumstances and thus if suitable experiments are carried out to investigate its wave properties, it will behave as a wave (i.e. interference, diffraction and polarisation experiments) but if a suitable experiment such as the photoelectric effect is carried out, it will behave as a particle. This is known as Wave-Particle duality. A diagrammatic representation is shown in Fig. 31.1.

---

**EXAMPLE**

Calculate the energy of a photon of violet light of wavelength $0.40\mu$m. Assume $h = 6.6 \times 10^{-34}$JS, $c = 3.0 \times 10^8$ ms$^{-1}$.

$$\text{Now} \qquad E = hf$$
$$\text{and} \qquad c = f\lambda$$
$$\therefore \quad E = \frac{hc}{\lambda}$$

Substituting the values

$$E = \frac{6.6 \times 10^{-34} \times 3.0 \times 10^8}{4.0 \times 10^{-7}}$$
$$= 4.95 \times 10^{-33} \text{ J}$$

$$\underline{\text{Energy} = 4.95 \times 10^{-33} \text{ J}}$$

---

## 31.2 THE PHOTOELECTRIC EFFECT

31.2.1  In the photo-electric effect, electrons are ejected from metal surfaces when a photon of electromagnetic radiation of high enough frequency falls upon them. The ejected electrons are known as photo-electrons and the effect is given by zinc exposed to X rays or ultra-violet, by sodium exposed to X rays, ultra-violet and visible light (except orange and red) and by caesium when exposed to infra-red.

In order to demonstrate the effect, ultra-violet radiation from a mercury vapour lamp is allowed to fall on a sheet of zinc which has been cleaned and attached to an electroscope, as shown in Fig. 31.2. If the electroscope is given a positive charge, the leaf is unaffected by the ultra-violet. However, when the electroscope is negatively charged, the leaf falls rapidly when the zinc is illuminated with the ultra-violet. When the zinc is positively charged, the photo-electrons fail to escape because they are attracted back by the positive charges. A negative charge on the electroscope however, repels the photo-electrons and the charge on the zinc and electroscope falls.

**FIG. 31.2**

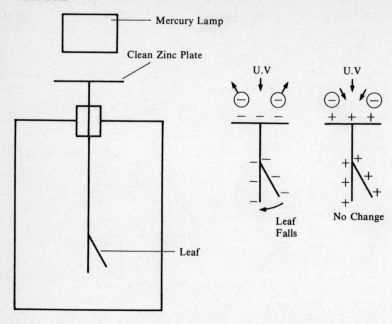

A full investigation shows
1) The number of photoelectrons emitted per second is proportional to the intensity of the incident radiation.
2) The kinetic energies of the photo-electrons range from zero up to a maximum which increases as the frequency and is independent of the intensity of the radiation.
3) For a given metal there is a certain minimum frequency of radiation called the threshold frequency, below which no emission occurs.

We would expect a certain number of photoelectrons to be ejected with greater speeds when the radiation intensity increases but this is not so, from 2, and this is inexplicable in terms of wave theory.

31.2.2   A certain amount of energy is required simply to liberate an electron from a metal. This amount of energy is called the Work Function of the metal, $\Phi$. If a photon is to liberate a photo-electron at all, the energy of the photon must at least be as great as the work function. If it is greater, the energy difference will appear as kinetic energy of the photo-electron.

Now the energy of a photon is given by

$$E = hf$$  f = frequency

Thus  h = Plancks' Constant

the kinetic energy of the photo-electron is

m = mass

$$\tfrac{1}{2}mV^2 = hf - \Phi$$  V = velocity

Now, in fact, V represents a maximum velocity and the actual value depends upon how much energy the electrons have inside the metal

$$\therefore \quad \tfrac{1}{2}mV_{MAX}^2 = hf - \Phi$$

A graph of K.E. against frequency is shown in Fig. 31.3.

**FIG. 31.3**

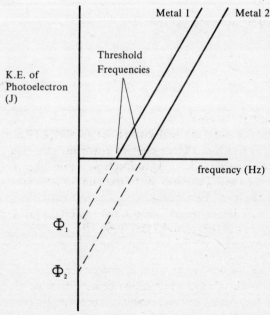

Note: As mentioned, the velocity achieved depends upon the energy of the electrons in the metal. The distribution of these electron energies varies quite markedly and this variation changes also with temperature. Thus, the velocity of the photoelectrons would be expected to follow some sort of distribution. An interesting experiment illustrating this fact has been designed by R.G. Keesing at the University of York.

---

**EXAMPLE**

A photo-emissive substance has a threshold frequency of $4.6 \times 10^{14} Hz$. Calculate its work function in J.

($h = 6.6 \times 10^{-34}$ Js).

$$\text{Now} \qquad \tfrac{1}{2}mV^2_{MAX} = hf - \Phi$$

At the threshold frequency the photoelectron is just released

$$\text{i.e.} \qquad \tfrac{1}{2}mV^2_{MAX} = 0$$

$$\therefore \quad \Phi = hf_0$$

where $f_0$ = threshold frequency

Hence, substituting the values:

$$\Phi = \begin{array}{c} 6.6 \times 10^{-34} \times 4.6 \times 10^{14} \\ 3.0 \times 10^{-19} \text{ J} \end{array}$$

Work Function = $3.0 \times 10^{-19}$ J

---

## 31.3 EMISSION AND ABSORPTION LINE SPECTRA

It was shown in Chapter 14 that electrons in orbits possess a certain energy. If an electron fell from one orbital to one nearer to the nucleus, energy was released in the form of electromagnetic radiation. If the initial energy is $E_i$ and the final is $E_f$ then the difference is $E_i - E_f$. This appears as a photon of frequency f.

$$\text{Hence} \qquad E_i - E_f = hV$$

Hence, the frequencies are discrete, because $E_i$ and $E_f$ are themselves discrete.

This may be verified by examining the radiation using a diffraction grating mounted on a spectrometer. Spectra will be observed at specific angles and thus are due to definite wavelengths.

If a source is emitting radiation and a material is placed between it and the observer, it will be noted that the material in the form of a monatomic gas will selectively absorb radiation at those frequencies at which, when excited, it radiates. This is because it can only accept energy in packets which correspond exactly in size with the possible differences in energy between pairs of the energy levels. The absorption spectrum of an element is thus the same as its emission spectrum except that whereas an emission spectrum consists of bright lines on a dark background, the absorption spectrum consists of dark lines on a bright background.

The presence of a cooler layer of gas around the sun causes the Fraunhofer lines in the solar spectrum, an example of an absorption spectrum. The lines indicate the presence of hydrogen, helium and sodium in the sun's atmosphere.

## 31.4   THE ELECTRON VOLT, STOPPING, EXCITATION AND IONISATION POTENTIALS

31.4.1   The energy gained by a charged particle accelerated by an electric field in a vacuum depends only upon its charge and the potential difference through which it is accelerated.

We define the electron volt, symbol eV, as the kinetic energy gained by an electron when it is accelerated through a potential difference of one volt.

Thus, an electron accelerated through V volts will have an energy of V electron volts.

If an electron is accelerated through a p.d. of 100V, it will have an energy of 100eV. Similarly, for a proton which has a charge of the same magnitude.

However, if we considered an $\alpha$ particle, it would gain 200eV energy because its charge is double the magnitude of that on the electron.
    By definition of the volt and electron volt, $1eV = 1.6 \times 10^{-19}J$

31.4.2   In the experimental verification of the photoelectric effect, use is made of the notion of stopping potential.

Rather than measuring a current of photoelectrons, we observe a nil current of them. Light is allowed to fall upon a plate which releases photo-electrons. The plate is then put at a positive potential so as to prevent these photo-electrons being liberated and being detected by a sensitive galvanometer. The minimum positive potential which must be applied so as to prevent the most energetic photo-electrons being emitted is called the stopping potential, $V_s$.

Hence from the definition of the electron-volt

$$\tfrac{1}{2}mV_{MAX}^2 = eV_s$$

31.4.3 In the undisturbed state, all the atoms in a gas are at their lowest possible energy level, the so-called ground state of the atom. For hydrogen this is $-13.6eV$ (See also Chapter 14). Thus, to ionise a hydrogen atom and theoretically remove an electron to infinity where it has no electric potential energy, $13.6eV$ of energy, at least, are needed. This energy must be given to it by some colliding particle. The amount of energy needed to remove an electron from the atom to infinity is known as the ionisation energy of the gas.

Thus, if the colliding particle itself is an electron, it must have a minimum energy of $13.6eV$ and thus must have been accelerated through a p.d. of $13.6V$ — the ionisation potential.

31.4.4 In the hydrogen atom, the energy level next above the ground state is $-3.4eV$ corresponding to the second orbital. Thus, if the atom gains $13.6eV - 3.4eV = 10.2eV$, it may be excited. This energy is known as the ionisation energy. In order to provide it, an electron would have to be accelerated through a p.d. of $10.2V$ — known as the excitation potential.

---

**EXAMPLE**

Calculate the kinetic energy and velocity of a proton after being accelerated from rest through a p.d. of $2.00 \times 10^5V$. (Assume proton mass $= 1.67 \times 10^{-27}Kg$).

Now $1eV =$ energy gained by an electron accelerated through a p.d. of $1V$

Further $\quad 1V = 1J\ C^{-1}$

But $\quad$ Charge on electron $e = 1.6 \times 10^{-19}C$

hence

$$1eV = 1.6 \times 10^{-19}J$$

The K.E. = 2.00 x 10⁵eV since proton charge is numerically equal to electron charge

$$\therefore \quad \text{K.E.} = 2.00 \times 10^5 \times 1.6 \times 10^{-19} \text{ J}$$
$$\text{K.E.} = 3.2 \times 10^{-14} \text{ J}$$

$$\text{K.E.} = \tfrac{1}{2}mV^2$$

$$\therefore \quad V = \sqrt{\frac{2 \text{ K.E.}}{m}}$$

Substituting values

$$V = \sqrt{\frac{2 \times 3.2 \times 10^{-14}}{1.67 \times 10^{-27}}}$$
$$= 6.19 \times 10^6 \text{ ms}^{-1}$$

Kinetic energy = $3.2 \times 10^{-14}$ J
Velocity = $6.19 \times 10^6$ ms$^{-1}$

## 31.5 CONSERVATION OF ENERGY FOR WAVES

Energy flux is defined as $\dfrac{\text{Energy}}{\text{Perpendicular Area}}$

Fig. 31.4 shows the rays and wavefronts from a point source S. The principle of conservation of energy requires that the energy flux through any of the spheres centred on S is the same, in the absence of absorption.

**FIG. 31.4**

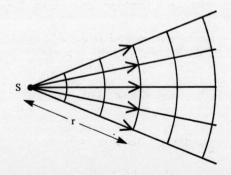

If the power of S is P, then the intensity, I at a distance r is given by

$$I \quad = \quad \frac{\text{Power}}{\text{Area}} \quad = \quad \frac{P}{4\pi r^2}$$

i.e. $\qquad\qquad I \quad \alpha \quad \dfrac{1}{r^2}$

The intensity obeys an inverse square law.

At a long way from the source the wavefronts are plane, since the rays are parallel, and hence the flux is constant.

## QUESTIONS

1) Calculate the energy of photons of wavelength $3 \times 10^{-7}$m ($h = 6.6 \times 10^{-34}$ JS, $C = 3 \times 10^8$ ms$^{-1}$.

2) Define ionisation potential and excitation potential.

3) By what factor does the intensity due to a point wave source change if the distance is trebled?

# ANSWERS TO QUESTIONS

**CHAPTER 1**
1.  $F = k\eta^2/\rho$
    k = constant, $\eta$ = coefficient of viscosity, $\rho$ = density of fluid.
3.  $V = k\sqrt{g\lambda}$
    V = velocity, k = constant, g = acc. due to gravity, $\lambda$ = wavelength.

**CHAPTER 2**
2.  5N
3.  Yes.
    e.g.  mass $= \dfrac{\text{force}}{\text{acc}}$
    i.e.  scalar $= \dfrac{\text{vector}}{\text{vector}}$

**CHAPTER 3**
2.  Repulsive
3.  $800 \, \text{Kg m}^{-3}$

**CHAPTER 4**
1.  $2 \, \text{ms}^{-2}$ from the South
2.  20m, 2s
3.  $0.4 \, \text{ms}^{-2}$, $12 \, \text{ms}^{-1}$

**CHAPTER 5**
2.  $3.3 \times 10^7 \text{N}$
3.  600

**CHAPTER 6**
1.  200Kg

**CHAPTER 7**
1.  $7.3 \times 10^{-5} \, \text{rad s}^{-1}$
2.  $4000 \, \text{ms}^{-2}$
3.  $3.1 \, \text{ms}^{-1}$
4.  0.23N, $1.7 \, \text{ms}^{-1}$

**CHAPTER 8**
1.  $0.64 \, \text{ms}^{-2}$
2.  $4 \times 10^{-5}$ J
3.  $0.2828 \, \pi$ s
4.  The drill is likely to set the glass in resonance. A full glass will be damped and, therefore, be less likely to break.

**CHAPTER 9**
1.  $\Theta°C = 100 \left( \dfrac{P_\theta - P_0}{P_{100} - P_0} \right)$
2.  $TK = 273.16 \dfrac{P_T}{P_{TR}}$
3.  20°C
4.  63.16°C

**CHAPTER 11**
2.  2.75 KW

**CHAPTER 12**
2.  $46.2 \, \text{W(MK)}^{-1}$
3.  0.221K

**CHAPTER 13**
1.  10C
2.  300J
3.  $2.0 \times 10^{-2} \, \Omega$
4.  480 $\Omega$

**CHAPTER 14**
1.  13, 13, 14
2.  2, 8, 18, 17
3.  Radius $= 1.2 \times 10^{-15} \times \sqrt{64}$
4.  $3.96 \times 10^{-19}$J

**CHAPTER 15**
1.  $^{234}_{92}$ U
2.  $^{237}_{93}$ N$_P$

3.  $1.76 \times 10^{-17}$ s$^{-1}$
4.  1.31 KBq
5.  1/22.9

## CHAPTER 16
2.  $2 \times 10^{-3}$ ms$^{-1}$
3.  11.2 $\Omega$

## CHAPTER 17
2.  $5.9 \times 10^{-2}$ m$^3$
3.  $2.56 \times 10^{-2}$ m$^3$

## CHAPTER 18
1.  $9.4 \times 10^4$ Pa
4.  $1.1 \times 10^{-3}$m

## CHAPTER 19
1.  Charge-electrons flow from the polythene to the perspex until both are at zero potential, i.e. uncharged.
2.  $4.4 \times 10^{-7}$N

## CHAPTER 20
1.  $7.5 \times 10^9$N
2.  23.27V
3.  21.44cm from $10^{-8}$C

## CHAPTER 21
2.  0.335m
3.  272 ms$^{-2}$
4.  $-1.26 \times 10^6$ JKg$^{-1}$

## CHAPTER 22
1.  $10^{-3}$C
2.  6
3.  0.67$\mu$F, 3 $\mu$F
4.  450V
5.  $1.07 \times 10^{-4}$m

## CHAPTER 23
1.  $2 \times 10^{-5}$N
2.  $1.83 \times 10^{-2}$m

3.  $1.73 \times 10^{-4}$ Nm
4.  26mV

## CHAPTER 24
1.  200V
2.  5A, 2As$^{-1}$

## CHAPTER 25
1.  163V, 0.0167s
2.  276W

## CHAPTER 26
5.  $-10$

## CHAPTER 27
2.  3cm, 7H$_z$, 21cm s$^{-1}$
3.  3.82 Kms$^{-1}$

## CHAPTER 28
2.  115 Hz
3.  215H$_z$, 645H$_z$, 1075H$_z$

## CHAPTER 29
1.  Similarities: all reflected, refracted, interfere, diffract, travel at $3.0 \times 10^8$ ms$^{-1}$ in air. Differences: different wavelengths (or frequencies), different energies.
2.  $3.96 \times 10^{-25}$ J
3.  Cut out most reflected light. Greater fraction of transmitted refracted light reaches observer.

## CHAPTER 30
1.  3mm
2.  13° 54'
3.  7°

## CHAPTER 31
1.  $6.6 \times 10^{-19}$ J
3.  $^1\!/_9$

# INDEX

# THE BASIC CONCEPTS SERIES

The Basic Concepts series attempts to explain in a clear and concise manner the main concepts involved in a subject. Paragraphs are numbered for ease of reference and key points are emboldened for clear identification, with self assessment questions at the end of each chapter. The texts should prove useful to students studying for A level, professional and first year degree courses. Other titles in the series include:—

## QUESTIONS AND ANSWERS SERIES

These highly successful revision aids contain questions and answers based on actual examination questions and provide fully worked answers for each question. The books are written by experienced lecturers and examiners and will be useful for students preparing for O and A level, foundation and BTEC examinations. Subjects include:—